The
Mind
of the Universe

The
Mind
of the Universe

*Understanding Science
and Religion*

Mariano Artigas

Templeton Foundation Press
Philadelphia and London

Templeton Foundation Press
Five Radnor Corporate Center, Suite 120
100 Matsonford Road
Radnor, Pennsylvania 19087

Library of Congress Cataloging-in-Publication Data

Artigas, Mariano.
    The mind of the universe : understanding science and religion /
    Mariano Artigas.
        p.   cm.
    Includes bibliographical references and index.
    ISBN 1-890151-32-7 (hardbound : alk. paper)
    1. Religion and science.   I. Title.
    BL240.2.A77   1999
    215—dc21   99-37740
                                                               CIP

Illustrations: Fernando Krahn
Cover art: Engraving of a diagram of the universe
            CORBIS/Bettman

Printed in the United States of America

00 01 02 03   10 9 8 7 6 5 4 3 2 1

Contents

Foreword

One of the major challenges faced by humanity at the threshold of the new millennium is that of surmounting the apparent conflict between science and religion so as to reach a new stage of fruitful dialogue and collaboration between them. For this purpose, it is vital to search for a common ground between science and religion and to examine how they may complement each other for the benefit of all humanity. As Pope John Paul II puts it, one of the main tasks of culture in our time is "that of integrating knowledge, in the sense of a *synthesis* in which the impressive whole of scientific knowledge would find its meaning within the framework of an integral vision of man and his universe, that is, of the *ordo rerum*."[1]

Religion and science engage one another as two very different but major components of world culture. Each has had and will continue to have a decisive impact on the development of human civilization. In the present context, in order to advance the cause of a more human and peaceful world, a greater striving toward unity is required. Unity, however, is not homogeneity—both religion and science must preserve their autonomy and distinctiveness. What is desired is not identity, but a kind of unity based on a constructive and dynamic interchange that respects the diversity and the integrity of each individual element.[2]

Fortunately, the dialogue between science and religion finds today a cul-

---

1. Pope John Paul II, Address to the Swiss world of culture, science and art in the University of Fribourg, 13 June 1984, no. 4, *L'Osservatore Romano,* English Weekly Edition, N. 27 (841), 2 July 1984, 3.

2. Cf. Pope John Paul II, Message to the Reverend George V. Coyne, S.J., Director of the Vatican Observatory, 1 June 1988: Robert John Russell, William R. Stoeger, S.J., George V. Coyne, S.J. (ed.), *Physics, Philosophy, and Theology: A Common Quest for Understanding.* Vatican Observatory [distributed by University of Notre Dame Press], Vatican City State 1988, M1–M14.

tural context that may be considered favorable in many respects. The cultural myth of a presumed contradiction between the scientific and the religious worldviews is now in decline. As Vaclav Havel, president of the Czech Republic, has noted, we are becoming gradually more aware of the fact that the "faith" of modernity—characterized by a purely scientific relationship with the world—lacks something which is essential for reaching the most intrinsic aspect of reality and for becoming a source of integration and meaning. We live in a context of crisis of the cultural paradigm. Science is becoming increasingly aware of its own limits and of its need for a foundation, yet, at the same time, it challenges religion, asking for more intellectual rigor in the presentation of its spiritual message. This challenge is a healthy appeal for greater thoughtfulness on the part of religion. Science and religion are called thus to a serious philosophical and epistemological reflection, and to build solid bridges which will allow mutual listening and enrichment.[3]

The service to truth which characterizes science is wholly compatible with the service to truth which characterizes religion. The autonomy conquered by science in modern culture is wholly justified by the requirements of the experimental method. But this autonomy has a reason for its existence—the search for truth. And it has a goal—the service of humankind. Science can thus be close to other ways of approaching the truth, and, more specifically, to those who search for the truth of the meaning of human life. If science were to ignore religion it would be very difficult to remain faithful to its own commitment in favor of humankind. In this state, it would easily be reduced to a set of theories appreciated only for their utilitarian functionality.

In this light, I want to recall a few words of Pope Paul VI. The year was 1963. Paul VI, who had just become Pope, received the members of the Pontifical Academy of Sciences for the first time. I was present as a young collaborator of the Pontiff. The Pope explained that he felt "encouraged by the certainty that our religion not only does not pose any objection to the study of natural truths, but that . . . it can promote scientific research, honor its results and help them to be better used for the good of humanity." He continued, saying:

> The religion which we have the happiness to profess is, in fact, the supreme science of life. It is thus the highest and most beneficent mentor in all those domains where life is manifested. It might seem to be absent when it not merely permits, but directs, the scientist to obey only the laws of truth. But looking more closely, it will be seen to be still beside him, to encourage him in his difficult task of exploration, assuring him that truth exists, that it is intelligible, splendid, divine; and also to remind him at every step that thought is an instrument for the conquest of truth and that it should be used with such

---

3. Cf. Giovanni Battista Marini-Bettólo Marconi—Paul Poupard (ed.), Scientific meeting on: *Science in the Context of Human Culture II. September 30–October 4, 1991.* Pontificiæ Academiæ Scientiarum Scripta Varia. Pontificia Academia Scientiarum—Pierre Téqui, Vatican City 1997.

respect for its own laws that one feels continually the transcendent responsibility that it imposes.[4]

Religion might seem to be absent from science, but it is not. Precisely with this spirit, Mariano Artigas tackles in this book the challenge of building a workable link, a "bridge" between empirical science and religion in general. This is not an easy task, especially if one is to respect meticulously the specificity of both fields and the methodological gap that guarantees their mutual autonomy. For this reason, Artigas focuses in his work on the presuppositions of science and on the implications of scientific progress, showing the profound coherence of this type of philosophical reflection with a metaphysical and religious perspective in which divine agency and human spirituality provide the deepest meaning for the scientific enterprise.

Artigas's reflection is philosophical in nature, but he does not take the principles of metaphysics as a point of departure. He rather focuses on some states of affairs that should be considered presuppositions of science since they are its necessary conditions: the intelligibility of nature, the human ability to know the natural order, and the values implied in scientific activity. He completes his study by reflecting on the connection of these general presuppositions with the achievements of scientific progress. Indeed, the fact that science works, and that it works so well, must have profound implications for our understanding and assessment of the ontological, epistemological, and ethical conditions that make science possible.

The presuppositions of science examined in *The Mind of the Universe* might seem, to a naïve mind, trivial and not worthy of a serious study; nevertheless, the philosophical and theological reflection on them is not at all a trivial matter. The analysis of Artigas is marked by its simplicity and straightforwardness, but it is certainly not superficial. In fact, he succeeds in building a philosophical bridge that serves to ground, on a solid foundation, a genuine dialogue between science and religion. Considering the novelty of its approach, its intrinsic value, and the richness of the perspectives that it opens for the reader, one can consider *The Mind of the Universe* not only an outstanding contribution, but also a significant breakthrough in the area of contemporary dialogue between faith and science.

Paul Cardinal Poupard
President of the Pontifical Council for Culture
The Vatican

---

4. Pope Paul VI, Discourse to the Plenary Session of the Pontifical Academy of Sciences, 13 October 1963: *Discourses of the Popes from Pius XI to John Paul II to the Pontifical Academy of Sciences: 1936–1986.* English version edited by Fr. Paul Haffner. Pontificiae Academiae Scientiarum Scripta Varia 66. Pontificia Academia Scientiarum, Vatican City 1986, 114.

Acknowledgments

I have used quotations taken from a great variety of sources. Thus, the reader will appreciate that my views are taken from, or shared by, a great number of well-known authors; in other cases, they are counterarguments to positions I do not share. I have used these quotations according to the needs of my argument; it may well happen that my response to other opinions of these authors would differ. In any case, I am grateful to all of them because they have helped me to develop my own opinion.

The ideas that form the main argument of this book have appeared in various books and articles over the past 10 years. In 1992 I published a paper in which these ideas were articulated.[1] I continued to develop them in subsequent years, until I was offered an award to write this book by Sir John Templeton, founder of the John Templeton Foundation. I am most grateful to Sir John and to the Foundation, especially to Dr. Robert Herrmann, for their support. They are directly responsible for the existence of this book, even though they bear no responsibility for the defects contained in it. I would especially like to acknowledge Ruth Mercado and Laura Porres for their editorial work in the revision of this book, to Theresa Talavera for preparing the index, and to the staff at Templeton Foundation Press for their encouragement and vision of the book. I am likewise most grateful to Fernando Krahn for the five excellent drawings he has provided as illustrations for this book.

1. Mariano Artigas, "Three Levels of Interaction between Science and Philosophy," in *Intelligibility in Science,* ed. Craig Dilworth (Amsterdam and Atlanta, Ga.: Rodopi, 1992), pp. 123–144.

God can be referred to as "the mind of the universe" not in a pantheistic sense, but to express the idea that our universe exhibits rationality, information, and creativity; that it makes possible the existence of human beings who are strictly rational and creative; and all this requires a divine foundation: a participation in God's creativity.

Introduction

The title I have chosen for my book is deliberately provocative. In fact, the expression *The Mind of the Universe* places before us the following dilemma: Either we identify the universe with a personal living being and accept some kind of pantheism, which will be full of difficulties, or we admit that the universe is formed by many different beings and then wonder why we should attribute to it a singular mind. Nevertheless, I have chosen this title because it has important advantages. Above all, the contemporary scientific worldview suggests that the universe is permeated in its innermost being by a rationality whose explanation requires the authorship of a personal mind.

Moreover, I suggest that the scientific worldview is most coherent with God's immanence in the world. This immanence, however, is that of a personal God who pervades the world and is at the same time completely separate from it. We should not identify God with any creature or with all of them because creatures are always limited and so cannot be identified with God.

The power, order, and beauty of the universe have always provoked reactions of awe and admiration. One of them, both philosophical and religious, was the doctrine of stoicism that was alive for several centuries and was eventually associated to pantheism. The stoic Seneca referred to God using the expression "The Mind of the Universe" in this way:

> What is God? The mind of the universe. What is God? The whole that you see and the whole that you do not see. Thus we return to him his magnitude, because we can think of nothing greater, if he alone is everything, if he sustains his work from within and from without.[1]

---

1. Lucius Annaeus Seneca, *Quaestiones naturales* (Paris: Les Belles Lettres, 1961), I, 13: volume I, pp. 10–11: "Quid est deus? Mens universi. Quid est deus? Quod vides totum et quod non vides totum. Sic demum magnitudo illi sua redditur, quia nihil maius cogitari potest, si solus est omnia, si opus suum et intra et extra tenet."

Seneca's words were borrowed 15 centuries later by Luis de Granada, one of the Spanish classical writers of Christian spirituality, who adopted them without any qualms, and even used them as a part of the argument that leads us from the contemplation of nature to the knowledge of its Creator. These are his words:

> What is God? The mind and reason of the universe. What is God? Everything that we see, because in all things we see his wisdom and assistance, and thus we confess his magnitude, which is so great that we cannot think of a greater one. And if he alone is everything, it is he who sustains his great work from within and from without.[2]

Nineteen centuries after Seneca, and four centuries after Luis de Granada, I use the expression "The Mind of the Universe" because it confronts the problem of the explanation of the universe. I think our universe exhibits rationality, functions by using information, has a certain kind of creativity, and makes the existence of human beings who are rational and creative, possible. All this requires a divine foundation and a participation in God's creativity.

For the first time in history, we have a scientific worldview that is complete, rigorous, and closely related to ideas of self-organization, rationality, and information. The development of epistemology permits us to combine logical, historical, and sociological perspectives, reaching a balanced view of the nature of empirical science. Finally, the development of science-based technology has made us more aware of the ethical implications of scientific progress. Using these developments as the framework of my argument, I intend to build a bridge connecting science and theology.

The dialogue between science and theology is developing rapidly but not easily. If we admit that there is a methodological gap between science and theology, we wonder what such a dialogue could mean at all. The distinction between the world of facts and the world of values poses a serious threat to any attempt at uniting both spheres. And last but not least, naturalism uses empirical science to present metaphysics and religion as meaningless or useless.

I want to show that our present scientific worldview provides a most suitable basis for a perspective that includes an end and religious values; I want to explore the implications of this worldview on our ideas about the universe as God's creation, man as God's collaborator, and God as the foundation of being, creativity, and values.

To achieve these goals, I shall try to show that empirical science should not be used as the basis for a reductionist or naturalist approach, because it comprises not only factual knowledge, but also a set of necessary conditions or

---

2. Luis de Granada, *Introducción del Símbolo de la fe,* first part, chapter I, ed. José M. Balcells (Madrid: Cátedra, 1989), pp. 129–130: "¿Qué cosa es Dios? Mente y razón del universo. ¿ Qué cosa es Dios? Todo lo que vemos, porque en todas las cosas vemos su sabiduría y asistencia, y desta manera confesamos su grandeza, la cual es tanta, que no se puede pensar otra mayor. Y si él solo es todas las cosas, él es el que dentro y fuera sustenta esta grande obra que hizo."

presuppositions for this knowledge. The analysis of these conditions is a philosophical and theological task.

These presuppositions are of three kinds. The first refers to the intelligibility or rationality of nature; it can be labeled as *ontological* and is closely related with the natural order. The second refers to the human ability to know the natural order; it can be labeled as *epistemological* and includes the different forms of scientific argument. The third refers to the values implied by scientific activity itself; it can be labeled as *ethical* and includes the search for truth, rigor, objectivity, intellectual modesty, service to other people, cooperation, and related values.

Scientific progress provides feedback on these presuppositions, because it retrojustifies, enriches, and refines them. Just as these presuppositions are necessary conditions for the existence of science, scientific progress is sufficient evidence of their existence and enables us to determine their scope.

Seen in the light of that feedback, the analysis of each of these presuppositions can provide a clue to the philosophical meaning of scientific progress and, therefore, to its theological relevance. This is the aim of my study, which is divided into four parts. In the first part, I consider which method should be used to study the philosophical and theological implications of science; then I analyze these implications in the following parts, which deal, respectively, with the ontological implications of scientific progress and the corresponding image of divine action, the epistemological implications of scientific progress and the corresponding image of man, and the ethical implications of scientific values. I conclude by examining the results of my study and the plausibility of the naturalistic and the theistic positions using criteria similar to those applied to evaluate scientific explanations. I also include some suggestions for further research.

My study should be considered a concrete proposal, centered on a particular perspective, which can be combined with many other approaches. The method I follow connects science and theology by means of a most interesting bridge, which belongs at the same time to science and to philosophy and theology. It belongs to science because the point of departure of my argument is the group of general presuppositions of science. But these presuppositions transcend the specific approaches used in the sciences, and thus their analysis is properly speaking a philosophical task. And this philosophical task in turn can serve to connect science and theology.

Contemporary science provides us with a marvelous worldview, which includes the very small and the very large, the living and the nonliving, the different branches of empirical science, the structural and dynamic features of nature, in a coherent and unitary whole centered on the concepts of self-organization. This worldview can be considered complete because it includes all levels of nature and their mutual relations. Nevertheless, every progressive step opens up new vistas and, with them, new, oftentimes, previously unsuspected problems. In this way scientific progress may serve to increase the sense of awe and admiration before the world and, above all, before its Creator. At the same time, we become increasingly aware of our own abilities and we improve them; therefore, we realize that we are creative and that we are becoming more and more creative, participating in the divine creativity which is the source of all being.

As my analysis is based on the fact of scientific progress, it will not be surpassed by that progress. Rather, the more the sciences progress, the more valuable this analysis will be. It would become useless only if that scientific progress were to cease. As long as empirical science continues to develop, the outline of my argument will continue to be valid and will provide a framework for further research.

PART I

Science Transcends Itself

Nature is very complex. Science is possible because we have learned to study particular phenomena in isolation. This book explores the connection of the scientific perspective with the broader concerns of the meaning of life.

1

Science and Beyond

Since its birth as a system in the seventeenth century, empirical science has become intertwined with religion in different ways, but it is only now that the relations between science and religion have become the subject of specific studies. Between the extremes represented by bold apologetics and radical naturalism, different combinations of separation, coherence, and dialogue have been proposed.

I think that today almost everyone would agree on two points. The first is that the perspective adopted by empirical science differs from that used by religion, so that there is a fundamental discontinuity between the two approaches. The second is that it is possible and even important to foster the dialogue between science and religion, because otherwise our life will suffer from a kind of intellectual schizophrenia that will have negative consequences in practice. With this in mind, I am going to identify the nature of the gap that exists between science and religion and will consider the means that may be used to bridge it.

I. THE MEETING OF SCIENCE AND RELIGION

I shall take as a frame of reference the fourfold classification of the ways of relating science and religion proposed by Ian Barbour, undoubtedly one of the most influential authors in this field. In particular I refer to two articles by Barbour, "Ways of Relating Science and Theology,"[1] and "Ways of Relating Science and Religion."[2]

1. Ian Barbour, "Ways of Relating Science and Theology," in *Physics, Philosophy, and Theology: A Common Quest for Understanding,* ed. Robert J. Russell, William R. Stoeger, and George V. Coyne (Vatican City State: Vatican Observatory, 1988), pp. 21–48.

2. Ian Barbour, "Ways of Relating Science and Religion," in *Religion in an Age of Science* (San Francisco: Harper, 1990), pp. 3–30.

A first difference between the two worth noting is in their titles. The difference may seem insignificant; and yet this small difference is interesting. The content of the two texts is nearly identical; the small change in terminology points to a controversial issue. This issue was examined when the "European Society for the Study of Science and Theology" was discussing its name a few years ago. The terms Science and Theology were chosen because these two terms are homogeneous, as they both refer to "sciences"; indeed, Theology is, according to the generalized usage, the science of religious affairs. Science and Religion, on the other hand, are apparently heterogeneous realities. I therefore find it interesting that Barbour has chosen "Religion" instead of "Theology" for his second text.

Should we relate Science to Theology, then, rather than to Religion? Also, why not to Faith, as is sometimes also done? And why not to Metaphysics or Spirituality in a broader sense? I do not intend to annoy the reader with discussions about terminology. What I want to stress at the onset is that my reflections will focus on the relations between Science on the one hand and Religion or Spirituality in a very broad sense on the other. I am concerned with the basic subjects common to most metaphysical and religious perspectives, namely the existence of a personal God who is the creator of the universe, and the existence of spiritual dimensions in the human person created by God with the gift of free will and with corresponding ethical responsibilities. My views contrast with those of scientific naturalism, which denies the existence of God and of spiritual dimensions in the human person and presents itself as if it were a consequence of scientific progress.

Returning to Barbour, he introduces his four-type classification of the ways of relating science and religion (or theology) with these words:

> In order to give a systematic overview of the main options today, I have grouped them in this chapter under four headings: *Conflict, Independence, Dialogue,* and *Integration.* Particular authors may not fall neatly under any one heading: a person may agree with adherents of a given position on some issues but not in others. However, a broad sketch of alternatives will help us in making comparisons in later chapters. After surveying these four broad patterns, I will suggest reasons for supporting *Dialogue* and, with some qualifications, certain versions of *Integration.*[3]

The four headings correspond approximately to three possible relations: hostility, indifference, and cooperation. Barbour distinguishes two steps in the last, namely a "weak" kind of cooperation represented by *Dialogue* and a "strong" one that corresponds to *Integration.* Barbour criticizes the "conflict" positions, represented by the different versions of "scientific naturalism" and by biblical fundamentalism as it is presented by the so-called "scientific creationists" in the United States, and he shows no sympathy toward the "inde-

---

3. Ibid., p. 3.

pendence" positions although stresses that independence is the first step toward a fertile dialogue.

The paragraph just quoted contains in the Vatican version a phrase that has been omitted in the later version; "The *Dialogue* viewpoint, in particular, may be combined with either *Independence* or *Integration* themes."[4] I do not know the reason for this change, but it indicates how difficult it is to set the relations between science and religion on steady ground. For instance, it is easy to describe the relations between science and religion with a word like "dialogue," but experience shows that it is not easy to actually establish that dialogue. There is a real gap between the two partners in the desired dialogue, and one that is not easy to bridge. As in the London tube, those in search of that dialogue should always be reminded to "Mind the gap!" Along the same lines, we should not be surprised when we realize that the major change between the Vatican and the Gifford versions of Barbour's text occurs in the last part, which is devoted to the different forms of Integration. Indeed, it is easy to describe the relations of hostility and independence, but it is much more difficult to explain how a real dialogue can be established between science and religion, and it is even more difficult to work out some kind of real integration.

Two other similar classifications represent perspectives different from that of Barbour but still coincide with it on the main features of the general map. The first comes from the Institute for Hermeneutic and Systematic Research (Switzerland). It was published in an essay by Clairette Karakash and Otto Schäffer-Guignier,[5] which proposes a classification of the relations between science and religion under the headings *Convergence, Conflict, Complementarity,* and *Refusal of the Articulation.* This classification is very close to that of Barbour, but these authors consider the positions of scientists and theologians separately. They rightly remark that these relations are seen quite differently by a scientist who thinks about religion than a theologian who thinks about science.

The second presentation comes from John F. Haught, a professor at Georgetown University and the first director of a center devoted to the study of the relations between science and religion recently created in that University. In a 1995 book on the relations between science and religion, he also organized his argument around a four-heading typology. Haught's explanation of this typology in his introduction reflects the wide acceptance of a Barbour-style typology not only at the level of the specialists, but also at a more introductory level:

> I see four principal ways in which those who have thought about the problem express their understanding of the relationship of religion to

4. Barbour, "Ways of Relating Science and Theology," cit., p. 21.

5. Clairette Karakash and Otto Schäffer-Guignier, "Typologie des articulations entre science et foi religieuse," in Pierre Bühler, Pierre-Luigi Dubied, Clairette Karakash, Otto Schäffer-Guignier, and Gerd Theissen, *Science et foi font système: Une approche herméneutique* (Genève: Labor et Fides, 1992), pp. 45–72.

science. (1) Some hold that religion is utterly opposed to science or that science invalidates religion. I shall call this the *conflict* position. (2) Others insist that religion and science are so clearly different from each other that conflict between them is logically impossible. Religion and science are both valid, but we should rigorously separate one from the other. This is the *contrast* approach. (3) A third type argues that although religion and science are distinct, science always has implications for religion and vice versa. Science and religion inevitably interact, and so religion and theology must not ignore new developments in science. For the sake of simplicity I shall call this the *contact* approach. (4) Finally, a fourth way of looking at the relationship—akin to but logically distinct from the third—emphasises the subtle but significant ways in which religion positively supports the scientific adventure of discovery. It looks for those ways in which religion, without in any way interfering with science, paves the way for some of its ideas, and even gives a special kind of blessing, or what I shall call *confirmation*, to the scientific quest for truth.[6]

Haught uses the outline of these four "cons" (*conflict, contrast, contact,* and *confirmation*) to study different aspects of the relationship between science and religion. Like Barbour, from the outset, he manifests his preference for the third and fourth "cons"—contact and confirmation. He also clearly criticizes the "conflict" approach, even as he tries to show in each particular case the reasons of its supporters.

We can therefore appreciate that the use of the four headings, with slight variations, has obtained wide acceptance, and also that while it is easy to see that agreement exists over the first two headings, those of conflict and independence (or contrast), differences easily arise when we consider the "positive" relations between science and religion: Haught's "confirmation" seems quite different from Barbour's "integration."

It is not necessary to enter into more detail regarding the typology of the relations between science and religion. The goal so far has been to present a general map of the ways of relating science and religion (or theology, or metaphysics), so that my later arguments may be better understood. Indeed, I am going to proceed beyond the four-heading scheme, as I shall concentrate on the problems that, in my opinion, underlie this typology.

I could present my position within this usual four-heading scheme. I certainly agree with Barbour and Haught in perceiving the "conflict" approach, as represented by scientific materialism and extreme religious fundamentalism, as completely mistaken. I also agree with them in considering the "independence" (or "contrast") position a good starting point to be followed by further "dialogue" (or "contact"), and even some moderate form of "integration" (or "confirmation"). Nevertheless, I am afraid that use of this scheme would not reflect my position well enough. Indeed, I think that the gap be-

6. John F. Haught, *Science & Religion: From Conflict to Conversation* (New York and Mahwah: Paulist Press, 1995), pp. 3–4.

tween science and religion is so wide that it cannot be properly bridged, so that I do not see what real dialogue would be about. This is not to say that I do not desire to reach an intellectual and practical unity between science and religion, but I think that the first step toward that unity is philosophical reflection rather than actual dialogue between the two different partners. Therefore, according to my perspective, a systematic integration will also have a philosophical character, which can in its turn be integrated into a strictly theological framework.

I do not recommend leaving aside dialogue and integration. But I prefer to face them in another form which is based on the sciences but which is, at the same time, openly philosophical. This coincides with Barbour's main ideas when he speaks about dialogue and systematic synthesis between science and religion, where he clearly underlines the necessity of philosophical mediation.

II. THE METHODOLOGICAL GAP BETWEEN SCIENCE AND RELIGION

A methodological gap exists between science and religion, because the aims, methods, and results of empirical science are different, in principle, from those of religion. This does not mean, however, as naturalism wrongly asserts that science contradicts religion and makes it useless. Actually, we can bridge the gap between science and religion; we need a philosophical connection.

1. THE SCIENTIFIC OUTLOOK

Empirical science may be characterized as the search for a knowledge of nature that can provide us with a controlled dominion over it. In the natural sciences we search for theories that can be subjected to empirical tests, or experiments that, under controlled circumstances, study the behavior of a system by means of some observable measurements.

Scientific experiments must be able to be replicated, at least in principle. Some will never be replicated, either because they refer to a unique isolated event, or because they are too expensive; this often happens today, as many experiments require large laboratories and an entire team of scientists devoted full time to the experiment. An exact replication would also be useless because further progress in pure science and technology makes it possible to perform new experiments that include the old ones as a particular case.

Empirical control is not enough if we desire to establish theories beyond all doubt. Today, any well-informed person knows that experimental testing is never complete. In epistemology we speak of this situation as the "empirical underdetermination of theories," which means that any theory contains so many particular instances that it is impossible to test all of them and that, therefore, no particular set of empirical data, however well chosen they might be, may be sufficient to establish the definitive truth of any theory. There is another more profound reason for the underdetermination of theories: namely that all empirical data, no matter how observational they may seem, are "theory laden"; in fact, any scientific observation requires the use of theoretical assumptions to define the concepts implied in it. Therefore, even the strictest experimental testing makes use of some assumptions and requires interpretation.

All this, together with the decline of classical determinism in physics, is sometimes interpreted as if scientific experiments were not so rigorous as previously thought, leading some authors to conclude that the difference between the natural sciences and the humanities has vanished. Nevertheless, there are good reasons to support the idea that a great difference exists between empirical science on the one hand and metaphysics, religion, and theology on the other.

One of these reasons, which is certainly quite important, is that empirical science is centered on the search for spatiotemporal patterns. Although nature does not consist only of patterns, it is organized around configurations (spatial patterns) and rhythms (temporal patterns). As Carsten Bresch puts it:

> If we were to describe the fundamental property of the matter of the universe in a single sentence, we would have to say that matter is formed—or created—so as to show continuously accelerating growth of patterns. . . . Everything around us consists of patterns.[7]

Actually, any scientific law, however stochastic or statistical or probabilistic it may be, always refers to the existence of some kind of pattern. Measurement implies the existence of repeatable patterns. Metaphysics, religion, and theology also deal with some kind of pattern, but it seems quite obvious that they are not centered around the particularized knowledge of spatiotemporal patterns as science is.

The existence of these stable spatiotemporal patterns in nature, and the possibility of using empirical science as a means of studying them, are the sources of both the distinctive reliability of empirical science and of its limitation. Too often, philosophers and theologians are afraid of admitting this reliability of empirical science, whereas some scientists disdain other approaches that do not possess such reliability. Both groups do not realize that the very same reasons that explain the distinctive reliability of empirical science point out its limits. Empirical science, by its very nature, is limited to those aspects of reality that can be studied using experimental control. Elementary reasoning may suffice to establish that, if there is a personal God and if the human person possesses spiritual dimensions, these spiritual realities will remain forever outside the possibilities of the methods of experimental science. The rigor and reliability of empirical science go hand in hand with its limits.

---

7. Carsten Bresch, "What is Evolution?" in *Evolution and Creation,* ed. Svend Andersen and Arthur Peacocke (Aarhus: Aarhus University Press, 1987), pp. 36–37.

No scientific method allows one to automatically obtain reliable knowledge from experience. The classical empiricist view of science, which considered scientific concepts as a mere result of inductive methods based on sense data, was simply mistaken. There are no sense data independent from any theoretical idea, nor purely inductive methods that would allow us to proceed from particular cases to general laws. We also know that scientific proofs always include some conventional elements, so that they can eventually be reformulated at a future point in time. Empirical science is a hermeneutic work that like any other work of human creation is in need of inventiveness and interpretation. Nevertheless, this should not lead us to deny that there is a distinctive reliability associated with the methods of empirical science.

All this can be explained following the "realist objectualism" approach proposed by Evandro Agazzi.[8] The term "realist objectualism" is used to express two ideas: (1) that in empirical science we must construct the "objects" of our theories, and (2) that following the scientific method we may obtain true knowledge of the reality we explore. Indeed, in every scientific discipline we adopt a concrete point of view: we must define a set of basic predicates and also the instrumental operations that serve to measure them. For instance, in Newtonian mechanics we define the basic magnitudes—mass, length, and time—and we describe the instrumental procedures used to measure their values. Thus we cut reality up in such a way that we have something akin to a mental cross section, and the object of our study is the ideal system we have constructed: in the case of Newtonian mechanics, the sun and the planets are considered to be mass points mutually related by the force of gravitational attraction, and any other property is considered irrelevant. We compare the behavior of our ideal models with the observed facts, and we modify the models whenever necessary. Obviously, any "objectification" of this kind has a historical element, as it depends on the concepts and instruments available at a particular moment in time.

Of course, the task of establishing a well-defined objectification in a new discipline for the first time is usually a very difficult one. Nevertheless, once we have the objectification, it is possible to establish intersubjective relations within it and deduce consequences from theoretical results that can be empirically tested.

Any scientific construct must always be interpreted within a particular objectification and, therefore, whatever the merits of a particular piece of natural science may be, we will always find a methodological gap between empirical science and the quest for the spiritual realities. We can safely conclude that the scientific method leaves room for a study of the radical principles of being, truth, goodness, beauty, ethical duties, and transcendence.

8. See Evandro Agazzi, *Temi e problemi di filosofia della fisica,* 2d ed. (Roma: Abete 1974); "Eine Deutung der wissenschaftlichen Objectivität," *Allgemeine Zeitschrift für Philosophie,* 3 (1978): 20–47; *Philosophie. Science, Métaphysique* (Fribourg: Éditions Universitaires, 1987); "L'objectivité scientifique," in *L'objectivité dans les différentes sciences,* ed. Evandro Agazzi (Fribourg: Éditions Universitaires, 1988), pp. 13–25.

2. NATURALISM: DIFFERENCE OR CONFLICT?

Scientific naturalism does not recognize such a gap, because it sees the scientific method as the only legitimate one. Barbour concludes, after an examination of some recent arguments in this line, that they assume that the explanation offered by empirical science is the only acceptable one; that, in those cases, scientific concepts are extended and extrapolated beyond their scientific use, so as to be inflated into comprehensive naturalistic philosophies; and that the abstract and selective character of science is ignored, so these authors fall into what Alfred North Whitehead called "the fallacy of misplaced concreteness."[9]

Naturalism gratuitously turns the difference of methods into contradiction, by denying the truth or correctness of any approach that does not coincide with the scientific one. Naturalism often asserts that scientific progress renders the arguments of metaphysics, religion, and theology less meaningful, so that it would be legitimate to conclude that one can get rid of them. By focusing on concrete events, naturalism can easily find some cases of conflict that were provoked by illegitimate extrapolations. Nevertheless, this tactic leaves the methodological problem untouched. The alleged replacement of theological explanations by scientific ones often corresponds to a lack of philosophical insight; this happens, for instance, when natural agency is seen as incompatible with the activity of a transcendent God.

Among scientists, as in any other social group, we find a great variety of religious views. Although many scientists are religious people, it is not difficult to find some who adopt an antireligious view. What should be stressed in those cases is that their naturalism is not a consequence or a necessary companion of their science, but is rather a personal, philosophical, and theological attitude.

Barbour refers to Jacques Monod, Carl Sagan, Francis Crick, and Edward O. Wilson as examples of scientists who adopt materialistic and naturalistic positions; Haught also provides examples of naturalistic positions. Two examples of scientific naturalism can be examined to illustrate this line of thought and the mistakes on which it is usually based.

Steven Weinberg received the Nobel Prize in physics for his contribution to the formulation of the electroweak theory, which unites in a single theory two of the four fundamental natural interactions—the electromagnetic and the weak nuclear forces. In his book *The First Three Minutes,* in which he explained the main features of the early universe, he alludes to the naturalist perspective. This assertion is present in his 1992 book *Dreams of Final Theory:*

> It would be wonderful to find in the laws of nature a plan prepared
> by a concerned creator in which human beings played some special
> role. I find sadness in doubting that we will. . . . The more we refine

---

9. Barbour, "Ways of Relating Science and Religion," cit., pp. 7–8.

our understanding of God to make the concept plausible, the more it seems pointless.[10]

An assertion such as this cannot be considered as a mere consequence of science. Indeed, the existence of the methodological gap between science and religion shows that we should not expect an answer to our religious questions from physics. The danger of confusion increases when such assertions are presented in works written by famous scientists and seem to be connected with the results of scientific progress.

The second example is even more explicit and refers to the spiritual dimensions of the human person, a subject that is the preferred target of present-day materialists, who think that God and soul have already been discarded from physics and biology, and consider anthropology the last place they should be expelled from. Francis Crick, in his 1994 book *The Astonishing Hypothesis,* has written:

> The Astonishing Hypothesis is that "You", your joys and your sorrows, your memories and your ambitions, your sense of identity and free will, are in fact no more than the behaviour of a vast assembly of nerve cells and their associated molecules. As Lewis Carroll's Alice might have phrased it: "You're nothing but a pack of neurones."[11]

Actually, what is really astonishing is that a scientist as important as Francis Crick, one of the codiscoverers of the double-helical structure of DNA, does not notice that the "nothing but" argument is entirely worthless, because the negative outcome of "the scientific search for the soul" could have been predicted in advance. Indeed, empirical science by itself will never reach God, divine action, spiritual dimensions in the human being, spiritual values, or moral laws, because these realities lie outside the goals of science and cannot be studied by using the experimental contol method.

One serious drawback of scientific naturalism is not only that it is mistaken, but also that it presents itself as if it were a part or a consequence of science. As naturalism or materialism are assuredly well-known philosophical doctrines, their scientific character is sometimes attributed to an alleged "scientific outlook," the general perspective that corresponds to scientifically informed thinking. This kind of argument sometimes receives attention even from authors who oppose naturalism but consider it as a part of the scientific perspective. Thus, Kurt Hübner admits that naturalism is the ontology of science, and then he turns the philosophy of scientific naturalism upside down by arguing that this ontology cannot be proven and that, therefore, its acceptance hangs on subjective opinions. He concludes that it is legitimate to accept, in our scientific age, views that contemplate nature as a reflection of

10. Steven Weinberg, *Dreams of Final Theory* (New York: Pantheon Books, 1992), p. 256.

11. Francis Crick, *The Astonishing Hypothesis: The Scientific Search for the Soul* (New York: Charles Scribner's Sons, 1994), p. 3.

transcendent dimensions.[12] I would prefer to call this alleged ontology of science "scientism" or "scientistic ontology," because it is really a pseudoscientific ideological view.

Science can provide very important material for philosophical and theological reflection, but it cannot by itself transcend its own boundaries. Any attempts to go beyond them must include philosophical reflection.

3. The Mediation of Philiosophy

I would like to underscore that, if I stress that a methodological gap exists between empirical science and the questions about transcendence, I do not do so for my own convenience or to prevent the abuses of materialism and naturalism. The gap really exists. Since this is the case, to bridge it we will need to use intellectual tools, which must include elements common to the opposite sides of the bridge.

This task cannot be accomplished by empirical science alone. I argue, instead, that it can be accomplished by philosophy.

When Barbour and other authors wish to establish a dialogue between science and religion, they usually see the methodological gap as a first approximation that should be carried out by considering the positive relations that exist between the two approaches. When we ask how we can conceive that those two mutually independent approaches may interact with each other, Barbour tells us:

> Any view of the relationship of science and religion reflects philosophical assumptions. Our discussion must therefore draw from three disciplines, not just two; science (the empirical study of the order of nature), theology (critical reflection on the life and thought of the religious community), and philosophy, especially epistemology (analysis of the characteristics of inquiry and knowledge) and metaphysics (analysis of the most general characteristics of reality).[13]

This is a very clear statement that refers to "any view of the relationship of science and religion." When Barbour presents his views on a systematic synthesis, he begins with these words:

> A more systematic integration can occur if both science and religion contribute to a coherent world view elaborated in a comprehensive metaphysics. Metaphysics is the search for a set of general categories in terms of which diverse types of experience can be interpreted. An inclusive conceptual scheme is sought that can represent the fundamental characteristics of all events. Metaphysics as such is the province of the philosopher rather than of either the sci-

---

12. Kurt Hübner, *Die Wahrheit des Mythos* (München: C. H. Beck, 1985); "La naissance de l'age scientifique, resultat des lois ou du hasard?" *Epistemologia,* 10 (1987): 27–38.

13. Barbour, "Ways of Relating Science and Religion," cit. p. 3.

entist or the theologian, but it can serve as an arena of common reflection.[14]

Here, Barbour might seem to concede too much to philosophy, as he sees the synthesis between science and religion as a kind of philosophical doctrine. I would rather speak of philosophical bridges that provide the basis for further theological reflections, and I would also like to remark that, like Barbour, I refer only to theoretical syntheses. There is also a practical or vital synthesis that is most important for the religious life. However, I prefer to pose the question anew from the very beginning.

If empirical science on the one hand, and metaphysics, religion, and theology on the other, represent different approaches toward different goals, an intellectual communication between the two will be possible only if a bridge can be found between them. That bridge is not ready-made however, we must build it. A scientific bridge would not be of use, because it would remain on the side of science and could not function as a bridge. The other possibility is that metaphysics, religion, or theology may incorporate scientific achievements into their realms. But when these achievements are described in purely scientific terms, they appear to belong solely to the province of science. We will not solve our problem unless we find in science something that may be considered under a philosophical, religious, or theological perspective. Once we have reached this point, we might suddenly feel that, after all, there are as many bridges as we desire, because every feature or part of science can be the subject of a philosophical, religious, or theological consideration. I would add that, in the case of religion and theology, we will always need some form of philosophical mediation; we can construct it, take it from an already existing philosophy, or work with a not too explicit philosophy, but a certain dose of philosophy will always be needed to translate scientific elements into humanistic terms.

In the current science-religion dialogue, the bridges between science and religion are often referred to as "boundary questions." I shall continue by examining whether such questions exist and, if so, what kind of questions they would be.

III. BOUNDARY QUESTIONS

If we do not forget the existence of the methodological gap between science and religion, we can wonder whether talk about boundary questions make sense at all. Most of what are usually considered boundary questions may be better labeled as "subjective connections" and "particular overlaps." But one type of boundary question is highly relevant: the study of the general presuppositions of science, especially when it is added to the study of the feedback on these presuppositions from scientific progress.

14. Ibid., p. 28.

1. Are There Genuine Boundary Questions?

Usually, theologians think the best way to approach the relations between science and theology is that of dialogue. In this context, it is often said that science leads to boundary questions that are connected with theology. The question then is: how can we describe these questions in order to identify them? A closely related question points to the root of our search: why should we search for boundary questions between science and religion?

Barbour asserts that the independence between science and religion is a good starting point because it preserves the distinctive character of each enterprise and is a useful strategy for responding to the difficulties posed by the "conflict" approaches. He reminds us that religion does indeed have its characteristic methods, questions, attitudes, functions, and experiences, which are distinct from those of science. But he also adds that the "independence" approach meets serious difficulties, which he summarizes in this way:

> If science and religion were totally independent, the possibility of conflict would be avoided, but the possibility of constructive dialogue and mutual enrichment would also be ruled out. We do not experience life as neatly divided into separate compartments; we experience it in wholeness and interconnectedness before we develop particular disciplines to study different aspects of it. There are also biblical grounds for the conviction that God is Lord of our total lives and of nature, rather than of a separate "religious" sphere. The articulation of a theology of nature that will encourage a strong environmental concern is also a critical task today. I will argue that none of the options considered above is adequate to that task.[15]

I think that these reasons are very sound. The problem is: how can we work toward the desired dialogue?

In his "Dialogue" section, Barbour examines two possible forms of dialogue—Boundary Questions and Methodological Parallels. He avers that both represent "indirect interactions" between science and theology. What kind of "indirect interaction" is involved in Barbour's understanding of boundary questions? An analysis of the issues and authors he mentions to exemplify that dialogue sheds some light on his thinking.

Barbour refers to Thomas Torrance as one of the partners in the dialogue between science and religion with these words:

> In recent writings he (Thomas Torrance) says that at its boundaries science raises religious questions that it cannot answer. In pressing back to the earliest history of the cosmos, astronomy forces us to ask why those particular initial conditions were present. Science shows us an order that is both rational and contingent (that is, its laws and initial conditions were not necessary). It is the combination of contingency and intelligibility that prompts us to search for new and unex-

---

15. Ibid., p. 16.

pected forms of rational order. The theologian can reply that God is the creative ground and reason for the contingent but rational unitary order of the universe.[16]

In this text we find three different candidates for boundary questions. The third one is the combination of contingency and intelligibility in nature. This is a very serious candidate; however, neither contingency nor intelligibility is, properly speaking, a part of science but is rather the result of a philosophical reflection on the presuppositions and achievements of science. The second candidate is the specificity of the initial conditions of the universe; it is often quoted as a very important boundary question, as for instance, in the form of the so-called "anthropic principle." The first candidate contains a kind of definition of a boundary question, when we are told that "at its boundaries science raises religious questions that it cannot answer."

John Polkinghorne has expressed a similar view. In one of his lectures he says:

> Secondly—and this is one of the points I most want to emphasize in this lecture—there are questions which arise from science and which insistently demand an answer, but which by their very character transcend that of which science itself is competent to speak. There is a widespread feeling among practising scientists, particularly those of us who have worked in fundamental physics, that there is more to the physical world than has met the scientific eye. As a result of that feeling, we are living at a time where there is a revival of natural theology taking place, largely at the hands of the scientists rather than the theologians.[17]

Obviously, if "there are questions which arise from science and which insistently demand an answer, but which by their very character transcend that of which science itself is competent to speak," these would be typical boundary questions. But can they exist at all? They should be closely related to science, as we are told that they "arise from science." However, they would not be, properly speaking, scientific questions. But what does it mean that, although they are not scientific, they "arise from science"? That they cannot be answered by science is much easier to understand, because if they are not strictly scientific, it is impossible to answer them by using the methods of science.

Properly speaking, genuine boundary questions cannot arise from science. This is a consequence of the methodological gap that should always be carefully respected. If boundary questions are contained in empirical science, they can be there only in an implicit way. The dialogue between science and religion will be based on an explicit reflection on some aspects that are only im-

---

16. Ibid., p. 18.

17. John C. Polkinghorne, "A Revived Natural Theology," in *Science and Religion. One World: Changing Perspectives on Reality,* ed. Jan Fennema and Ian Paul (Dordrecht: Kluwer, 1990), p. 88.

plicit in scientific work. This perspective makes it possible to understand how genuine boundary questions can arise and also how they can be examined.

Barbour also refers to Ernan McMullin as a proponent of dialogue and quotes a passage in which McMullin expresses a very balanced view that fosters dialogue while avoiding too close commitment to scientific achievements:

> The Christian cannot separate his science from his theology as though they were in principle incapable of interrelation. On the other hand, he has learned to distrust the simpler pathways from one to the other. He has to aim at some sort of coherence of worldview. . . . He may, indeed *must,* strive to make his theology and his cosmology consonant in the contributions they make to his worldview. But this consonance (as history shows) is a tentative relation, constantly under scrutiny, in constant slight shift.[18]

The above reflections may lead us to distinguish three different kinds of boundary questions. The first kind includes particular scientific problems that could serve as a subjective source of religious reflections; this kind can be called "subjective connections." In this line, the astrophysicist who studies scientific theories about the origin of the universe may feel impelled to think about the metaphysical and theological issue of the ultimate explanation of the universe; astrophysics can play a role in this affair, but the question itself lies beyond the purely scientific province and cannot be tackled seriously unless we adopt a metaphysical and theological perspective. The second kind of boundary question refers to "particular overlaps" that may exist between science and religion. The third kind refers to the general presuppositions of science and to general insights as to its achievements. This third group provides the best material for boundary questions and my examination of them shall be central to my proposal. But first I shall discuss the other two to examine what can be said about subjective connections and particular overlaps.

2. Subjective Connections

Although I am ready to admit the assertions that "there are questions which arise from science and which insistently demand an answer, but which by their very character transcend that of which science itself is competent to speak" and that "there is a widespread feeling among practising scientists that there is more to the physical world than has met the scientific eye," I am not sure that they lead to true boundary questions. I would rather label such questions as "subjective connections." I describe them as "subjective" because they depend on the sensibility of the individual scientist. Although they may corre-

---

18. Ernan McMullin, "How Should Cosmology Relate to Theology?" in *The Sciences and Theology in the Twentieth Century,* ed. Arthur Peacocke (Notre Dame, Ind.: University of Notre Dame Press, 1981), p. 52.

spond to an objective problem situation, this kind of problem can be bracketed or left aside in scientific work.

Scientists are human beings who must, like any other person, face philosophical and theological problems; and they may sometimes be moved by particular scientific situations to confront such problems. I would even say that many scientific situations may lead people to reflect on those deeper problems. However, when scientists ask such questions, they behave not like scientists but rather as philosophers or theologians. Doubtless they have the right to behave this way, but their reflections are no longer purely scientific, and they should be evaluated according to philosophical or theological criteria. The origin of these problems can be labeled as scientific only in a loose way, in that a scientific situation has served as the stimulus to activate a philosophical or theological attitude. In addition, the same situation may inspire metaphysical thoughts in one scientist and not in another. If a problem is a genuine scientific question, it cannot properly be considered a metaphysical one.

A good example is cosmology, which is usually regarded as a source of alleged boundary questions. Christian thinkers agree that the arguments used by scientific cosmology about the origin and evolution of the universe can neither prove nor disprove the Christian doctrine of creation.[19] But there is also an increasing bibliography supporting the idea that "there is sufficient evidence at present to justify the belief that the universe began to exist without being caused to do so."[20] However, intriguing as quantum fluctuations and quantum gravity may be, there is little rigor involved when the question is posed as if a self-creation of the universe out of nothing according to physical laws were a real possibility. Indeed, when problems are posed this way, we may have as many boundary questions as we desire. Nevertheless, one can only wonder whether this kind of problem really arises from science or if it should rather be considered as some kind of theology-fiction. If we pose the problem of the ultimate existence and meaning of the universe, what we really face is a philosophical and theological problem. When studying the problem, we should include the relevant empirical knowledge provided by the sciences, but this is by definition not a scientific problem.

The "anthropic principle" is usually also considered to be a boundary question. At first sight, it seems a good candidate to occupy that place. Nevertheless, it should rather be regarded as a new instance of scientists' tendency to establish a link between metaphysical questions and their scientific concerns. Insofar as scientists are human beings who share every human concern, we can find as many boundary questions as we desire. But this would not serve as an answer to our problem. Science may be seen as a catalyst to set off meta-

19. See Stanley L. Jaki, "From Scientific Cosmology to a Created Universe," *The Irish Astronomical Journal,* 15 (1982): 253–262; McMullin, "How Should Cosmology Relate to Theology?" cit.

20. Quentin Smith, "The Uncaused Beginning of the Universe," *Philosophy of Science,* 55 (1988): 39.

physical attitudes, but this does not mean that science by itself implies any metaphysical problem at all; rather it adopts a nonmetaphysical point of view.

In short, I wonder if any specific problem that can be formulated within empirical science may be seen as a boundary question. Insofar as we deal with substantive questions that are properly scientific, we do not need to appeal to extrascientific reasons; indeed, if we need metascientific reasons to formulate or solve a concrete problem, this would indicate that the problem cannot be strictly considered a scientific one.

Therefore, I would conclude that substantive scientific problems cannot be properly called boundary problems. It is understandable that metaphysicians and theologians may consider it a positive sign that scientists sometimes relate particular scientific problems with metaphysics. However, these connections are contingent and subjective events. Scientific problems, when property formulated, have scientific solutions. Metaphysical questions do not properly arise from specific scientific achievements; they rather belong to a perspective that surpasses the scientific realm, and they should be studied from the metaphysical point of view. We can speak in this context of boundary questions if we desire, but we should keep in mind that they do not correspond to the objective relations that exist between the two different methodological approaches.

3. PARTICULAR OVERLAPS

From the historical point of view, the boundaries between science, on the one hand, and philosophy and religion, on the other, have sometimes changed. In such a case we can speak of particular overlaps. One obvious example is the case of the Copernican system. Geocentrism seemed to be backed by common sense and religion, but science finally showed that it was wrong. Such a situation, however, can hardly be considered a genuine boundary question; it is rather a question of fact that does not challenge the existence of the methodological gap between science and religion. Very specific, contingent historical circumstances must be taken into account to place the Galileo affair in its real perspective: we cannot forget, for instance, that neither Galileo nor anyone else was able at that time to provide a proof of the heliocentric theory, but that it was only possible to decide the issue later on by using later scientific arguments. Therefore, no genuine boundary question was at stake then. Empirical science extended its sphere to include a problem that had previously been considered from a different perspective. This is not a boundary question, however, because the problem could be formulated and solved using purely scientific arguments.

In those cases, when the same problem is tackled by science and metaphysics or religion at the same time, I would prefer to speak of "particular overlaps," which should be resolved by clarifying the corresponding arguments. The science–religion debates often center around such problems; and currently the vast majority are due to the abuse of science in the hands of a scientistic naturalism that presents itself as if it were a consequence of science when it, in reality, consists only of pseudoscientific extrapolations.

A different kind of "particular overlap," and certainly a very important one, is the use of pieces of scientific knowledge within metaphysical or theological arguments. Most so-called boundary questions belong to this category. The most usual overlap occurs when scientific information is used as part of the arguments of natural theology, such as the proofs of the existence of God or arguments about the attributes of God.

Theologians rightly aim to emphasize that it is unsound to argue along the lines of the so-called "God of the gaps." They are usually careful about the possibilities of natural theology, saying, for instance, that "natural theology today should avoid any attempt to build its foundation on apparently unfillable gaps in the scientific picture of the universe" and that, as a consequence, "only a radically metaphysical argument, from the very existence of a determinate world, or the existence of any dynamic order at all, has a fair chance of succeeding."[21] There is a clear awareness about "the extreme fluidity whereby models of nature designed to highlight divine activity have so readily lent themselves to reinterpretation in secular terms."[22] Theologians following these principles contemplate arguments such as the fine-tuning of the universe as compatible, coherent, or consonant with theism, and not as real proofs of it.[23]

It can be safely said that scientific information can be used within natural theology in the same way as any other information. However, it must first be submitted to epistemological evaluation, and this is not a trivial exercise. This is why even authors who have devoted great effort to examining the arguments of natural theology sometimes do not use scientific information at all. Thus, when Alvin Plantinga examines in detail cosmological and teleological arguments, he focuses on the logical point of view and only makes occasional, trivial references to scientific knowledge; for instance, when speaking about the causes of existence, he refers to elementary particles only to add immediately "or for that matter a full-grown horse." This is easily understandable if we note that, when speaking about scientific acceptability, Plantinga says that "the relationship between a scientific theory and the grounds for accepting it is still a black and boundless mystery," so that, if we try to use scientific information for theological arguments, "our understanding of scientific theory is too meager to make it more than a shot in the dark."[24]

To use scientific information in a metaphysical or theological context, we

21. W. Norris Clarke, "Is a Natural Theology Still Possible Today?" in *Physics, Philosophy, and Theology: A Common Quest for Understanding,* cit. p. 105.

22. John H. Brooke, "Science and the Fortunes of Natural Theology: Some Historical Perspectives," *Zygon,* 24 (1989): 16.

23. McMullin, "Natural Science and Belief in a Creator: Historical Notes," in *Physics, Philosophy, and Theology: A Common Quest for Understanding,* cit., pp. 70–71; Clarke, "Is a Natural Theology Still Possible Today?" cit., pp. 103–104.

24. Alvin Plantinga, *God and Other Minds: A Study of the Rational Justification of Belief in God* (Ithaca and London: Cornell University Press, 1967), pp. 3–25, 95–111, 269.

should first reflect philosophically on it; indeed, philosophy is homogeneous with metaphysics and natural theology, whereas empirical science is not. This should be kept in mind, for instance, when evolution is used as a counterargument to arguments for divine design, as if the scientific explanations of the structures and adaptation of plants and animals rendered implausible the argument for a divine design.[25] Actually, divine action conceived as the activity proper to a First Cause is absolutely compatible with the agency of natural causes, and criticisms such as this would only be effective against arguments lacking in philosophical insight.

When we use science within natural theology, the only way to achieve rigorous arguments is to consider the reach of scientific explanations. Richard Swinburne distinguishes what he calls full, complete, ultimate, and absolute explanations, and carefully analyzes what should be considered to be scientifically inexplicable. According to his view, there are two categories of such phenomena, those too odd to fit into the established pattern of a scientific explanation and those too big to fit into any pattern of scientific explanation.[26] The more interesting phenomena would be the second type, as they lead to fundamental questions; for instance, why anything exists at all, or why the most general laws of nature hold. In any case, when we use scientific knowledge in metaphysical or theological arguments, we must examine its value first of all, taking into account the epistemological perspective.

Once again, I conclude that the methodological gap between empirical science and natural theology is broad and deep. It is possible to bridge it, but the bridge must include philosophical reflections that, even though consistent with science, cannot be regarded as a mere consequence of it. Discussions about natural theology, even when science is considered to be their source or a central point in them, inevitably fall outside science and focus on philosophical arguments.

IV. THE QUEST FOR INTEGRATION

So far, my comments on boundary questions have been rather restrictive. However, I am not against dialogue and integration; on the contrary, I would like to foster them, but I am trying to avoid the temptation of turning the desire for dialogue into wishful thinking. One should begin by selecting the boundary questions carefully and by exercising equal caution in articulating them. My own proposal, which I will briefly sketch here, focuses on one kind of boundary question: *the presuppositions and implications of scientific progress.* My ideas, to a certain extent, partly correspond to some of the proposals already advanced by other authors.

25. John L. Mackie, *The Miracle of Theism: Arguments For and Against the Existence of God* (Oxford: Clarendon Press, 1982), pp. 132, 141–142.

26. Richard Swinburne, *The Existence of God* (Oxford: Clarendon Press, 1989), pp. 71–72.

1. GENERAL PRESUPPOSITIONS AND INSIGHTS

In the two versions of Barbour's text cited earlier, there is an apparently slight difference when he speaks about boundary questions. I am most interested in that difference, because it points directly to the approach that I am going to develop. The words appear, in both cases, at the very beginning of the section "Boundary Questions" in Barbour's texts; this gives them a certain flavor of solemnity. In the Vatican text the starting phrase reads: "Boundary questions refer to general presuppositions of the whole scientific enterprise"; the Gifford text runs this way: "One type of boundary question refers to the general presuppositions of the whole scientific enterprise."

In the first case, "general presuppositions of the whole scientific enterprise" are presented as *the* boundary questions, as the only candidate for that important place in the dialogue between science and theology; in the later version of the text they are presented only as "one type of boundary question," this type is the first one considered by Barbour in some detail.

Barbour's reference to the general presuppositions of the scientific enterprise centers around the influence of Christianity in the systematic birth of modern empirical science; these presuppositions are therefore presented as historical factors that played a significant role in that birth. It is a well-known fact that positivism presented religion as a first childish stage in the history of humankind which would have been overcome by scientific progress; in this perspective, history is seen as the struggle of the scientific mind against all sorts of religious obstacles. The cliché of the Middle Ages as the "dark ages" when scientific progress was hindered by religious obstacles fits well with that viewpoint. The facts, however, do not fit so well with this view, as was made apparent when in the late nineteenth and the early twentieth centuries, the French physicist Pierre Duhem discovered in the Paris archives a huge number of manuscripts clearly showing that the systematic birth of modern empirical science was prepared by centuries of patient work in the medieval universities of Oxford, Paris, and others.

This long preparation included some specific scientific achievements that were most important, such as the famous theorem of Merton College. The law of accelerated motion, which would play a central role in the development of Galileo's physics, was established explicitly in Oxford and Paris in the fourteenth century. In Paris, Nicole Oresme explained it using a geometric figure which coincides with the one used by Galileo two centuries later to study the same problem.[27] We now know, therefore, that when Galileo for-

27. See Edward Grant, ed., *A Source Book in Medieval Science* (Cambridge, Mass.: Harvard University Press, 1974), pp. 243–253. Oresme's original work is contained in one of his books, edited by Marshall Clagett under the title *Nicole Oresme and the medieval geometry of qualities and motions. A treatise on the uniformity and difformity of intensities known as "Tractatus de configurationibus qualitatum et motuum"* (Madison: University of Wisconsin Press, 1968). Galileo's explanation is contained in Galileo Galilei, *Discorsi e dimostrazioni matematiche intorno à due nuove scienze,* 1638, giornata terza, theorema I, proposito I, in *Opere,* national edition, ed. G. Barbèra, vol. VIII (Firenze: Barbèra 1968), pp. 208–209.

mulated the law of falling bodies, which is considered one of his most important achievements, he worked on a solid basis established several centuries before. Of course, this is what should be expected, and it does not diminish in any way the enormous merit due to Galileo. The work of Duhem has been continued in a variety of fields, which not only include critical editions of medieval manuscripts, but also systematic studies about the conditions that actually prepared the modern birth of empirical science.

Indeed, modern empirical science was born in a particular place and time after many centuries of slow but continuous preparation that included several factors, such as the development of mathematical and technological skills. I will only mention, as an example of the instrumental factors that were needed, that it was difficult for science to develop before modern clocks existed, because measurements of time play a central role in any branch of empirical science.

Some of these factors had an intellectual character. The development of empirical science as a self-sustaining enterprise required, for instance, a kind of faith in the rationality of the world and also in the human capacity to know that world. In short, empirical science is possible only if our world possesses a strong kind of order and if we are capable of investigating it. Actually, after sharing the Christian faith for several centuries, Medieval and Renaissance Europe was built on a common ground that included, as a basic tenet, the doctrine of creation with all its implications: that the world had been created by an omnipotent and wise God and that, therefore, a natural order exists; that the natural order is contingent, because God's creation is free and thus the world cannot be a necessary product of God's action; that human beings, as creatures who participate in God's nature, can reach a knowledge of that natural order; and finally that owing to the contingent character of the world, in order to reach that knowledge we must not only think, but also perform experiments that allow us to know how our world really behaves.

The relevance of these antecedents and their relationship to Christian culture is generally acknowledged today. Barbour's "general presuppositions of the entire scientific enterprise" are closely related to them. He refers, for instance, to the orderly and intelligible character of the world, which goes hand in hand with its contingency, and also to the "desacralisation" of nature that encouraged scientific study. These points are closely related to the biblical doctrine of creation. Barbour points out that we should not exaggerate the relevance of Christianity because there are other important factors that operated at the same time, such as the recovery of the ancient Greek tradition, Arab science, and the humanistic interests of the Renaissance. Then he adds:

> I believe the case for the historical contribution of Christianity to the rise of science is convincing. But once science was well established, its own success was sufficient justification for many scientists, without the need for religious legitimation. Theistic beliefs are clearly not explicit presuppositions of science, since many atheistic or agnostic scientists do first-rate work without them. One can simply accept the

contingency and intelligibility of nature as givens and devote one's efforts to investigating the detailed structure of its order. Yet if one does raise wider questions, one is perhaps more open to religious answers.[28]

At this point, I would pose the following question: are those presuppositions mere historical factors, as Barbour seems to accept, or do they have a relevance that surpasses the historical realm?

Stanley Jaki, who has devoted entire specialized volumes to this subject, refers to the "Christian cultural matrix" that permeated Western Europe for several centuries and provided a common ground where the new scientific enterprise found its only viable birth.[29] Jaki does not limit his thesis to the historical influence of Christianity at the beginning of modern science but extends it to the subsequent development of science as well. Jaki centered his Gifford Lectures around this thesis and entitled them *The Road of Science and the Ways to God.* In his own words:

> The aim of these lectures is to demonstrate what is intimated in their title, namely the existence of a single intellectual avenue forming both the road of science and the ways to God. Science found its only viable birth within a cultural matrix permeated by a firm conviction about the mind's ability to find in the realm of things and persons a pointer to their Creator. All great creative advances of science have been made in terms of an epistemology germane to that conviction.[30]

Thus, Jaki extends his ideas about the general presuppositions of science to any truly creative piece of science. He sees those presuppositions as a necessary condition that must always be present; sometimes explicitly, otherwise implicitly.[31]

Polkinghorne considers intelligibility as a good candidate for a boundary question: "Because I do indeed believe that we live in 'One World,' I also believe that the search for truth will always prove a path to God." He adds that one of the pillars of a new natural theology rooted in science is the appeal to intelligibility, saying that we should then speak of "insight," that is, "of a way of looking at the totality of things which has coherence and intelligibility." It is thus that "theism offers a more satisfying and more extensive explanation of what is going on."[32]

That reference to "insight" introduces a new factor related to the achieve-

28. Barbour, "Ways of Relating Science and Religion," cit., p. 17.

29. Stanley L. Jaki, *Science and Creation: From Eternal Cycles to an Oscillating Universe,* 2d ed. (Edinburgh: Scottish Academic Press, 1986).

30. Stanley L. Jaki, *The Road of Science and the Ways to God* (Chicago: The University of Chicago Press; Edinburgh: Scottish Academic Press, 1978), p. vii.

31. Stanley L. Jaki, "Theological Aspects of Creative Science," in *Chance or Reality and other Essays* (Lanham, Mass.: University Press of America, 1986), pp. 161–181.

32. Polkinghorne, "A Revived Natural Theology," cit. pp. 88–89.

ments of science rather than to its presuppositions. Although it may appear that these two aspects are not connected at all, I relate them in such a way that my entire proposal is based on this connection. In doing this, I follow a way opened up by Nicholas Rescher, who holds that one of the presuppositions of science is metaphysical realism, which refers to ontological features such as natural order and also to the cognitive human abilities to obtain true knowledge of that order. He refers to the "retro-justification" of that metaphysical realism by what he terms the "wisdom of hindsight" on the grounds of its pragmatic and explanatory efficacy.[33]

There is an obvious connection between the presuppositions of science and its achievements, and it belongs in some way to the connection between the necessary conditions of a state of affairs and actual existence of that state of affairs. Indeed, speaking in a very general way, we can say that if A is a necessary condition for B to exist, then the existence of B shows that A is true. In our case, if A represents the presuppositions of science, then the success of the scientific enterprise should be interpreted as a confirmation of A. We can also guess that any piece of scientific progress will allow us to know in further detail some concrete features of those presuppositions, namely of the natural order and of the human ability to know it. We can speak of the implications of scientific progress and also of the feedback of this progress on its presuppositions.

Of course, the reference to "presuppositions," "necessary conditions," and "implications" in this context is in need of further clarification. Indeed, these terms are usually employed in quite a technical way in the specialized field of logic, and their meaning here is wider than the one they have in that field.

2. Bridging the Gap

The preceding reflections can be summed up in a few words. We considered some Christian ideas as elements of a cultural matrix that, jointly with other factors, provided a fertile soil for the birth of modern empirical science. These ideas can be considered presuppositions of science, because they implied a faith in the existence of a natural order that could be explained by science. Those presuppositions are always present, in some way, when science continues to progress. We also noticed that scientific progress provides insight that confirms the value of the presuppositions of science and even amplifies them. Therefore, we are dealing not only with presuppositions that played an important role in the birth of modern science, but also with some aspects of scientific progress that continue to be relevant to the present and the future as well.

Along these lines, I would add that Polkinghorne refers to "the curious way in which modern science seems, almost irresistibly, to point beyond itself."[34] I think that my proposal gives a new meaning to these words. Actu-

---

33. Nicholas Rescher, *Scientific Realism* (Dordrecht: Reidel, 1987), p. 126.

34. John C. Polkinghorne, *One World* (London: SPCK; Princeton, N.J.: Princeton University Press, 1987), p. 63.

ally, the presuppositions of science form a part of science as necessary conditions. They are present only implicitly, so that one can work in science and even make relevant contributions to it without caring in any way about those presuppositions; nevertheless, they continue to be present, not as a kind of philosophical ornament, but as a real part of science itself. When we study the presuppositions of science, we are studying science itself in a strict sense, and our conclusions, if they are correct, should also be considered to belong to the realm of science. In addition, the analysis of the implications of scientific progress and of their feedback on those presuppositions can seriously be said to be a part of science. And the analysis of the presuppositions and implications of science may provide a way to show how science transcends itself.

As I use these words, "presuppositions" refer to the foundations of science, and "implications" or "insights" to its achievements. My proposal begins with the analysis of the presuppositions and then continues with the analysis of the feedback of scientific progress on them. As I see it, this perspective has the following advantages:

- It is closely related to the kind of insight that leads toward transcendence. Indeed, it is rooted in a philosophical basis that includes ontological, epistemological, and ethical problems whose foundations can be easily related to anthropology and natural theology. Nevertheless, this relationship is not an immediate one because metaphysical and theological studies require specific perspectives that cannot be directly obtained from the analysis of science alone. The proposed bridge respects the specific character of the different approaches involved.
- The basic outline refers to the general features of scientific progress, so that the more the sciences progress, the stronger the bridge between science, metaphysics, and religion becomes. This bridge completely overcomes the difficulties involved in the God-of-the-gaps approach, because it is not centered on the holes in scientific knowledge.
- This bridge does not imply any commitment to the particular achievements of science at any given moment. Nevertheless, it provides a good framework for examining the metaphysical and theological implications of any concrete scientific achievement.
- As the bridge is built on some implicit assumptions and implications of scientific progress, even if it undoubtedly has a philosophical character, it is closely connected to science and shows that in some way science transcends itself.

2

The Presuppositions
and Implications
of Science

Belief in an underlying natural order and in the human ability to know it were factors that contributed to the systematic development of modern empirical science and continue to foster its progress today. Insofar as these beliefs have helped to bring about some scientific achievements and preceded them, they can be considered genuine presuppositions of science.

The problem of the presuppositions of science is, however, much broader. On the one hand, it is closely related to the explanation of the autonomy of science: indeed, to say that science is based on extrascientific presuppositions apparently contradicts its autonomy. On the other hand, one may also dispute whether the label "belief" is the most appropriate one to use when referring to presuppositions. Scientific achievements, even when they have been attained with the help of some kind of belief, should be evaluated with objective standards completely independent of any belief system. Apart from the presuppositions already mentioned, there are other candidates that could be also considered genuine presuppositions, and the problem arises as to whether some criterion exists that could help determine which candidates should be considered genuine presuppositions. There is no general agreement about the very existence of presuppositions. Finally, the problems related to the presuppositions of science are seldom considered in a systematic way and, in consequence, the entire issue usually appears as if it were surrounded by a kind of cloud.

I. WHY PRESUPPOSITIONS?

1. The General Presuppositions of Science

The terms "supposition" and "presupposition" have been used in different ways in logic throughout the history of philosophy, including recent times.

In the middle of the twentieth century, analytical philosophy was a predominant trend in the intellectual arena and, therefore, logical analysis played a most important role. In *The Encyclopedia of Philosophy* (1967), the notions of "presupposing" and "contextual implication," which are considered within the specialized context of logic, are said to "have come to play increasingly prominent roles in the philosophical literature of the English-speaking world during the past 25 years. This development is not accidental but arises from the stress the twentieth century puts upon analysis as a fundamental mode of philosophical inquiry." The encyclopedia identifies two kinds of presupposition. The first is linked with the Oxford philosopher Peter F. Strawson, who defined what it means to say that a statement presupposes another one in his *Introduction to Logical Theory* (1952).

That second kind of presupposition is associated with Robin G. Collingwood who "distinguishes between absolute and relative presuppositions," arguing that "metaphysics is the science that ascertains what these absolute presuppositions are. His view is that absolute presuppositions form the basis of the civilisations developed at various times in history and the ground of the science developed in such civilisations. When a civilisation changes, its presuppositions change and are succeeded by others. According to this view, metaphysics is therefore a branch of the historical sciences."[1]

Collingwood's ideas about presuppositions transcend the strict ambit of formal logic and imply a historicist interpretation of metaphysics, which is very problematic, to say the least. To admit that science evolves in time and that some of its presuppositions also change does not imply that we should endorse a historicist view of metaphysics, for metaphysics should concentrate on those concepts and principles that reflect central features of reality.

According to *The Oxford Dictionary of Philosophy*, a presupposition is "Informally, any suppressed premise or background framework of thought necessary to make an argument valid, or a position tenable. More formally, a presupposition has been defined as a proposition whose truth is necessary for either the truth or the falsity of another statement."[2] Obviously, the first meaning is wider and can be applied to arguments and positions, whereas the second is narrower and refers to a relation between two statements.

The Cambridge Dictionary of Philosophy offers two meanings for "presupposition": "(1) a relation between sentences or statements, related to but distinct from entailment and assertion; (2) what a speaker takes to be understood in making an assertion. The first notion is semantic, the second pragmatic."[3] The two notions are said to be logically independent.

---

1. Avrum Stroll, "Presupposing," in *The Encyclopedia of Philosophy* Vol. 6, ed. Paul Edwards (New York: Macmillan & The Free Press, 1967), pp. 446, 449.

2. Simon Blackburn, "Presupposition," in *The Oxford Dictionary of Philosophy* (Oxford and New York: Oxford University Press, 1994), p. 300.

3. Rod Bertolet, "Presupposition," in *The Cambridge Dictionary of Philosophy*, ed. Robert Audi (Cambridge: Cambridge University Press, 1995), p. 641.

I choose as my definition one that cannot be identified with any of the meanings just quoted, but corresponds to the common meaning of the word. We use several terms that are closely related: To "assume" means to take something for granted as the basis of an argument or an action. To "presume" means to assume or take for granted, to presuppose, to anticipate. To "suppose" is said of actions, conditions or facts, and means to involve something as a ground or basis, to require something as a condition, to imply, to presuppose. Finally, to "presuppose," when it is said of a thing, means to require it as a necessary preceding condition, to involve or imply it as an antecedent; when it is said of a person, means that the person supposes something a priori, or believes something in advance of actual knowledge.

In this context, when we speak about the presuppositions of science, we can think of them in two basic senses: as "beliefs" of the scientists, or as "statements" or "principles" that provide the basis of scientific theories. The first sense sounds rather subjective; the second has an objective character.

In the first sense, the presuppositions are "beliefs" of the scientists prior to the formulation or testing of their theories. Actually, everyone would agree that scientists may have their personal beliefs and also that these beliefs may have an influence on the results obtained. However, this influence will be regarded as something accidental and therefore irrelevant unless we may show that some particular beliefs must be shared by all scientists as a part of their job.

In the second sense, the presuppositions are "statements" or "principles" that should be assumed as a basis for the scientific theories. Nevertheless, if we assert that the theories of science must be built on some extrascientific basis, the autonomy of science seems to be in danger.

The two senses of the term "presupposition" come up against some difficulties: the first sense seems irrelevant to science and to any objective appreciation of its value, and the second seems to be contrary to the autonomy of science.

I am going to use the term "presupposition" in a different way. My use does not refer to "beliefs" or "statements," but rather to "states of affairs." It does not directly refer to the beliefs of the scientists; it refers to objective states of affairs implicitly included in the practice of science. For instance, "natural order" is a presupposition of science because the very existence of science would be impossible if nature did not exhibit any kind of order at all. I do not mean that we must assume that nature behaves in a completely deterministic way, but that nature must possess some kind of still-unknown order if we are to achieve any scientific progress. In this sense, the existence of the presuppositions of science is required as a necessary preceding condition if science is to exist at all.

I shall focus on three presuppositions: *natural order, human abilities,* and *scientific values.* All three have an objective character; values can be considered objective if we define them as the internal goals of the scientific enterprise.

These presuppositions can remain unnoticed, and their existence can be denied as happens when scientists adopt a positivistic attitude. But although they can adopt such an attitude about philosophy or the scientific method, they cannot adopt it when they work as scientists.

Empirical science is a "state of affairs," a goal-directed human activity whose existence and progress are necessarily grounded on some assumptions about the natural order and about our ability to know it. The general presuppositions of science can be considered necessary conditions of science; natural order, human cognitive ability, and science as a goal-directed enterprise are "states of affairs" that exist in nature, in the human being, and in society, respectively.

If we consider the presuppositions of science in this way, we can also understand how they relate to those presuppositions considered as "beliefs," "statements," or "principles." Indeed, if a state of affairs such as natural order is a necessary condition of the scientific enterprise, then all scientists will believe that that order exists, and yet any one of them can deny this and continue working successfully in the scientific field. Again, natural order may be explained by means of particular statements or principles, but this does not contradict the autonomy of science; indeed, those statements should not be included among the principles, axioms, or postulates of scientific theories: they only express preconditions of science or, put in other words, the soil that science needs if it is to grow at all. The "belief" and the "statement' character of the presuppositions of science can be accepted while avoiding, at the same time, the disadvantages that they could provoke.

When speaking about the presuppositions of science I refer to the general presuppositions that serve as the basis of the entire scientific edifice, which differ from those that refer only to single theories or branches of empirical science. Every scientific theory has to be built on axioms or principles that cannot be proved from within the theory in which they appear. These axioms or principles are, therefore, presuppositions of those particular theories, but cannot be considered presuppositions of the entire scientific enterprise. Also, some branches of the sciences presuppose the validity of other, more fundamental branches; in this sense, for instance, chemistry assumes to a great extent the validity of many theories of physics, and this may also be said of biology with respect to chemistry and physics.

The particular presuppositions that are used within science can be called presuppositions "in" science, and the general presuppositions that are the basis of the entire scientific enterprise can be called presuppositions "of" science. This terminology is used by Kurt Hübner.[4]

2. SCIENCE WITHOUT PRESUPPOSITIONS?

To begin a discussion of presuppositions, we must first overcome a basic difficulty: why should we admit these presuppositions at all? Some misunder-

---

4. Kurt Hübner, "The Problem of Metaphysical Presuppositions in and of Science," in *The Nature of Metaphysical Knowledge,* ed. George F. McLean and Hugo Meynell (Washington, D.C.: University Press of America, 1988), pp. 129–134.

standings originate from historical confrontations; for example, presuppositions are usually considered a piece of "metaphysics," and the logical reaction
to a discussion about them is to say that there is no reason to introduce something extrascientific into science.

This kind of polemic can be traced back to the birth of a modern empirical science in the seventeenth century. The new science presented itself as a
substitute for ancient physics, which was made up of both science in the modern sense and a kind of physical philosophy. This ancient natural philosophy
was replaced by a mechanistic philosophy, which to some extent was shared
by Descartes, Galileo, and Newton.

In the philosophy of Descartes, as later in that of Kant, natural science was
considered a branch of the tree of knowledge which had its roots in metaphysics. The metaphysics of Descartes included a divine action that was seen
as the guarantee of the conservation of the quantity of motion; the metaphysics of Kant was a set of laws of human knowledge that would allegedly
act as the basis for the principles of science. Until the middle of the nineteenth century, philosophers were really interested in the development of
empirical science and sometimes helped to foster it, and scientists were interested in philosophical and theological issues. The idealistic philosophies of
Schelling and Hegel changed the situation dramatically. Empirical science
was considered by Hegel as a tool that should change when necessary to accommodate his philosophical ideas. At that time, scientists began to look with
suspicion on any kind of philosophical claim and attempted to reinforce the
methodological gap between science and philosophy. Stanley Jaki refers to
"the violent reaction of nineteenth-century physics against Schelling, Hegel,
and their followers, who tried to derive the whole of physics not from observations and measurements, but from their own fancies, which they identified with metaphysics." He includes in this context a quotation from the
physicist Hermann Helmholtz, written in 1862, that offers clear firsthand testimony of the rupture that occurred then between physicists and philosophers:

> The philosophers accused the scientific men of narrowness; the sci-
> entific men retorted that the philosophers were crazy. And so it came
> about that men of science began to lay some stress on the banishment
> of all philosophic influences from their work; while some of them,
> including men of the greatest acuteness, went so far as to condemn
> philosophy altogether, not merely as useless but as mischievous
> dreaming. Thus it must be confessed, not only were the illegitimate
> pretensions of the Hegelian system to subordinate to itself all other
> studies rejected, but no regard was paid to the rightful claims of
> philosophy, that is, the criterion of the sources of cognition, and the
> definition of the functions of the intellect.[5]

5. Stanley L. Jaki, *The Relevance of Physics* (Chicago and London: The University of Chicago
Press, 1966), pp. 333–334.

One of the ways to reinforce the gap between science and philosophy is to deny that empirical science is in need of any philosophical basis, foundation, or presupposition. The autonomy of science became a crucial issue not only for scientists, but also for those philosophers who saw in empirical science an ally in their fight against metaphysics and religion. Whenever someone spoke about the presuppositions of science, they would say that this kind of talk was outdated and did not respect the autonomy of science. After all, why should scientists listen to outsiders evaluating their own work? What could metaphysics add to scientific rigor? Where would extrascientific criteria come from?

An example of such an attitude can be found in the work of Arthur Pap included in two classic anthologies of philosophy of science published in the mid-twentieth century.[6] Pap poses the question: "Does science have metaphysical presuppositions?" His answer is no. According to Pap, many metaphysicians react against the positivistic worship of science by saying that "the scientists themselves are metaphysicians, only they are not aware of their own metaphysical presuppositions." To evaluate that claim, Pap distinguishes three meanings of the word "presupposition" and tries to show that none of them can be called a metaphysical presupposition of science.

First Pap considers "presupposition" as a "necessary condition" and offers as an example "a proposition which a metaphysician might claim to be presupposed by science without nonetheless belonging to science: the principle of causality," expressed in the simple form: "every event has a cause." He immediately adds that it cannot be said that any specific causal law presupposes this principle, because the statement "some events are uncaused" is certainly consistent with "this event has a cause." Then he alludes to "another proposition which a follower of Kant might wish to call a presupposition of empirical science: there are physical constants," and labels this an existential statement verified by some singular statements, adding that this is not a reason to label it as "metaphysical."

The second meaning offered is "the relation of an inferred conclusion to a part of its premises." In that sense it is said that some sciences presuppose others and logic is presupposed by all the sciences. In this context, Pap refers to "the beliefs which the scientist expresses by his activities and which motivate his behavior as scientist," and more concretely, to believing in the simplicity of nature, or to the belief that the same cause always will produce the same effect. Pap holds that such beliefs should not be considered "metaphysical," unless "metaphysical" means only a very general belief. Moreover, he adds that, whatever relevance those beliefs have, they belong to the psychology of scientific inquiry and cannot lend any logical weight to the propositions of science.

---

6. I quote from Arthur Pap, "Does Science Have Metaphysical Presuppositions?" in *Readings in the Philosophy of Science,* ed. Herbert Feigl and May Brodbeck (New York: Appleton-Century-Crofts, 1953), pp. 21–33. A briefer text under the same title is contained in Philip P. Wiener, *Readings in Philosophy of Science* (New York: Charles Scribner's Sons, 1953), pp. 480–484.

The third meaning of "presupposition" given by Pap is the psychological reason for the behavior of scientists; he notes that some of these beliefs are necessary for scientists to act as they do. However, Pap comments that he does not see any reason why these beliefs should be viewed as "metaphysical."

Pap's attitude is best expressed when he refers to "the belief that physics is built on certain 'a priori' principles which are a genuine source of physical knowledge." Certainly, if this were the meaning of the presuppositions of science, Pap would be right in rejecting them. A Kantian or, in general, a rationalist attempt to provide a "metaphysical" basis to empirical science by means of some a priori assumptions involves a mistaken approach. This does not reflect my understanding of the term, which focuses on presuppositions that are necessary conditions for the entire scientific enterprise. Natural order, human abilities, and scientific goals are conditions necessary for the very existence of science.

Pap recognizes that there are presuppositions underlying the behavior of scientists, but he insists that this is a psychological issue. But I hold that if some of those presuppositions are *necessary* conditions of the behavior of the scientists, they cannot be confined merely to the psychological realm. Pap would seem to argue that this kind of presupposition is irrelevant because it is too general and therefore is trivial. He illustrates this viewpoint using the metaphor of fishing.

Let us consider, Pap suggests, the case of someone who goes to fish in a lake. Obviously, we must presuppose that there are fish there; otherwise we should consider that person a fool. In that sense, the assumption that there are fish in the lake is a presupposition for the activity of fishing. Nevertheless, this assumption can only be confirmed empirically, that is, if we find fish there. Then, every fished fish is a confirming instance of our presupposition. But, according to Pap, this sense of "presupposition" is trivial.[7]

Pap uses this metaphor to illustrate his rejection of the principle of causality as a presupposition of the entire scientific activity. The same metaphor can be used to demonstrate the nature and relevance of the general presuppositions of science.

Like fishermen, assuming the presence of fish in a body of water, scientists must assume that some kind of natural order exists that can be grasped using the scientific approach, and they must also assume that this effort is worthwhile despite the absence of a guarantee that their enterprise will be successful. Every success is a confirmation of the possibility and value of their effort. What is more, a new success may provide clues and new stimuli about new possibilities for the development of science. Of course, in science as in fishing, any success is contingent and cannot provide a guarantee of future success. But what actually happens in science is exactly the contrary: again and again we discover unsuspected new fields, new methods, revolutionary applications, even as experts predict the end of science. If we consider the va-

7. Arthur Pap, *Analytische Erkenntnistheorie* (Wien: Springer, 1955), n. 65.

riety of natural phenomena and the limits of our knowledge, it is hardly conceivable that our quest for new knowledge will ever reach an end.[8]

New findings contribute to reshaping our previous ideas about nature and human knowledge and provide new means to achieve practical goals and pose new problems. All this can hardly be considered trivial. It is a source for major events in human history. This perspective does not come from study of the presuppositions of science alone; it requires considering the feedback from scientific progress to these presuppositions.

The prejudice against the metaphysical foundations of science can be partly explained, as already noted, as a reaction against the excesses of some philosophers. The Kantian approach has played a central role in this issue. Kant appreciated the progress of science and built his philosophy, to a great extent, as a justification of that progress. However, he thought that empirical science could not provide its own foundations and that, therefore, it was the task of philosophy to develop the "principles" that would constitute the "pure" or foundational part of the sciences. It is understandable that this approach provoked a reaction among scientists, who felt that their autonomy would be threatened if philosophers were needed to provide the basics of science. Another real danger existed that a particular stage of science would be canonized as definitive. In summary, speaking about the presuppositions of science was feared as a dangerous form of interference that should be avoided.

I propose viewing this from a completely different perspective. As I see them, the presuppositions of science form a part of science but are not concrete pieces of knowledge that should be added as explicit premises in scientific work. They are rather necessary conditions that are usually only implicit in the work of scientists without interfering in that work. Their relevance comes from their interplay with scientific progress. In this way they provide a means for science to transcend itself, as they are a part of science that can be used within philosophical and even theological contexts to discover the meaning of science.

Some could argue that we should not accept the existence of presuppositions of science because we cannot anticipate whether they will work. We find an echo of this argument when David Miller, one of the most orthodox followers of Karl Popper, tries to answer the objections that have been formulated against Popper's falsificationism. He writes:

> The first, and perhaps most fundamental, objection is found in the claim that science, and even pre-scientific inquiry, cannot get started without some assumption or presupposition of order and regularity in the world. This objection was considered (by Popper), and set aside, already in *Logik der Forschung*, Section 79, but it recurs from time to time.[9]

8. See Gerald Holton, "The End of Science is Nowhere in Sight," *Scientific American,* 273, no. 4 (October 1995): 191.

9. David Miller, *Critical Rationalism: A Restatement and Defence* (Chicago and La Salle, Ill.: Open Court, 1994), p. 15.

When Miller analyzes this objection, he tells us that, "although falsificationism does not make any metaphysical assumption concerning the immutability of natural processes, Popper recommends the adoption of the corresponding methodological rule: to search for spatio-temporally invariant laws," and he concludes:

> In sum, science need contain no metaphysical assumption concerning the immutability or order of nature. It need contain no assumption not explicitly available for testing (though it will inevitably have consequences that cannot be tested). Scientific hypotheses propose order for the world; they do not presuppose it.[10]

Indeed, Popper spoke of "the metaphysical faith in the existence of regularities in our world" as "a faith which I share, and without which practical action is hardly conceivable," but, at the same time, he proposed to shift from the stronger metaphysical "principle of the uniformity of nature" to a methodological rule that leads us to search for those regularities.[11]

Popper's remarks, and Miller's as well, clearly show that, if science is to progress at all, we must advance hypotheses that propose that some new, previously unknown order exists. But we have no guarantee that these hypotheses will be correct and, even if they pass our tests successfully, we cannot know whether they are and will always be universally valid in space and time. This is completely coherent with my idea about the presuppositions of science. I do not say that science must presuppose that there exists an immutable natural order. I think that this is not true: I prefer to think of the natural order as contingent and evolving in time. Nevertheless, we must admit that empirical science can only develop insofar as a stable natural order exists and insofar as we can connect the different stages of that natural order by means of some causal link.

II. SCRUTINIZING PRESUPPOSITIONS

I am going to examine now several positions that underline important features of the presuppositions of science and come from different perspectives. I have chosen authors who combine science, philosophy, and religion, covering a spectrum from religious orthodoxy to pure materialism. For the sake of clarity and rigor, I shall examine each position separately.

1. Ontological and Epistemological Realism as Presuppositions

In Stanley Jaki's publications regarding the relations between science, philosophy, and theology, the presuppositions of science are a central topic. His ap-

---

10. Ibid., pp. 26–27.

11. Karl Popper, *The Logic of Scientific Discovery* (London and Cambridge, Mass.: Unwin Hyman, 1990), pp. 252–254.

proach involves two main lines of argument. His first argument holds that the Christian cultural matrix that made possible the birth of modern science included ontological and epistemological realism, which should be taken as the basic preconditions of empirical science. These presuppositions hold not only for a particular moment in time, but also extend their influence to any later developments of truly creative science. Here, "ontological realism" means that we accept the existence of a natural world that has its own consistency and is intelligible, and "epistemological realism" stands for our capacity to know that world, even if our knowledge is always imperfect. Jaki's second argument, in his examination of the relation between physics and metaphysics, concludes that not a few philosophical assumptions have to be used if physics is to exist at all.

Jaki devotes a chapter ("Physics and Metaphysics") in his book *The Relevance of Physics* to underlining the existence of philosophical ideas that must be admitted if empirical science is to exist and have any meaning at all. Like a good historian, he "teaches by examples" and presents selected testimonies of first-rate physicists who speak about a kind of philosophical "faith" as the basis of empirical science. For instance, Hermann Weyl says that "science would perish without a supporting transcendental faith in truth and reality." Albert Einstein and Leopold Infeld say that "without the belief that it is possible to grasp the reality with our theoretical constructions, without the belief in the inner harmony of our world, there could be no science. This belief is and always will remain the fundamental motive for all scientific creation." When Jaki analyzes these testimonies, he speaks of the "metaphysical roots" of the methods and basic concepts of science. Then he refers to some "basic assumptions" about the realm of reality that are used in science:

> The principal one of these basic assumptions is the intelligibility of nature. If this is mentioned by physicists only on occasion, it is only because we don't talk too much about the air we breathe, unless the situation becomes critical. There are other assumptions, too, often and explicitly used by physicists, without being any the less metaphysical for that. The first to mention is simplicity. . . . Not a bit different is the case of the principle of symmetry. . . . The pure rationalist, the extreme positivist, the antiphilosophical physicist are clearly at a loss when coming face to face with the task of accounting for the constant use of assumptions, the nature of which they try to ignore. Yet, without recourse to philosophy, one is indeed hard put to find justification for the fact without which physicists simply cannot do their work: the unavoidable necessity of translating mathematical formalism into a conceptual system based on sense perception.[12]

---

12. Jaki, *The Relevance of Physics,* cit., pp. 348, 351, 353. Chapter 8, "Physics and Metaphysics," occupies pages 330–370.

Jaki analyzes these ideas and includes among them the idea of causality. Then he summarizes his list of the philosophical assumptions of science:

Faith in the existence of the external world, faith in the existence of a typical order in nature, assumptions used by the scientific method to detect this order, the necessity of referring the mathematical formalism to commonsense terms, the indispensability of non-univocal, analogous concepts even within the framework of science characterized by emphasis on using univocal terms whenever possible, all these are not the only instances of the unavoidable involvement of physics in metaphysics.[13]

The word "faith" is not used by accident in these texts; Jaki insists on the "philosophical faith" needed by scientists and has also devoted an article, "The Role of Faith in Physics," to this subject.[14]

Jaki's "philosophical faith" and "assumptions" can be identified with the "presuppositions" of science and can be summarized under the headings "ontological realism" and "epistemological realism," if we limit ourselves to the more general presuppositions. Indeed, some of them, such as simplicity or symmetry, should not be considered general presuppositions because they have a more particular character, and others refer to commonsense concepts that could be considered presuppositions of any human activity whatsoever. In his monographs Jaki defines the general presuppositions of science as "ontological realism" and "epistemological realism."

I agree with this view. These are the most basic general presuppositions of science. Ontological realism refers to the natural order; in empirical science we aim at knowing a world whose existence and behavior do not depend on our will: we may transform it and even create new systems, but to do this we have to follow the laws of nature. Epistemological realism refers to our ability to know that objective natural order. Even if our knowledge necessarily includes conventional features, we can in some way grasp nature's objective character.

I would add that I do not like to speak about "philosophical faith" or simply "faith" in this context, even if this word is borrowed from people like Einstein. Indeed, to work in science we do not need to "believe" in the tenets of ontological and epistemological realism or in any particular assumptions whatsoever; it is sufficient that we "suppose" them.

The general presuppositions of science have to be regarded as the basis of scientific work because they are necessary conditions of it. They are a part of science itself, as they are its necessary conditions. The use of the word "faith" tends to introduce some confusion precisely because it refers to subjective factors. Surely, some scientists could say that they do not have that faith, and perhaps they would be right. Instead, if we stop speaking about "faith" and we

13. Ibid., p. 359.

14. Stanley L. Jaki, "The Role of Faith in Physics," in *Chance or Reality and Other Essays* (Lanham, Mass.: University Press of America, 1986), pp. 144–160.

speak about "presuppositions," we will avoid those difficulties. Presuppositions refer to objective states of affairs; therefore, even if many scientists refused to accept them, this would not change the objective situation.

Jaki intends to show the failures of the positivist account of science, and so he argues that scientific procedures contain many aspects that should be considered as philosophical or metaphysical. I agree with his view and would add another presupposition related to the aims of scientific inquiry; namely, that this inquiry is worthwhile. This presupposition is the most basic one derived from an analysis of science itself.

2. Presuppositions and the Limits of Science

In a collection of essays on the structure and development of science, the Oxford nuclear physicist Peter Hodgson considered the presuppositions of science in connection with its limits. He focuses on the inability of empirical science to solve all kinds of problems, especially ethical ones, and tries to show that the very nature of science implies the existence of limits in reference to metaphysical, ethical, and religious matters.

In this context, Hodgson follows Jaki in his appraisal of the historical role Christian ideas played in the birth of empirical science. Gunnar Andersson writes in his introductory essay:

> Hodgson thinks that science cannot even begin if the prospective scientist does not believe that the world is ordered and rational. Otherwise he would think that the scientific enterprise is doomed to failure. In this sense certain metaphysical presuppositions are necessary for the very beginning of science. According to Hodgson this can explain why science was born in Europe and not elsewhere. The Christian belief in a rational and omnipotent Creator firmly implanted in the European mind the conviction that the universe is ordered and rational and opened the way for science.[15]

In his essay, Hodgson refers, briefly but explicitly, to three levels of the presuppositions of science: ontological, epistemological, and ethical. He summarizes thus:

> Science cannot even begin to exist unless the prospective scientist firmly and implicitly holds a rather special and interlocking set of beliefs about the world and about his proper attitude to it. He must believe that the world is ordered and rational, and that this order and rationality is open to the human mind, for otherwise his enterprise would be foredoomed to failure. He must believe that it is good to study the world, and that the knowledge he gains is precious and yet must be shared freely among all men. Finally he must believe that the order of the world is contingent, that the world could have been

---

15. Gunnar Andersson,"Presuppositions, Problems, Progress," in *The Structure and Development of Science*, ed. Gerald Radnitzky and Gunnar Andersson (Dordrecht, Boston, and London: Reidel, 1979), p. 7.

made otherwise, so that he cannot hope to unlock its secrets by pure contemplation but must embark on the arduous course of observation and experiment.[16]

The three kinds of presupposition correspond to the three levels of science as a goal-directed activity in which characteristic methods are employed to obtain a specific result. The first necessary condition for science to exist is that we consider its goals as valuable and worth pursuing. The second is that those goals are achievable and this includes two conditions: "that the world is ordered and rational, and that this order and rationality is open to the human mind."

Hodgson's insistence on the "natural" and "necessary" character of the presuppositions of science is especially interesting. He speaks about "the natural presuppositions of science" and "the presuppositions that are necessary for science." When he examines what the effect of denying any one of these presuppositions or all of them would be, he concludes: "thus the presuppositions of science seem to be essential and unchangeable." I would add that while the presuppositions of science possess some general characteristics that do not change, they also include some specific points that could evolve as a result of the feedback received from scientific progress.[17]

Hodgson also refers to those presuppositions as "beliefs." I would prefer to avoid this word in this context, precisely because, as Hodgson most aptly notes, the general presuppositions of science are objective necessary conditions for it. Hodgson writes that they are rarely explicitly denied because they "are usually at a deeper level of consciousness; indeed they have to be mainly of this character if they are to be effective."[18] But this is hardly compatible with a "faith" or a "belief," as these words usually suggest a conscious attitude.

In conclusion, Hodgson's essay contains a clear and explicit reference to the three kinds of presuppositions of science that I shall take to be the central ones, and he underscores the idea that they are necessary conditions for the scientific enterprise.

3. THE NONSCIENTIFIC BASES OF SCIENCE

Langdon Gilkey, in a book that aims to build bridges between science, philosophy, and theology from the point of view of a theologian, articulates a critique of scientism that would make room for the humanities. He clearly indicates that his criticism is not directed at science, but at scientism:

> My critique is not of science, its methods, or its results but of this way of knowing as understood in relation to other, complementary ways of knowing. The view of science that I criticize (1) sees science

---

16. Peter Hodgson, "Presuppositions and Limits of Science," in *The Structure and Development of Science,* cit., p. 136.

17. Ibid., pp. 136–137.

18. Ibid., p. 138.

as the only way to know reality and so the only responsible means for defining reality for us and (2) views the results of science as providing an exhaustive account of reality or nature and hence as leaving no room for other modes of knowing, such as aesthetic, intuitive, speculative, or religious modes. . . . This book devotes its first attention, then, to a critical investigation of the scientistic side of the debate present at Little Rock.[19]

A professor of theology in the University of Chicago, Gilkey participated as a witness in the creationist trial in Little Rock, Arkansas, in 1981. Since then has tried to show how the extreme positions that underlie a trial like that— a "scientific creationism" that searches scientific knowledge in the Bible and "scientific naturalism" that seeks to oppose religion in the name of science— can be overcome.

Gilkey's main argument is centered around four ideas that are present in both science and religion: nature as power, as life, as order, and as unity of meaning. In the section entitled "The Nonscientific Bases of Science," Gilkey argues that empirical science is based on a double foundation that lies outside science itself: on the existence of a subject capable of carrying out the scientific enterprise and on the existence of an orderly nature that can be scientifically studied. This double foundation corresponds quite well to two of my three general presuppositions, which are also affirmed by Jaki and Hodgson.

The phrase "nonscientific bases of science" expresses quite well that this double foundation is not, and cannot be, the result of scientific proofs. A scientistic position which presents empirical science as the only legitimate way of knowing is untenable, because science itself must rely on a nonscientific basis. I have sometimes used similar expressions. Yet, when we speak specifically about the presuppositions of science, I would prefer to avoid it. In fact, as we have already noted, the three general presuppositions of science form part of science itself as necessary conditions of it, and in this sense they are scientific. Obviously, they do not figure among the specific results of science, as a part of any theory. But they have to be admitted, at least in an implicit way, by anyone who works in the field of empirical science. They are "nonscientific" only in the precise sense that their study requires a philosophical perspective that is different from the particular points of view used in empirical science (although in some way they can also be studied scientifically), but they constitute a part of the entire building of empirical science as its foundation.

The existence of the natural order is considered by Gilkey to be a central presupposition of the entire scientific enterprise:

Finally, the assumption of an order spanning all of space and time is essential to all modern scientific thinking and inquiry. This assumption is unprovable because it is the basis of all proof. Without it there

---

19. Langdon Gilkey, *Nature, Reality, and the Sacred: The Nexus of Science and Religion* (Minneapolis, Minn.: Fortress Press, 1993) p. 2.

are no data at all, data from yesterday in time or from somewhere else in space; and without data there is no empirical proof. As Alfred North Whitehead put it, that yardsticks used to measure distances yesterday in Cambridge should hold good today in New Haven is a faith based on general intuition and not provable by any use, however ingenious, of yardsticks. This faith in order, Whitehead continued to explain, is not only basic to science but also to all human (he says "civilized") life.[20]

Here there is a further reference to "faith" I do not like; I would rather speak of "assumptions" or "presuppositions." Actually, some assumptions that were once considered evident or commonsense were later modified, and the content of the presuppositions of science is affected by this qualification. In fact, when I say that a natural order is a general presupposition of science, I do not intend to include in my assertion any fixed specific types of order such as the yardstick. It might eventually happen that the yardstick could change, and we should be prepared for such eventualities. What would happen in that case is that a part of the general presupposition would have to change. As I shall explain later, a central aspect of my argument is that there is a kind of feedback from scientific progress on the general presuppositions of science in such a way that progress retrojustifies, broadens, and eventually refines the presuppositions. The refinement of our presupposition takes place when we realize that some part of it must be corrected or changed, and it is hardly conceivable how this can happen if the entire presupposition must be admitted by faith.

Regarding the presupposition that refers to the knowing subject, Gilkey points out that the existence of a self-aware subject is a precondition of empirical science, and takes this as evidence against the account of reality provided by scientism:

> In any case, it is clear that science as an operation demonstrates the reality and the effectiveness of spirit: of mind, freedom, and commitment; of the transcendence of spirit over past, present and future; and of the power of spirit to project plans into the future. Despite this, many scientists say that they cannot find any sign of spirit among the objects they investigate. Of course they cannot; what they investigate are objects, and all objects of inquiry lack inwardness, as all such objects also already lie in the past of the observer. Spirit is known only by intuitive awareness, by disclosures, of self and of others, not by inquiry into objects. This is one important reason for why scientific knowledge cannot represent all we know: it leaves out the creative subject of science, the scientists, and thus has only half the story. The subject must be added to reality in any full account of nature.[21]

This text is an excellent account of some features of the epistemological presuppositions of science. Gilkey shows that the existence of a knowing subject

---

20. Ibid., p. 38.

21. Ibid., pp. 41–42.

who possesses the necessary abilities to work in science is a part of science; this part does not appear in the technical formulations of the theories but is necessarily presupposed in any full account of science. This explains why I do not oppose labeling this kind of presupposition as "nonscientific" and prefer to consider it a part of science whose specialized study requires a philosophical approach.

Finally, I also agree with Gilkey when he says that a coherent reflection on the presuppositions of science shows that in some way science transcends itself. He puts it this way:

> If the arguments put forth in this chapter, and those that preceded them, are sound, then I have shown that an intelligent and self-consistent science points beyond itself to an ontological or metaphysical ground.[22]

I can safely conclude that Gilkey's position is completely consonant with my claims about the presuppositions of science and about the way in which science transcends itself.

4. CAN SCIENCE EXPLAIN EVERYTHING?

As a professor of philosophy, Roger Trigg faces the problem of the grounding of science from a strictly philosophical point of view. He speaks about two kinds of assumptions, foundations, or preconditions of science, which refer to the orderliness of the contingent world and to our ability to know it. He asserts that those preconditions are not a part of the subject matter of science but have to be considered its necessary conditions.

The background of Trigg's arguments is aptly explained by the subtitle of his book: "Can Science Explain Everything?" Trigg notes that "we have to stand outside science in order to judge its validity"; to say that science can explain everything, one should reason *about* science and not just within it. Therefore, he argues, "physical science can never, it seems, explain its own existence," so that "claims that *only* scientific procedures provide a proper basis for knowledge can never be made from within science."[23] Then, Trigg offers clear, straightforward arguments referring to the epistemological and ontological presuppositions of science. In reference to the epistemological level, Trigg says:

> Any scientific theory is put forward on the tacit assumption that its proponents can recognise what is true, or at least what seems to be so. If the reply comes, as it inevitably will, that most scientists have been mistaken most of the time, it must be accepted that even the power to recognise falsehood is important. Believing something on the

---

22. Ibid., p. 74

23. Roger Trigg, *Rationality and Science: Can Science Explain Everything?* (Oxford: Blackwell, 1993), pp. 219, 223, 226.

grounds of its truth, or not believing it because of its falsity, both depend on the ability to see what is the case because of the way things are. . . . Science has been one of the great achievements of human rationality. Those who wish to equate scientific procedure with rationality as such are not wholly wrong. Science is reason in action, and if the power of human rationality is challenged or decided, the status of science itself must be put at risk. Yet if rationality itself is in turn apparently undermined by science, the situation rapidly becomes absurd.[24]

Indeed, the scientific enterprise requires as a necessary precondition the ability to argue about truth and falsehood, and this ability cannot be explained in terms of science alone. If empirical science were considered the ultimate explanation, we would be entrapped in a vicious circle.

Trigg refers clearly to the epistemological and ontological presuppositions of science when he says:

If reality were unstructured and disorderly, indeterminate and fundamentally chaotic, science would be impossible . . . genuine science would be impossible without an ordered and regular world which humans can to some extent get to know.[25]

He refers again to those presuppositions, calling them "assumptions":

The pursuit of science has to rest on certain assumptions, whether explicit or implicit. It must certainly be concerned with an objective world. Otherwise it is participating in a very elaborate form of novel writing. Yet its practice must only be possible if those engaged in it are able to reason towards conclusions. This rationality will very often not be deductive in form but will need its own leap of creativity. It will have sometimes to proceed from the known to the unknown and from the present to the future. As justification, it will have to invoke the character of the world. That means that the subject must be detachable to some extent from its physical and social context to see what is true both about the world and about its own place in it. The very existence of science as a successful route to knowledge is testimony to the distinction between subject and object. So far from being an unscientific concept, that of the subject lies at the very heart of science. It is what makes science possible.[26]

Trigg does not devalue empirical science. On the contrary, he clearly states that "The physical sciences have always provided some of the most impressive examples of the human ability to reason towards truth." But he rightly stresses that these sciences are in need of a basis that is not part of their specific content: "The preconditions necessary for science cannot be subsumed

24. Ibid., pp. 220–221.

25. Ibid., p. 224.

26. Ibid., p. 229.

within science as a part of its subject matter."[27] In my opinion, these pre-conditions can be considered a part of science as necessary conditions for it, but their study requires that we adopt a philosophical perspective. It is pre-cisely because they are double-sided that they can serve as a bridge between science and philosophy and theology. They belong to science but do not add specifically scientific contents to it in such a way that they do not clash with the autonomy of science. Rigorous philosophical or theological reflection on them may serve as a real bridge uniting the objective world of natural facts with the personal world of meaning.

Other aspects of Trigg's reflection are worth noting, as for example, his emphasis that the idea of contingency is essential to science because contin-gency demands an empirical method.

5. Retrojustification of the Presuppositions of Scientific Inquiry

In Nicholas Rescher's discussion of scientific realism, he insists on the exis-tence of the ontological presuppositions of science and emphasizes two ideas essential to my argument: (1) he speaks about the presuppositions of scientif-ic inquiry rather than of science in general, which corresponds to my em-phasis on the presuppositions of science as a goal-directed activity; and (2) in his analysis, the validity of those presuppositions lies in their potential func-tional utility, and then in their being retrojustified by the "wisdom of insight" that we reach through them.[28]

The idea that the retrojustification of the presuppositions of science by the achievements that could not be obtained without them is a typical feature of what would be considered necessary conditions. If A is a necessary condition for B, then the existence of B is a sufficient condition for A. In other words if B exists, A must be true. But because there are many types of necessary and sufficient conditions, the application of that rule sometimes is not easy. For instance, the natural order must be a necessary condition of scientific inquiry because if no order existed at all in nature, our search would be pointless. Nevertheless, the idea of "natural order" must be carefully analyzed because it refers to an enormous collection of states of affairs; this also holds true in the case of "scientific inquiry." Although in principle there is no difficulty in arguing that the success of empirical science demonstrates the adequacy of the presupposition of the existence of a natural order, this reasoning is sel-dom used in the epistemological field.

Rescher is an exception. He introduces the notion of the "retrojustifica-tion" of a postulate (here, the existence of natural order) on grounds of its pragmatic and explanatory efficacy. Rescher also provides an illustration rep-resenting the "practical loop of retrojustification."[29] One may or may not

---

27. Ibid., p. 231.

28. Nicholas Rescher, *Scientific Realism: A Critical Reappraisal* (Dordrecht-Boston: Reidel, 1987), p. 126.

29. Ibid., p. 144.

agree with the details of his argument, but the notion itself is really important.

I shall use the notion of "retrojustification" as a part of my argument. Indeed, I focus on the feedback of scientific progress on its presuppositions because it is a matter of fact that science progresses, and its success shows that its preconditions must be valid. "Retrojustification" is the first part of that feedback, which also includes "amplification" and eventual "refinement" of the presuppositions of science. This provides an interesting basis for the bridges that connect the sciences and the humanities.

Other ideas of Rescher are relevant to my argument. His discussion of realism begins with that statement that, at the existential and ontological level, there is a real world of objective physical reality, and also that, at the cognitive and epistemic level, we can to some extent obtain information about that world independent of the mind. Obviously we are looking again at the two general presuppositions that constitute a kind of common ground of agreement. But Rescher adds that the second component, that we can reach some knowledge about the world, presupposes the first, that is, the existence of the world. He labels this ontological presupposition as "metaphysical realism" and says that it is not the result of an inductive inference, but is rather "a regulative presupposition that makes science possible in the first place," "a *precondition* for empirical inquiry," and "a presupposition for the usability of observational data as sources of objective information." He writes: "We do not learn or discover that there is a mind-independent physical reality, we *presume or postulate* it." He adds: "it is a presupposition for our inquiries rather than a result thereof," so that it is "a *formative assumption* that undergirds our view of the nature of inquiry" and "a postulate whose justification pivots on its functional utility in enabling us to operate as we do with respect to inquiry."[30]

This sounds like my ontological presupposition, but there are some differences. My presupposition refers to the existence of natural order, which must include the existence of a mind-independent world that is the subject of that order and has its own consistency, but my emphasis is on order and intelligibility. Rescher's emphasis is on the very existence of a mind-independent world: he poses a kind of Cartesian or Kantian problem in which realism would be confronted with idealism. Rescher refers to Kant and says that, as Kant clearly saw, objective experience is possible only if the existence of a real world is *presupposed* from the outset. Because of his stress on the Kantian problem, I conclude that, even though Rescher's discussion seems quite close to my argument, the two discussions refer to two different subjects. When I speak about the ontological presupposition I understand it as referring to the existence of a real natural *order.*

The distinction between our two arguments has an important consequence regarding the common use of the idea of "retrojustification" of realism as a presupposition of science. In both cases there is a reference to a retro-

30. Ibid., pp. 126–127.

justification of "something" related to realism, but that "something" differs and therefore the meaning of the term "retrojustification" is also different. The identification might seem unavoidable when Rescher says "In summary, then, we need that postulate of an objective order of mind-independent reality,"[31] but I think that this is a verbal coincidence only.

I dare say that Rescher probably has natural order in mind as a part of his "metaphysical realism." Perhaps his preoccupation with the classical question of realism versus idealism leads him to pay little attention to that aspect of the problem. In any case, surely there is a basic agreement about the epistemological and ontological presuppositions of science. And, above all, Rescher's ideas about the retrojustification of the presuppositions of science by its results are closely connected with my argument. His assertion that "Science must (and can) retrovalidate itself by providing the materials (in terms of a science-based worldview) for justifying the methods of science"[32] is included, to a great extent, in the core of my argument.

6. Philosophical Hypotheses in Science

Although the presuppositions of science can be related to theological considerations, their existence and role are independent of those considerations. The position of Mario Bunge, who cannot be suspected of alliances with religion, can be used to illustrate this point.

From the point of view of epistemology, Bunge speaks about "philosophical hypotheses in science":

> Scientific knowledge contains no philosophical assumptions. From this it is often concluded that scientific research has neither philosophical presuppositions nor a philosophical import, whence science and philosophy would be water-tight compartments. But this is a hurried conclusion. Philosophy may not be found in the finished scientific buildings (although this is controversial) but it is part of the scaffolding employed in their construction . . . scientific research does *presuppose and control* certain important philosophical hypotheses. Among these the following stand out: the reality of the external world, the multilevel structure of reality, determinism in an ample sense, the knowability of the world, and the autonomy of logic and mathematics.[33]

My argument coincides in three important points with Bunge's ideas. First, Bunge stresses that philosophical assumptions do not belong directly to the results or the theoretical constructs of empirical science, because they are concerned with science as a research activity. He states clearly that scientific re-

31. Ibid., p. 133.

32. Ibid., p. 143.

33. Mario Bunge, *Scientific Research*, vol. 1 (Berlin: Springer, 1967), p. 291.

search not only presupposes some philosophical hypotheses, but also controls those hypotheses; this corresponds to my ideas about the feedback of scientific progress on its presuppositions. Finally, the presuppositions listed and examined by Bunge include a healthy dose of realism, as do mine.

Once he has examined the presuppositions mentioned above, Bunge states that the existence of philosophical presuppositions in science means that science is not philosophically neutral; he notes that this should not be interpreted as if philosophy had to play a role in deciding the correctness of scientific theories:

> There are other philosophical hypotheses relevant to factual science but it is not our (impossible) task to examine them all. The aim of the preceding study has been to show that scientific research logically presupposes certain wide scope philosophical hypotheses: that science is not philosophically neutral but partisan. It should not be concluded that science needs a solid philosophical *basis,* in the sense that a philosophy is needed to *validate* scientific hypotheses.[34]

Bunge calls the presuppositions "philosophical hypotheses." One may wonder, however, whether they are philosophical and whether they should be considered as hypotheses. Regarding the first question, I would prefer to repeat that, as necessary conditions of science, they are a part of science whose explicit examination requires a philosophical perspective that leads to philosophical conclusions; in this precise sense they may be called "philosophical." Regarding the second question, I would say that the presuppositions, insofar as they are preconditions or assumptions, have a hypothetical character, but I would add that they cease to be hypothetical when they are corroborated by the success of scientific inquiry. We might say that they have a permanent core that is corroborated and enlarged by advances in science, so that they may also include some features that evolve in time. For instance, natural order is a general ontological presupposition corroborated by the progress of science, but it is also enriched with new pieces of knowledge that provide new perspectives: this is the case, for instance, with the theories about the self-organization of nature.

7. The Unreasonable Effectiveness of Science

Paul Davies, the physicist, strongly avers that the entire scientific enterprise is based on the supposition that we live in an intelligible world that can be the object of a rational scientific quest; he also states that the success of science serves as a clear confirmation of that supposition.

Davies considers the success of empirical science to be a kind of miracle. Under the heading "The Scientific Miracle," he writes:

> The success of the scientific method at unlocking the secrets of nature is so dazzling it can blind us to the greatest scientific miracle of

---

34. Ibid., p. 300.

all: *science works*. Scientists themselves normally take it for granted that we live in a rational, ordered cosmos subject to precise laws that can be uncovered by human reasoning. Yet why this should be so remains a tantalizing mystery.[35]

Here we find a clear reference to the ontological and epistemological pre-suppositions of science, which Davies considers something scientists take for granted. This is the plain truth. The sense of awe and mystery that the pre-ceding quotation reflects corresponds to the experience of many people who reflect on those issues. In this line, Davies adds:

the fact that science works, and works so well, points to something profoundly significant about the organization of the cosmos. . . . What is a surprise is that human reasoning is so successful in fram-ing an understanding of those parts of the world our perceptions can't directly reach. It may be no surprise that human minds can deduce the laws of falling objects, because the brain has evolved to devise strategies for dodging them. But do we have any right to ex-pect extensions of such reasoning to work when it comes to nuclear physics, or astrophysics, for example? The fact that it does work, and works "unreasonably" well, is one of the great mysteries of the uni-verse.[36]

And again:

The success of the scientific enterprise can often blind us to the as-tonishing fact that science works. Although most people take it for granted, it is both incredibly fortunate and incredibly mysterious that we are able to fathom the workings of nature by use of the scientific method.[37]

The emphasis on the success of science is important when we consider the basis that makes possible that success. Davies refers explicitly to this basis as the presuppositions of science when he examines the question "Why Is the World the Way It Is?":

Underlying all these questions is a crucial assumption: that the world is both rational and intelligible. . . . The entire scientific enterprise . . . is built upon the assumed rationality of nature.[38]

Davies also speaks of the success of science as a proof in favor of the ra-tionality of nature. Although he does not consider this to be a complete or definitive proof, he considers it a strong argument:

35. Paul Davies, *The Mind of God: The Scientific Basis for a Rational World* (New York-London: Simon & Schuster, 1993), p. 20.

36. Ibid., pp. 21, 24.

37. Ibid., p. 148.

38. Ibid., p. 162.

I concede that one cannot prove the world to be rational. . . . Yet the success of science is at the very least strong circumstantial evidence in favor of the rationality of nature.[39]

In conclusion, I would say that Davies accepts both ontological and epistemological realism as the basis of the astonishing success of the scientific enterprise. He stresses that this success requires and proves, to a certain extent, the existence of an objective rationality in nature and also of the human cognitive abilities needed to represent that rationality. These reflections appear as part of an even stronger argument: that our existence cannot be an accidental result of blind forces.

III. WHAT PRESUPPOSITIONS?

I shall briefly review the three main types of presuppositions of science, showing how they are related to science considered as three separate dimensions: as a goal-directed human activity, as a method to achieve the goals of that activity, and as a set of results obtained by the application of that method.

1. Presuppositions in the Three Dimensions of Science

Empirical science is a complex reality that includes many branches, methods, and results. Nevertheless, it is possible to describe it in a very general way as including three main features. First of all, science is a *goal-directed activity*, that is, a human activity directed toward the achievement of two specific aims: the knowledge of nature and the controlled dominion of nature. To achieve these goals we must use some specific means; these can be labeled the *scientific method*. Finally, considered as a body of knowledge obtained using the scientific method, science contains *theoretical constructs:* concepts, statements, and theories (Figure 2.1).

When I say that the goals of the scientific enterprise are the knowledge of nature and its controlled dominion I am not ignoring the problems that such a realist position must face. I shall consider them in detail later on. But as a starting point, I think that it can be safely assumed that the general aim of the scientific enterprise is to explain natural phenomena by using theories that can be submitted to experimental control and may therefore serve as a basis for achieving a controlled dominion over nature.

Although the three dimensions of science are closely related, they should be carefully differentiated when we reflect on the character and main features of empirical science. Indeed, when we talk about the presuppositions of science, what we mean depends on which dimension we consider.

39. Ibid., p. 191.

If we consider science as a *goal-directed human activity*, we can easily note that its existence depends on the presupposition that its goals can and should be achieved. Therefore, the first general presupposition of science is that *scientific goals* can be achieved and that they possess a value, so that scientific activity is a worthwhile enterprise that deserves our efforts. As self-evident as this may seem, it is most important. It can be labeled as an *ethical presupposition,* because it refers to values. From the historical point of view, we know that one factor that contributed to the birth of empirical science was the emphasis on the value of a knowledge that could serve as the basis for practical applications. Francis Bacon is considered the great prophet of modern empirical science because he realized that the enterprise was worthwhile and helped spread this conviction. Today, the magnitude of scientific achievements, which can be applied for both good and evil, has provoked a renewed interest in the relationship between science and values (Table 2.1).

The use of the *scientific method* presupposes the existence of some specific *human abilities* that we are able to transcend ordinary knowledge through the formulation of hypotheses that can be submitted to empirical tests. This is an *epistemological presupposition.* A fully developed scientific method is anything but trivial. It took many centuries to develop. This method includes a series of successive steps: building theoretical models, relating these models to experimental tests, defining magnitudes that at the same time are theoretical constructs and can be measured, and evaluating the validity of the models by using the empirical evidence available at each moment in time. The progress of science clearly shows that we possess an astonishing ability to tran-

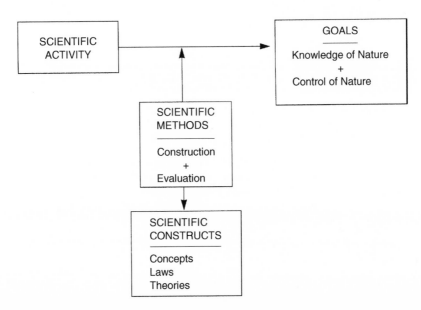

Fig. 2.1 Three levels in science: aims, methods, and constructs.

Dimensions of Science	Presuppositions	Character of the Presuppositions
Goals	Scientific values	Ethical
Methods	Argument and proofs	Epistemological
Constructs	Natural order	Ontological

Table 2.1 *The general presuppositions in the three dimensions of science.*

scend our immediate experience and to reach deepest levels of nature by using extremely subtle methods.

In the third place, the success of the *scientific constructs* resulting from using
the scientific method of construction and control presupposes, as a necessary
condition, that they reflect in some way a *natural order* that cannot be reduced
to the order that we impose on our own theories. This is an *ontological presupposition.* The empirical testing of our theoretical models is only possible if
some kind of objective natural order exists. We can even say that the more
the sciences progress, the more we can be certain of the existence and characteristics of an objective natural order.

I shall therefore concentrate on these three general presuppositions of science: *scientific goals, human abilities,* and *natural order.*

2. THE CHARACTERISTICS OF THE PRESUPPOSITIONS

I would like now to examine the main characteristics of these presuppositions. My presuppositions are *scientific* insofar as they are related to empirical
science as its necessary conditions. My presuppositions are *philosophical* insofar as their study requires that we adopt a philosophical perspective. They can
even be considered *theological* in two respects: first, because historically they
were partly derived from theological ideas, and because their study may eventually have a theological import. Therefore, they should be distinguished from
scientific presuppositions such as theories, which must be accepted as the basis of other scientific theories, and from the stipulations that must be accepted to establish an intersubjective discussion in science.

My presuppositions cannot be thought of as scientific as if they were statements of the same type as a usual scientific statement nor as philosophical as
if they were metaphysical principles needed to provide a foundation to the
sciences.

My presuppositions are not *constitutive,* as if they were a part of science
among others, but *regulative,* for they provide a clue to understanding science
itself and to reflect on its meaning. In some way, they participate in the regulative character of metaphysics as expressed by Thomas Aquinas' introduction to his commentary on Aristotle's *Metaphysics:*

> As the Philosopher teaches in his *Politics,* when several different things
> are ordained to a single one, one of them has to be regulative or di-

rective, and others regulated or directed. . . . But all sciences and arts
are ordained to a single thing, namely the perfection of man, which is
his happiness. Therefore one of them has to be directive of all the
rest, and this one rightly should be called wisdom, because it is a
character of the wise man to direct others.[40]

My argument does not take metaphysical principles as a point of departure.
Rather, it focuses on some states of affairs that should be considered presuppositions of science because they are its necessary conditions. I will try to reflect on them to show that analysis of them is most coherent with a metaphysical and religious perspective, in which divine agency and human
spirituality provide the deepest meaning for the scientific enterprise.

I have already stressed that my presuppositions are not *particular,* but *general.* Natural order, human abilities, and scientific goals refer to the entire scientific enterprise. Doubtless, specific or particular presuppositions may also
have interesting implications, but they should be the subject of specialized
studies that concentrate, for instance, on relativity, quantum theory, or other
specific subjects. Nevertheless, when concentrating on the feedback of scientific progress on the presuppositions of science, I will consider the implications of many particular scientific achievements.

My presuppositions can be labeled as *pragmatic* rather than *logical.* This is
why I have not focused on the specialized meaning of presuppositions in formal logic.

My presuppositions are *necessary conditions* of the scientific enterprise, not
only *psychological assumptions.* Actually, scientists working in their specialized
field can be completely oblivious of them and can even deny their existence
when they reflect on their research; however, from an objective point of view,
these presuppositions are the basis of the whole scientific enterprise and of
every one of its parts. My presuppositions are so important and, at the same
time, so trivial in themselves, because they are the basic necessary conditions
for science to exist and develop, and express precisely the "conditions of possibility" of the three dimensions of empirical science.

One major objection to consideration of my proposed presuppositions
would be to say that although they really exist, they are not worthy of a serious study; just as a fisherman must suppose that there actually are fish in the
sea and that they have certain characteristics, but his presuppositions are only
guesses that can be wrong. I would answer that though it is true these presuppositions are in some sense trivial, the philosophical and theological reflection on them is not a trivial matter.

It is important to underscore that these presuppositions refer to scientific
progress. They are necessary for science to progress in every particular case.
Although each one of them has a general character that does not change, they
also possess a changing part that evolves with scientific progress. In this sense,

40. Thomas Aquinas, *In duodecim Libros Metaphysicorum Aristotelis Expositio* (Torino-Roma: Marietti, 1964), p. 1.

they are *evolving,* not *fixed* presuppositions. Scientific progress brings about some important changes in them. For instance, natural order shows itself now as a process of self-organization, and this suggests new philosophical and theological insights. The use of new methods shows that dynamic systems are a central feature of our world; therefore the relationship between causality and determinism, an issue relevant for philosophy and theology, has to be revisited.

Because the presuppositions evolve, my argument about them will continue to be useful as long as science continues to progress. The experimental research methods of today are not those of the seventeenth century. The pioneers of modern science had to rely on some kind of faith, expecting that nature would be intelligible and that they could manage it by using the new methods. Scientists now must hope that new scientific avenues of exploration that can be explored using our cognitive abilities will open. We must suppose that there are new dimensions to be explored if we are to continue the scientific adventure at all. If there were no perspectives of further progress, my talk about the presuppositions of science would cease to have any interest. Only if the death of science, which has been announced so many times, were to actually come to pass would my presuppositions cease to work.

I do not think, however, that we may meaningfully speak about the real end of science, even if we only make reference to its basic features. Because the limits of our knowledge are so great, we necessarily have to adopt particular perspectives that can always be completed by other perspectives. The historical record suggests that every new advance opens unsuspected avenues. All this is most important for my argument because I do not consider science as a static entity, but as a dynamic goal-directed activity that never ceases to aim at achieving new goals.

IV. THE FEEDBACK OF SCIENTIFIC PROGRESS

The presuppositions of science are important, above all, because the progress of science interacts with them. The fact of scientific progress acquires a specific meaning when considered against the background of the preconditions of science.

The feedback of scientific progress has three effects on the presuppositions: *retrojustifies, enlarges,* and eventually *refines* them.

1. Implications for the Presuppositions

So far I have spoken about the *presuppositions* of science. Now I am going to discuss the *implications* of scientific progress on them.

The meaning of "implication" which appears closest to my area of interest refers to the philosophical or theological implications of singular scientific advances. But since I have concentrated on the *general* presuppositions of science, I will now focus on the general implications of scientific progress on them rather than focusing on particular advances. I cannot, however, simply ignore particular advances: we can speak of "general presuppositions" underlying the entire scientific enterprise, but there exists no such a thing as a "general advance," because scientific progress always consists of particular advances.

Therefore the situation is somewhat intriguing. I cannot in this discussion focus on the implications of particular theories, interesting as they may be, but, at the same time, I must consider at least the main features of the most relevant scientific advances. I am interested in the feedback of scientific progress on its presuppositions, and any advance contributes to that progress.

As with my use of the item "presuppositions," I use the term "implication" not in the technical sense it has within formal logic, but in a sense closer to its ordinary meaning. An "implication" usually means something "implied" or "implicit," a necessary logical consequence but not actually stated openly. As in the case of presuppositions, implications may refer to persons, ideas, feelings, or states of affairs. As I refer my presuppositions mainly to states of affairs, I am also going to consider the implications of scientific progress mainly as states of affairs, and I shall do so from an objective point of view that can be analyzed by anyone.

The idea that serves as the skeleton of my argument has two aspects: (1) I assert that there exists a feedback of scientific progress on its presuppositions as it *retrojustifies, enlarges,* and eventually *refines* them, and (2) I add that this feedback provides a most interesting basis for reflections in the philosophical and theological realms (Figure 2.2).

This idea is anything but obvious if we consider the methodological gap between the sciences and philosophy and theology. As a consequence, scientific progress properly considered can only have scientific implications. I will therefore examine the skeleton of my argument with this in mind.

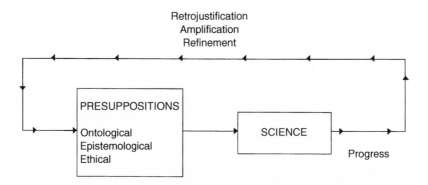

Fig. 2.2   The feedback from scientific progress to its presuppositions.

My argument includes three successive steps. The first, the identification of the general presuppositions of the entire scientific enterprise, includes a philosophical reflection on science, as study of the presuppositions requires a philosophical perspective. The second step, identifying the implications of scientific progress on its presuppositions, requires an analysis of the main advances of science and reflections on how these advances retrojustify, enlarge, and refine their presuppositions. The third step, a reflection on the philosophical and theological meaning of the second step, obviously must be philosophical and theological in character.

Thus I do not assert that empirical science by itself has any philosophical or theological implications. But the first two steps of my argument have a philosophical character, and the third step supposes them and adds further philosophical and theological reflections. Nevertheless, because the argument begins with a reflection on science and on scientific progress, this acts as the basis for the philosophical and theological reflections developed in the third step. In this sense it can be said that the argument is developed following closely the real development of science, and also that it focuses entirely on the significance of scientific progress.

That the analysis of scientific progress provides us with clues which are interesting from the humanistic point of view is the central idea of many antimetaphysical and antireligious doctrines such as positivism, neopositivism, scientific materialism, and the different versions of scientific naturalism widespread in the contemporary intellectual arena. My argument did not arise from those pseudoscientific ideologies nor has it been developed in reaction to them; it has a positive character and stands on its own feet. Nevertheless, an understanding of my argument clarifies the misrepresentations of science and of scientific progress common to those ideologies.

Some parts of my argument can partly be found in other works. As I have shown, authors from different philosophical and theological perspectives recognize some general presuppositions of science and agree on the main characteristics of some of them. Some agreement also can be found concerning particular features of the second and third steps of my argument. Jaki shows that scientific progress is incompatible with idealistic or empiricist epistemologies, Bunge says that scientific research controls the philosophical hypotheses that it assumes as presuppositions, and Rescher speaks about the retrojustification of the metaphysical realism presupposed by the scientific quest.

My argument is partly based on the purely logical idea that "P is a sufficient condition of Q iff Q is a necessary condition of P"[41] (here, "iff" stands for "if and only if"). If we are able to identify the three general presuppositions of science, and we know that they are necessary conditions of the entire scientific enterprise, then the very existence of scientific achievements

---

41. Ernest Sosa, "Condition," in *The Cambridge Dictionary of Philosophy,* ed. Robert Audi (Cambridge: Cambridge University Press, 1995), p. 149.

can be considered a sufficient condition for the existence of those presuppositions. Therefore, any piece of scientific progress may be considered as evidence in favor of them.

Some difficulties may arise because there are different kinds of presuppositions: for instance, some are factual conditions of logical arguments, others are factual conditions of real facts, and others are logical conditions of logical consequences. But these uncertainties are resolved in my argument as I define the term "presupposition" following its contemporary dictionary meaning. "To presuppose" is defined thus: "If one state of affairs presupposes another, the first state of affairs cannot be true unless the second is also true." And a "presupposition" is defined as "something that you assume to be true, especially something which you must assume is true in order to continue with what you are saying or thinking."[42] These explanations are clear enough to avoid any misunderstanding.

It is also easy to grasp what the precise meaning of the three components of the feedback of scientific progress on its presuppositions are. "Retrojustification" means that scientific progress reveals the validity of its three preconditions, as they are necessary conditions of the kind of result actually achieved. To say that the presuppositions are "enlarged" means that the progress of science provides a more complete and detailed knowledge of them, so that completely new perspectives may be opened. And to say that the presuppositions are eventually "refined" means that scientific progress sometimes leads us to change older ideas that do not fit with new advances.

I have compared the presuppositions of science with those of a fisherman. To explore this metaphor further, insofar as both the fisherman and the scientist are successful, they will reach a more detailed knowledge of their field of exploration and will find further stimuli to continue their search. But I would add that a great difference exists between the two: the success of the fisherman may mean that fewer fish will exist, so that his presuppositions could eventually lose their validity, but each new scientific achievement means that new vistas are opened. The presuppositions of science would collapse only if we could reach a thoroughly complete knowledge of nature. This seems very improbable if we consider the enormity of the limits of our knowledge and our extraordinary capacity to overcome those limits.

What actually happens is that new scientific advances provide the basis for further philosophical and theological reflection. We have to distinguish carefully what belongs to the ambit of science in its strict sense from our analysis and our eventual interpretations in the philosophical and theological ambits. My argument provides, first of all, a general framework in which we can easily integrate the achievements of the sciences with our reflections on them, respecting the distinction of the different levels of analysis and seeking at the same time their integration. And this framework always will remain open, be-

---

42. "Presuppose" and "Presupposition," in *Collins Cobuild English Language Dictionary,* John Sinclair, editor in chief (London and Glasgow: Collins, 1987), p. 1136.

cause it represents a particular perspective which can be completed and combined with other perspectives.

2. A GUIDE TO THE BRIDGES

The main lines of my argument have been sufficiently explained. Now I will only add a few indications about the method I shall follow to develop them.

I shall examine first the ontological level, then the epistemological one, and finally the ethical one. The reverse order would perhaps conform better to the nature of the issues, since scientific goals are the first determinant feature of empirical science, followed by the methods used, and then by the results. Moreover, epistemological considerations apparently should be placed before ontological ones. Nevertheless, the order I have chosen permits a clearer explanation, because the worldview is easier to explain than epistemological or ethical issues, and its analysis provides an initial perspective that will be of great help in reflecting on the nature of our knowledge and of our goals. Also, considerations about goals raise ethical issues that can be best seen as the coronation of the argument.

PART II

Self-Organization
and Divine Action

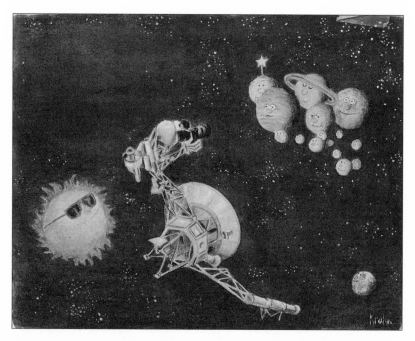

For the first time in history we have a scientific worldview that provides a unified picture, including all natural levels and their mutual relations. The new worldview provides a good basis for renewed study of purpose in nature and can be used to argue in favor of a personal God.

3

Natural Creativity

In empirical science we search for a knowledge of nature that can be submitted to empirical control. We therefore presuppose the existence of a certain degree of order in nature. The existence of this natural order can be considered an ontological presupposition of science, because it refers to something that does not depend on our will. The entire scientific enterprise may be summarized as a progressive knowledge of natural order.

The systemic birth of empirical science in the seventeenth century was accompanied by polemical confrontations with the ancient worldview. And since then, scientific progress had continued to provoke changes in our worldview. Now, for the first time in history, we have a scientific worldview that provides a rigorous and unified picture of the world, because it includes all natural levels (microphysical, macrophysical, and biological) and their mutual relations. Moreover, the new worldview is centered around a dynamic process of self-organization and provides us with new ideas that can illuminate our knowledge of the relations between nature and divine action.

In this chapter I shall concentrate on the analysis of natural order as an ontological presupposition of science and shall examine the impact of scientific progress on our understanding of order, considering the main features of the new scientific worldview. This analysis will show how scientific progress retro-justifies, enlarges, and refines its ontological presuppositions and will pave the way toward an understanding of the theological implications of this progress.

I. THE SCIENTIFIC QUEST FOR ORDER

The concept of order is extremely general and can be applied to a wide range of phenomena, in the natural world as well as in human affairs. Natural order is a presupposition of empirical science. Such a presupposition is not a changeless picture or idea, but an evolving idea enriched by scientific progress. This progress provides us with different features that refer to natural order and serve to build up a scientific worldview.

1. Natural Order

Many authors consider natural order to be a property of nature that must be presupposed if the scientific enterprise is to make any sense at all. Jaki speaks about "faith in the existence of a typical order in nature" as a precondition of science, and quotes Einstein and Leopold Infeld about "the belief in the inner harmony of our world." Hodgson, following Jaki, states that "the Christian belief in a rational and omnipotent Creator firmly implanted in the European mind the conviction that the universe is ordered and rational and opened the way for science." Gilkey says that "the assumption of an order spanning all of space and time is essential to all modern scientific thinking and inquiry. This assumption is improvable because it is the basis of all proof." According to Trigg, "If reality were unstructured and disorderly, indeterminate and fundamentally chaotic, science would be impossible." Davies writes that "underlying all these questions is a crucial assumption: that the world is both rational and intelligible. . . . The entire scientific enterprise . . . is built upon the assumed rationality of nature." In fact, if we did not assume that there are underlying orderly features to be discovered in nature, science would be completely meaningless. The existence of order in nature is a necessary condition for any piece of scientific work.

Insofar as natural order is considered to be a precondition for science, it is often equated with the "rationality" or the "intelligibility" of the world. These terms mean that the world is structured or organized in such a way that it can be grasped by our intellectual constructs. They are quite similar to the classical concept of "ontological truth." In classical metaphysics it is said that ontological truth or intelligibility is a transcendental property of being as such, which amounts to saying that no real being exists that is unintelligible. Of course, full intelligibility can exist only in the case of divine knowledge. However, the concept of ontological truth clearly fosters a confidence in the intelligibility of nature with respect to human beings, who are created as the image of God and participate in God's perfection.

If we consider natural order in a strict sense as a presupposition of empirical science, we are not obliged to assume a strong idea about ontological truth. We only have to assume, in every particular case, that there is some kind of order in nature which is yet unknown and can be known. This assumption does not require a strong commitment to metaphysics. It has two parts: (1) a permanent feature, the existence of natural order, which, always necessary as a basis for science, is still only a very general idea, and (2) an evolving aspect which depends on the state of the sciences at any particular time, because we must always suppose that there is more order to be uncovered if we are to continue working in science. Therefore, when we speak of natural order as an ontological presupposition of science we are not obliged to admit a strong changeless metaphysical commitment, let alone a belief in a full intelligibility based on the divine wisdom. Our ontological presupposition is more modest and includes that changing and evolving aspect. It is precisely this evolving feature of our presupposition that provides the basis for my argument. If natural order were a changeless presupposition, the feedback of scientific progress on the presuppositions that is the basis of my argument could hardly exist.

The concept of order is a classical concept that has survived down the centuries and today occupies a central place in the philosophy of science. It is mainly a relational concept, insofar as it refers to relations rather than to absolute properties. Therefore, it always depends on some criteria that are chosen as a reference, so that a state that is very ordered in some respects may be very disordered in others. This relational character also explains why the concept of order can be applied to any natural state of affairs. A completely disordered state of affairs would mean a state in which no relation existed between its components. Such a state can be considered impossible. It is hardly conceivable that in the natural world a state might exist that would not exhibit any kind of order at all.

In his introduction to *The Concept of Order*, Paul Kuntz analyzes the different meanings of "order." The most general is as "a relation of definite sort"; its opposite would be "nothing." In this sense, it is sometimes said that the concept of order is quasi-transcendental, for it can be applied in some way to any real state of affairs. Kuntz mentions other, more specific meanings of order; when he refers to the order of the material world, he speaks of "chaos" as its opposite and discusses the impossibility of experiencing real chaos:

> This state is the undifferentiated. Notably, we must conceptualize chaos by negation of order which we now take for granted. Chaos is then only a hypothetical state. We may introduce "chaos" by supposing the undifferentiated consciousness of the infant to be "a blooming, buzzing confusion." But the evidence seems to be that the infant does differentiate its mother from the rest of the world. So "chaos" is hardly even then experienced; we have only a hypothesis of the state of affairs to which categories do not apply. Theoretically this is not nothing, for there are relations, but not of specificable kinds; and since relations are of all kinds as well as types, we may not hope ever to experience chaos. For one thing, probably no sentient being could survive long enough in chaos to know what had happened to it in this state.[1]

Certainly, we speak about chaos and chaotic states in some branches of science that are rapidly expanding now. But we should not forget that the chaos

---

1. Paul G. Kuntz, "Introduction," in *The Concept of Order,* ed. Paul G. Kuntz (Seattle and London: The University of Washington Press, 1968), p. xxxv.

studied in the sciences does not correspond to completely disordered states, rather it follows some rules. Even the usual scientific denomination of "deterministic chaos" clearly represents this situation. Speaking about this topic, John Haught writes:

> After all, can we really separate the deep question of a thing's existence or "being" from the fact of its patterning? For anything to exist at all would it not have to possess some degree of organised structure? Without at least some internal ordering of its components, could anything even have actuality? Our position, as articulated by Whitehead, is that things simply cannot exist without being ordered in a definite way. Indefiniteness would be equivalent to non-existence.[2]

We could perhaps suppose that in some extraordinary circumstances, such as the very first moments after the origin of the universe, there was or should have been a kind of chaos, a completely disordered state of matter. However, this hypothetical state would remain forever outside the reach of empirical science and could hardly be represented in any meaningful way. Authors who speak seriously about chaotic beginnings or states in the natural world usually identify chaos with an extremely violent or disordered state, but the progress of science shows the existence of different kinds of order underlying even the most violent and disordered states.

That the concept of order is relational implies that we may distinguish as many types of order as there are types of relations. Two types of order play a unique role in empirical science: *patterning* and *organization*. Patterning is relevant in empirical science because empirical control is achieved through experiments whose possibility depends on the very existence of patterns in the natural world. Patterns refer to fixed ways of being and behaving, and progress in science always depends on the possibility of achieving some kind of empirical control, and therefore on the existence of repeatable patterns. We could even say that empirical science is centered around the study of spatial and temporal patterns.

Speaking about patterning in nature, Haught writes:

> The very possibility of doing science in the first place *presupposes* the fact of patterning as science's field of exploration.[3]

This assertion apparently coincides with my point, however our meanings differ. Haught includes it within an argument that refers not only to the presuppositions of science, but also to the theological implications of the very existence of patterning in nature. In addition, this consideration is included in a discussion of the recent development of the sciences of complexity and therefore to the present worldview. In that context, the concept of "patterning"

---

2. John F. Haught, *Science & Religion: From Conflict to Conversation* (New York-Mahwah, N.J.: Paulist Press, 1995), p. 151.

3. Ibid., p. 151.

refers to the formation of new patterns. Certainly, these topics are central in my argument; here I emphasize the central place of patterns in nature and their role as a part of the ontological presuppositions of science and also of the implications of scientific progress.

In this line, Carsten Bresch begins an article thus: "Our world is made up of patterns." To quote it more extensively:

If we were to describe the fundamental property of the matter of the universe in a single sentence, we would have to say that matter is formed—or created—so as to show continuously accelerating growth of patterns. . . . Everything around us consists of patterns. Matter is patterned, atomically and molecularly. Organisms are enormous patterns of cells, each of which in turn consists of a wealth of biological patterns. The arrangement of the houses in a human settlement is just as much a pattern as are the positions of the pieces of furniture in a room. A song is a time-pattern of sequences of notes; a book is a pattern of letters. We are so used to being surrounded by patterns that we do not give a thought to this fundamental property of our world. But it is matter *and* pattern (structure, form) that determine the properties of an object.[4]

Obviously, Bresch stresses the central place that patterns occupy in our world. But he also goes further, as he speaks of this world being made up of patterns that grow in a continuous way.

Patterns are closely linked to organization, which is a specific and very important kind of order. Organization includes the idea of parts that are related because they play a role within a whole, and this could be taken as a sign of rationality and, therefore, of the existence of a plan.

As we will see later on, scientific progress highlights the existence of a continuous process of patterning, which leads to patterns that possess a considerable degree of organization. The resulting worldview, centered around patterning and organization, will represent a considerable refinement of our knowledge of natural order and of its implications.

Last but not least, that new worldview may facilitate the recovery of some central ideas of the ancient worldview that seemed lost forever. This is especially true in the case of ideas associated with purpose or natural teleology. Indeed, in ancient times nature was seen above all as the world of living beings, where purpose played a very important role. Later on, the success of modern empirical science centered mainly around the physical sciences, where apparently there was no room for purpose. More recently, however, the extensive development of the physical sciences has provided the basis for a new biology that once more occupies a central place within the natural sciences, and so it has become fashionable again to speak about teleology in the scientific context.

4. Carsten Bresch, "What is Evolution?" in *Evolution and Creation,* ed. Svend Andersen and Arthur Peacocke (Aarhus: Aarhus University Press, 1987), pp. 36–37.

The progress of science provides us now with a worldview in which natural order is seen as a gigantic process of self-organization. This fact, full of interesting implications about teleology, provides a most interesting bridge between natural science and theology. This bridge will be useful only if we use it properly, and this task is not easy. We must be careful when we speak of teleology in nature, and we must avoid ingenuous and illegitimate anthropocentrisms. Therefore, before analyzing the present worldview and its implications, I will analyze the modalities of order as represented in the natural sciences and will then introduce the present worldview by considering the evolution of the ideas that have led to it.

2. The Scientific Knowledge of Order

Even if we admit that our scientific knowledge reflects in some way the characteristics of the real world, we should realize that it is not a mere copy of them. Indeed, in empirical science we adopt particular perspectives that depend on the concepts and instruments available at a concrete moment. Consequently, our knowledge of natural order depends on the peculiarities of different scientific approaches. In addition, the concept of order does not always have the same meaning in the sciences, and so we must interpret what kind of order is involved in each particular case. For instance, sometimes we consider the state of a system in physics as very ordered when it corresponds to a maximum homogeneity, whereas order in biology usually refers to the organization of heterogeneous parts within a whole organism. Of course, this fits well with the relational character of the concept of order. When we speak about order we should always explain which criterion we are using in every particular case.

In some way, any scientific achievement can be interpreted as an advance in our knowledge of order. I shall illustrate this assertion using two examples that, at first sight, could be interpreted as supporting the existence of disorder in nature and in science: the theories about chaos and Heisenberg's uncertainty principle.

The theories about chaos are not an exception in the scientific quest for order. Indeed, they refer to phenomena that are extremely sensitive to small variations in the initial conditions, in such a way that it is impossible to determine exactly the future behavior of the system under study. However, even in those cases we can determine the existence of patterns that are precisely the subject studied by those theories, and so this branch of science is labeled "deterministic chaos." This seemingly contradictory expression aptly reflects the fact that the physical phenomena under study are not completely chaotic or disordered. As Haught expresses it:

> Chaos, in common discourse, means "disorder." However, science is
> primarily interested in order. In fact, only the assumption that the
> universe is in some way organized gives scientists the incentive to
> search for its inherent intelligibility. In what sense then can science

be interested in chaos? It is interested in chaos because many natural processes start out with a simple kind of orderliness, move through an incalculable phase of turbulence, but then end up manifesting surprisingly rich forms of unpredictable order in the midst of chaos, an order that can best be mapped by computer imagery.[5]

Theories about chaos are especially relevant because they not only provide knowledge about some ordered features of the natural world, but also allow us to understand the emergence of new—previously nonexisting—patterns.

My second example of the presence of order in scientific achievements refers to the uncertainty relations formulated by Werner Heisenberg in 1927. These relations establish the impossibility of measuring at the same time and with any desired precision the values of two magnitudes such as position and momentum, or energy and time. According to Heisenberg's principle, a limit to attainable precision exists so that the more precise the measurement of one magnitude is, the less precise the measurement of the other will be (Figure 3.1).

Heisenberg's uncertainty relations are one of the cornerstones of quantum physics. They are often interpreted as the expression of the impossibility of speaking about the objective or real characteristics of the natural world, as if they implied that the very concept of reality is in some way blurred. Nevertheless, as quantitative relations between physical magnitudes, they can be used as a tool for achieving progress in our knowledge of natural order. The same physics that is sometimes regarded as supporting subjectivism is used by physicists in their work as a means to uncover new features of reality.

As these relations are one of the main arguments used against the existence of an objective real order, I examine the writings of some well-known physicists to show how they have used those relations to obtain new knowledge about natural order in the field of subatomic particles.

Research conducted at Brookhaven Laboratory (New York) led to the discovery of the upsilon particle and to the introduction of a fifth quark. In that experiment high-energy protons, accelerated in a synchrotron, were directed against uranium nuclei. The pairs of leptons produced in the collisions were treated as if they were the result of the decay of a virtual photon. However, analysis of the results demonstrated the phenomenon characterized as resonance, an indication that the lepton pairs emanated from some real particle. The researchers applied the following reasoning:

> On the basis of Werner Heisenberg's uncertainty principle we could then estimate the size of whatever material within the colliding nucleons had served as the source of the new particle. Heisenberg's principle suggests that the greater the particle's mass, the smaller the size of its source. This meant that if we discovered sufficiently massive resonances, we would in fact be detecting extremely small structures

5. John F. Haught, *Science & Religion,* cit., pp. 142–143.

$$\Delta x \ \bullet \ \Delta p \ \geq \ h/2\pi$$

Fig. 3.1 Heisenberg's uncertainty principle. When we try to measure two conjugate magnitudes such as the position (x) of a particle and the momentum (p) of that particle at the same time, we cannot surpass a certain limit of accuracy. Specifically, the product of the uncertainties in the measures of "x" and "p" (represented as "Δx" and "Δp") is equal to or greater than h/2π, which has a constant value ("h" stands for Planck's constant, and the value of "π" is 3.14159). Therefore, supposing that we measure "x" with complete accuracy, our measurement of the momentum will be affected by an uncertainty of h/2π. Though this principle refers to a limit in the accuracy of measurement, it is also used as a positive heuristic to find new properties of the microphysical world.

within the target nucleons. Our search for such lumps within the target nucleons was undertaken in 1967.[6]

Note that in this case we are far from the usual epistemological discussions about the extent of Heisenberg's principle, which, in spite of the fact that it points toward a limitation in our knowledge, is used here as a positive heuristic to uncover the existence of a new basic component of matter. This example is not an isolated case. In fact, in the same report we can read:

According to Heisenberg's uncertainty principle, a narrow, or well-defined, mass implies a lifetime that is long compared with that of most other subatomic particles.[7]

Other authors explain how they applied this reasoning, used when physicists try to detect particles whose lifetime is very short, in their research:

The method of detection employed is an application of Werner Heisenberg's uncertainty principle and it consists in searching for an enhancement at a particular energy in the probability of interaction between known particles. Such an enhancement is called a resonance. One expression of the uncertainty principle relates the uncertainty in the energy at which the resonance is found to the lifetime of the particle being created: the greater the uncertainty, the longer the lifetime.[8]

In a similar vein, in an article about the proofs of the existence of quarks inside the hadrons, we are told:

A test particle colliding with a hadron at high energy inspects the behavior of the constituent quarks over very small distances and during a very brief interval. This fact is established mathematically by the

6. Leon M. Lederman, "The Upsilon Particle," *Scientific American,* 239, no. 4 (October 1978): 62.

7. Ibid., p. 64.

8. David B. Cline, Alfred K. Mann, and Carlo Rubbia, "The Search for New Families of Elementary Particles," *Scientific American,* 234, no. 1 (January 1976): 50.

uncertainty principle, which relates the time and distance in which a measurement is performed to the energy and momentum of the test particle.[9]

Finally, Heisenberg's principle is also applied to the study of quantum vacuum. Obviously, the vacuum studied in physics cannot be identified with the idea (or pseudoidea) of nothingness:

One usually thinks of a vacuum as a space with nothing in it, but in physics the vacuum is defined more precisely as the state in which all fields have their lowest possible energy.[10]

The structure of the vacuum is associated with Heisenberg's principle by another physicist in this way:

The structure of the vacuum is a consequence of the uncertainty principle of Werner Heisenberg. One version of the uncertainty principle states that for any physical event there is an uncertainty about the energy released during the event that is related to the uncertainty about the exact time of its occurrence. More precisely, the product of the uncertainty about the energy and the uncertainty about the time is not less than some numerical constant. For an event confined to an extremely short interval there is a correspondingly large uncertainty about its energy. During any short interval, therefore, there is a substantial probability that the quantum-mechanical vacuum has some nonzero energy.[11]

These examples concerning the theories of chaos and the use of Heisenberg's uncertainty principle show that even when scientific advances seem to show the existence of some kind of disorder, they provide us with new knowledge about natural order. Heisenberg's principle is used as a positive heuristic for the advancement in subatomic physics, and theories of chaos provide important clues about how new patterns emerge in nature.

We can safely say that scientific progress means progress in our knowledge of natural order. Our scientific results need not be a copy of real order such as it exists in nature. Very often they are encoded statements formulated in a mathematical language that, while being a powerful means to foster progress in science, cannot be considered a photograph of natural order. The mathematical features of science exercise some kind of fascination, but we should not forget that they are human constructs. In addition, very often the mathematics used in science, even in the most formalized disciplines, include not a few simplifications that are necessary for their application to the study of

9. Yoichiro Nambu, "The Confinement of Quarks," *Scientific American*, 235, no. 5 (November 1976): 56.

10. Gerard 't Hooft, "Gauge Theories of the Forces Between Elementary Particles," *Scientific American*, 242 no. 6 (June 1980): 126.

11. Claudio Rebbi, "The Lattice Theory of Quark Confinement," *Scientific American*, 248, no. 2 (February 1983): p. 40.

physical phenomena. Physicists are familiar with this situation, which can be aptly exemplified by the work of Lord Rayleigh.

In the second half of the nineteenth century, John William Strutt (Lord Rayleigh) achieved outstanding results in the mathematical study of dynamics, acoustics, optics, and electricity. A graduate in mathematics, he considered mathematics to be only an auxiliary technique when applied to physical problems. In his introduction to Rayleigh's *The Theory of Sound,* R. B. Lindsay discusses Rayleigh's mathematical training in Cambridge: "it was not *rigorous* mathematics in the pure sense, but it was *vigorous* mathematics." And Lord Rayleigh himself discussed his mathematics thus:

> In the mathematical investigations I have usually employed such methods as present themselves naturally to a physicist. The pure mathematician will complain, and (it must be confessed) sometimes with justice, of deficient rigour. But to this question there are two sides. For however important it may be to maintain a uniformly high standard in pure mathematics, the physicist may occasionally do well to rest content with arguments which are fairly satisfactory and conclusive from his point of view. To his mind, exercised in a different order of ideas, the more severe procedure of the pure mathematician may appear not more but less demonstrative.[12]

These examples show that we cannot identify the statements of the sciences with the natural order as it exists in reality, and that, nevertheless, scientific progress always means progress in our knowledge of the natural order, even when it seems to impose limits on it.

There are as many types of scientific representation of the natural order as there are scientific statements and theories. A special relevance can be attributed to the functional relations between magnitudes, an all-pervasive element of every branch of mathematical natural science. Functional relations can always express some feature of natural order as far as they always express regularities.

Many scientific laws are functional relations. For instance, some describe relations between properties of systems in equilibrium, and others describe the motion of physical systems. Especially interesting for a study of natural order are those laws that express general conditions of order, such as the laws of maximum or minimum values, the laws of symmetry, and the laws of conservation.

3. Scientific Worldviews

A worldview is a unified picture of the world that reflects our basic ideas about natural order and includes in a general framework our real or alleged knowledge about particular kinds of natural order.

---

12. Quoted by John N. Howard, "Principal Scientific Contributions of John William Strutt, Third Baron Rayleigh," in *Springs of Scientific Creativity, Essays on Founders of Modern Science,* ed. Rutherford Aris, H. Ted Davis, and Roger H. Stuewer (Minneapolis: University of Minnesota Press, 1983), p. 167.

A remarkable unanimity exists among authors concerning the worldviews that have played a central role in Western thought. Almost everyone speaks of three great worldviews that roughly correspond to three periods: from the ancient times until the birth of empirical science, from the development of classical empirical science until the scientific revolutions of the twentieth century, and the current epoch. Agreement about the main ideas of the ancient and the modern worldviews is common; differences mainly arise regarding the contemporary worldview, but steadily increasing agreement on these ideas has emerged in the last decades of the twentieth century.

To fully appreciate the character, meaning, and consequences of our present worldview, I present it against the background of the previous pictures of the world.

II. DESCRIBING WORLDVIEWS

I have chosen five positions that analyze and evaluate the different worldviews that have had a strong impact on Western history. These are taken from authors who differ widely in their perspectives and doctrines, so as to provide a sufficiently rich perspective about our present position.

1. FROM NATURE TO HISTORY

Robin George Collingwood's posthumous book *The Idea of Nature* discusses three views of nature: the Greek, the Renaissance, and the modern. Collingwood distinguishes different postures in each stage; for instance, discussing the Ionians, the Pythagoreans, Plato, and Aristotle, when outlining the Greek view. However, it is possible to focus on the essential traits that paint a unified picture of the whole process, following Collingwood's own statements.

Collingwood adopted a historicist position in which metaphysics was viewed as depending on the historical circumstances. His overall view can be labeled "From Nature to History." He characterizes the three great worldviews using the metaphors of the organism (Greek), the machine (Renaissance), and human history (Modern), and presents the last worldview as surpassing the two previous ones (Table 3.1).

The first two metaphors are a commonplace, as they are used by many authors. According to Collingwood,

> Greek natural science was based on the principle that the world of nature is saturated or permeated by mind. Greek thinkers regarded the presence of mind in nature as the source of that regularity or orderliness in the natural world whose presence made a science of nature possible. . . . Since the world of nature is a world not only of ceaseless motion and therefore alive, but also a world of orderly or regular motion, they accordingly said that the world of nature is not

	Greek	Renaissance	Contemporary
Analogy	Organism	Clock	Self-organization
Kind of order	Teleology	Regularity	Patterning
Rationality	Panpsychism	Contrivance	Information
Key features	Substances	Laws	Processes
Key patterns	Forms	Configurations	Rhythms

Table 3.1   *Three great worldviews.*

only alive but intelligent; not only a vast animal with a "soul" or life of its own, but a rational animal with a "mind" of its own. The life and intelligence of creatures inhabiting the earth's surface and the regions adjacent to it, they argued, represent a specialised local organisation of this all-pervading vitality and rationality.[13]

The Renaissance worldview (corresponding roughly to the scientific revolution of the sixteenth and seventeenth centuries) is depicted by Collingwood as a reaction against this ancient picture:

> The central point of this antithesis was the denial that the world of nature, the world studied by physical science, is an organism and the assertion that it is devoid both of intelligence and of life. It is therefore incapable of ordering its own movements in a rational manner, and indeed of moving itself at all. The movements which it exhibits, and which the physicist investigates, are imposed upon it from without, and their regularity is due to "laws of nature" likewise imposed from without. Instead of being an organism, the natural world is a machine: a machine in the literal and proper sense of the word, an arrangement of bodily parts designed and put together and set going for a definite purpose by an intelligent mind outside itself. The Renaissance thinkers, like the Greeks, saw in the orderliness of the natural world an expression of intelligence: but for the Greeks this intelligence was nature's own intelligence, for the Renaissance thinkers it was the intelligence of something other than nature: the divine creator and ruler of nature. This distinction is the key to all the main differences between Greek and Renaissance natural science.[14]

Even if the organism and machine metaphors are very limited, they capture some important features of the corresponding worldviews. The Greek view not only made room for mind and purpose, but required them. The mechanistic world was totally deprived of internal purpose; it was seen as a consequence and a manifestation of God's ordering activity, but matter was

13. Robin G. Collingwood, *The Idea of Nature* (Oxford: Clarendon Press, 1945), pp. 3–4.

14. Ibid., p. 5.

thought to be ruled by blind forces: the way to God was paved by that internal indifference of matter that required an external intelligent being if it was to be organized. Indeed, the mechanistic worldview was based on the assumption that matter by itself is something completely passive that needs an action coming from outside if it is to achieve a coherent organization.

The metaphysical and religious implications of these two worldviews were in no way antithetical. The ancient worldview was widely accepted and used by Christian authors, who found it very easy to combine it with the existence of a personal God who is the purposeful creator of the world. It was also easy to combine it with the central role played by human beings in God's plan. However, both aspects could also easily be integrated within the mechanical view, which strongly stressed the primacy of spirit over matter and the impossibility of attributing the many contrivances that exist in nature only to blind laws.

We may suppose that Collingwood's view coincides, to a great extent, with the view he labels "the Modern view of nature," which he sees as still in the making. The transition to that view begins with Hegel, and the main elements and authors that intervene in it are three: evolutionary biology with Bergson, modern physics with the new theory of matter, and modern cosmology as represented by Alexander and Whitehead. The organism and mechanism as metaphors are substituted by history:

> the modern view of nature, which begins to find expression towards the end of the eighteenth century and ever since then has been gathering weight and establishing itself more securely down to the present day, is based on the analogy between the process of the natural world as studied by natural scientists and the vicissitudes of human affairs as studied by historians. . . . Modern cosmology could only have arisen from a widespread familiarity with historical studies, and in particular with historical studies of the kind which placed the conception of process, change, development in the center of their picture and recognized it as the fundamental category of historical thought.[15]

It is a matter of opinion whether one should agree with Collingwood's insistence on the role of history and historians in the construction of the new worldview. According to Collingwood, this modern worldview originated first in the field of history and then spread to the field of natural science. I doubt that he is right on this point. He says that, by the beginning of the nineteenth century, history had already "been established as a science, that is, a progressive inquiry in which conclusions are solidly and demonstratively established. It had thus been proved by experiment that scientific knowledge was possible concerning objects that were constantly changing," and he concludes:

> Once more, the self-consciousness of man, his historical consciousness of his own corporate doings, provided a clue to his thoughts

15. Ibid., pp. 9–10.

about nature. The historical conception of scientifically knowable change or process was applied, under the name of evolution, to the natural world.[16]

This is too hard to swallow. As I see it, Collingwood was also influenced by Hegel and Hegel's followers. He presents Hegel as representing the transition point to the modern view of nature, but it should be recalled that Hegel's historicism refers directly to the world of spiritual affairs and has little in common with empirical science and scientific worldviews. For one thing, it is important to remember that Hegel, in the introduction to his *Philosophy of Nature*, explicitly stated that physical and biological evolution must be completely excluded from philosophical reflection, a cause of no small embarrassment to some modern Hegelians.[17]

What seems indisputable is that evolutionary thinking plays a central role in the modern worldview, and Collingwood stresses the relevance of Bergson in this context. He rightly points out a serious drawback of Bergson's philosophy when he says that "what is wrong with Bergson's philosophy, regarded as a cosmology, is not the fact that he takes life seriously but the fact that he takes nothing else seriously."[18] But he aptly regards emergent or creative evolution as an idea that forms part of the central core of the modern view of nature.

Collingwood examines the consequences of the modern view. Two of them—that change is no longer cyclical but progressive, and that substance is resolved into function—should be rather considered as features of the mechanistic worldview, and the dissolution of the concept of substance is, in my opinion, a mistake which Collingwood shares with many other authors. Indeed, the concept of substance underlying these criticisms is usually that of a changeless subject as it is proposed in the mechanical view of nature. It seems possible, and even necessary, to assert the existence of systems that possess a high degree of individuality and can be considered real totalities rather than aggregates. In fact, one of the outstanding features of nature when seen under the light of the contemporary progress of empirical science is the existence of wholes that cannot be reduced to the mere sum of their components, which corresponds extremely well to the classical concept of substance.

Collingwood recognized two other consequences of the modern view, which are closely related and are very important: nature is no longer considered as being mechanical, and teleology is reintroduced into nature. Colling-

16. Ibid., pp. 9–13.

17. Georg Wilhelm Friedrich Hegel, *Enzyklopädie der philosophischen Wissenschaften im Grundrisse*, in *Gesammelte Werke*, herausgegeben von der Rheinisch-Westfälischen Akademie der Wissenschaften, Band 20 (Hamburg: Felix Meiner Verlag, 1992), n. 249, pp. 238–239. It is important to recall that the relevant text is contained in the preceding quotation—in the third edition of the Encyclopedia, the last revised by Hegel. The text is not as complete in the second edition of that work: see *Gesammelte Werke*, Band 19 (Hamburg: Felix Meiner Verlag, 1989), n. 249. p. 186.

18. Collingwood, *The Idea of Nature*, cit., p. 141.

wood refers to Bacon's and Molière's celebrated criticisms against final causes, and he aptly says that during the birth and establishment of modern empirical science,

> The doctrine especially selected for attack was teleology, the theory of final causes, the attempt to explain nature as permeated by a tendency or endeavour to realise forms not yet existing.[19]

That the attacks against teleology have been superseded by further scientific progress can doubtless be seen as one of the main characteristics of the contemporary worldview.

Collingwood speaks about "the new theory of matter" and, although his reflections were set down in 1945, his points are most relevant for the contemporary worldview. One of them is that scientific progress uncovers the existence of dynamic patterns, which play a most important role in an updated worldview. Collingwood says that by examining the role of electron patterns,

> we also get a very important new conception of chemical quality, as depending not upon the merely quantitative aspect of the atom, its weight, but upon the pattern formed by the electrons that compose it. This pattern is not a static pattern but a dynamic pattern, a pattern constantly changing in a definite rhythmical way, like the rhythmical patterns discovered by the Pythagoreans in the field of acoustics. The idea of rhythmical pattern as a link between quantity and quality is important in the modern theory of nature not only as providing a connexion between those hitherto unconnected notions, but, what is more important still, as revealing a new significance in the idea of time.[20]

This can be viewed as an anticipation of ideas that have come to occupy a central position in the contemporary worldview thanks to the progress achieved throughout the twentieth century. Collingwood also proposes that

> we take seriously the modern view that not only mind and life but matter too is inherently and essentially activity.[21]

Although I do not agree with his statement that substance is nothing but its activity, I think his stress on the essential dynamism of matter is one of the main features highlighted in the contemporary worldview.

Finally, Collingwood studies, under the label of "modern cosmology," the philosophy of Samuel Alexander and Alfred North Whitehead. He points out that the world appears to Alexander "as a single cosmic process in which there emerge, as it goes on, higher orders of being." He recalls that Alexander bor

19. Ibid., p. 93.

20. Ibid., p. 146.

21. Ibid., p. 150.

rows the word "emergent" from Lloyd Morgan, who used it in his works *Instinct and Experience* (1912) and *Emergent Evolution* (1923). Collingwood follows Alexander in considering that the word "emergent" is used to describe how

> the higher orders of being are not mere resultants of what went before . . . thus the higher is not a mere modification or complication of the lower but something genuinely and qualitatively new, which must be explained not by reducing it to terms of the lower out of which it grew but according to its own proper principles.[22]

"Emergence" to Collingwood is therefore a purely descriptive concept that does not fully explain the appearance of new qualities and beings. In all this, Collingwood anticipates much of the discussions of the late twentieth century. Collingwood's final conclusion, which is consistent with his historicism, includes the warning that his reflections refer to the progress reached in science up to a concrete date, so that we cannot anticipate what kind of progress will be made in the future and what consequences will accompany it. He ends by asserting that the higher form of thought upon which our reflections on nature depend is history.

2. A Purposeless World

Nicolai Hartmann's *Philosophy of Nature,* published in 1950, belongs to a series on ontology published by Hartmann from the 1930s onward. It can be considered the last attempt made by an important professional philosopher in the twentieth century to build an entire philosophy of nature. In those days, philosophy of science seemed to be definitively replacing the old-fashioned philosophy of nature. Nevertheless, around 1990 it was apparent that the great problems of philosophy of nature were not only still alive, but had also reappeared with renewed vigor due to the new developments in science.

Hartmann presents the goal, method, and main ideas of his natural philosophy, which is conceived as an analysis of the categories of the natural world closely linked to the development of the empirical sciences. Hartmann adopts a realist perspective, and in some way he aims at developing the Kantian line. Although some of his reflections can be used to reformulate the classical philosophical ideas, he strongly criticizes the Aristotelian ideas of substance, form, and finality, and he tries to destroy any bridge that could establish links between philosophy and theology. Hartmann rightly noticed that the affirmation of purpose in the natural world is especially relevant if we seek to connect the sciences with metaphysics and theology, and devoted an entire work undermining the foundations of teleology in all its forms.[23]

In the introduction to his *Philosophy of Nature,* Hartmann presents an overall view of the development of natural philosophy throughout history that,

---

22. Ibid., pp. 158–159.

23. Nicolai Hartmann, *Teleologisches Denken* (Berlin: Walter de Gruyter, 1951).

to a great extent, encompasses the three worldviews, but also introduces other details.[24] He distinguishes four periods, with their corresponding worldviews, and a later interlude. The first two periods correspond to those distinguished by Collingwood and other authors. The first period includes the Aristotelian and Scholastic teleological worldview, from Plato to the sixteenth century, which Hartmann strongly criticized as anthropocentric. The second, which reaches maturity in the seventeenth century, corresponds to the classical physics of Galileo and Newton; it is a cosmology without purpose, based on exact lawfulness: forms are substituted by laws, matter by forces, teleology by processes without beginning or end, and causality is reduced to efficient causes.

Differences between Hartmann and other authors arise when the later events are considered. Hartmann speaks of a third period, represented by Kant alone. Hartmann attributes a decisive importance to Kant as a turning point in the history of thought; in more than one respect, he tries to update some of Kant's main ideas. According to Hartmann, the worldview corresponding to classical physics reaches its peak with Kant, and Kant inaugurates a new philosophy of the organic world, definitively destroying the remnants of teleology that had survived until his time. Hartmann then describes a brief fourth period, consisting of the idealistic metaphysics of nature of Schelling and Hegel; it included a return to teleology, so that nature was seen as a kind of unconscious intelligence based on spirit, but it was shortly afterward overcome by the progress of the sciences. Finally, there was an interlude in which the sciences dominated; the corresponding worldview was that of positivism, which limited the realm of the knowable to the results of empirical science.

Hartmann criticizes the positivist views and, in spite of the insistence of the positivists on the meaninglessness of philosophy of nature, he formulates an entire philosophy of nature. Nevertheless, he does not consider it as having a strong philosophical consistency. He rather reduces the task of his natural philosophy to that of analyzing the categories used by the sciences at a concrete moment in time. Therefore, the results would always be provisional, depending on the stages reached by the sciences. Moreover, we should not expect anything like the ancient problems related to teleology, spirituality, and transcendence. As I have already said, Hartmann strongly criticizes any form of teleology and the concepts traditionally associated with teleology, especially those of substance and form. Neither does he leave any door open to the divine. Regarding humanism, he certainly recognizes the special status of human beings and their emergent character with relation to the merely natural levels, but he carefully avoids connecting all this with any theological view.

The difficulty with Hartmann is that his analysis of particular issues is often correct, but he is wrong when he refers to the most important concepts

24. Nicolai Hartmann, *Philosophie der Natur. Abriss der speziellen Kategorienlehre* (Berlin: Walter de Gruyter, 1980), "Einleitung," nn. 1–10, pp. 1–20.

that can give a meaning to philosophy. This is probably due to his utterly antiteleological and antitheological attitude, which leads him to some contradictions. For instance, although he repeatedly denies any real meaning to the Aristotelian and Scholastic concept of substance, when he explains his ideas about natural wholes he proposes ideas, such as dynamical complexes and central predetermination, which can easily be used to reformulate the classical concept of substance in the contemporary context. In the same way, he denies the existence of any kind of finality in nature, but at other times, especially when analyzing the biological realm, he introduces ideas that could serve to support teleological thought.

The relevance of Hartmann's philosophy of nature lies in two points: first, in the subtlety of many of his particular analyses, and above all in the fact that his criticisms remind us that the problem of the bridges between science and theology is a permanent source of concern even to those who deny the existence of the divine.

3. THE WORLD AS A PATTERN OF NUMBERS

Another threefold scheme of the worldviews has been proposed by Stanley Jaki, who devoted to this subject the first part of *The Relevance of Physics,* under the heading "The Chief World Models of Physics." There, he studies three worldviews which he calls "The World as an Organism" (centered mainly on Aristotle), "The World as a Mechanism," and "The World as a Pattern of Numbers."[25] The first and the second correspond to the first two views of Collingwood and Hartmann. Jaki's originality with respect to other authors lies in his characterization of the third worldview, which corresponds to the contemporary scene.

Jaki's book is not devoted to science in general, but specifically to physics. Therefore, it is hardly surprising that we do not find there any consideration regarding biological evolution. One could perhaps wonder why there is no reference to cosmic evolution, which plays a very important role in the contemporary worldview. This can be understood upon noting the date of publication; 1966 is just after the discovery by Arno Penzias and Robert Wilson of microwave background radiation, when the Big Bang model was beginning its successful career in the scientific world. In later writings Jaki has paid great attention to both cosmic evolution and biological evolution.

Jaki criticizes the excesses involved in the organicistic and mechanistic worldviews. At the end of his analysis of the first worldview he explains how the second one emerged and writes:

> Yet, in ultimate analysis, what changed was only the object of scientific faith, not its degree. For three centuries machines were to be

---

25. Stanley L. Jaki, *The Relevance of Physics* (Chicago and London: The University of Chicago Press, 1966), pp. 1–137.

idolized with as little second thought as had been the concept of organism for over two thousand years.[26]

Jaki's criticisms of the organicistic view are directed not only to Aristotle, but also to some of his predecessors and to the modern followers of that view: Goethe, Schelling, and Hegel. Although I agree with Jaki's sharp criticisms, I also believe that that view contained some important ideas that are being re-covered now after having been neglected for several centuries. I do not ad-vocate organicism or romanticism or idealism, but the modern romantic movement contained some interesting features that counterbalance the ex-cesses of the mechanistic worldview; however, these doctrines do not provide a solution along the right lines. And yet, the development of science makes it possible to recover the positive features of the organicistic view.

This point is most important regarding Aristotle. Of course, one may find in his works as many drawbacks as one desires if we seek to compare them to modern physics. Nevertheless, I think that it would not be fair to consider Aristotle the main obstacle to the development of modern science for two thousand years. Certainly, the beginning of modern physics required new ideas that in some cases explicitly contradicted Aristotle's doctrines. But the elaboration of the new physics was an extraordinarily difficult task only pos-sible thanks to many conceptual and empirical developments taking place over centuries, and the conceptual developments, in many cases, arose from dis-cussion of Aristotle's ideas. In any case, Aristotle was truly interested in sci-ence and contributed to the progress of biology, the field in which he could cultivate empirical work with some probability of success.

Aristotle cannot be considered an enemy of empirical science. In a book on 20 great experiments that changed our view of the world, Rom Harré chose as the first Aristotle's study of chicken embryology.[27] This experiment is the only experiment from the ancient era chosen. When Harré explains the criteria that he used to choose the 20 experiments, he comments:

> Aristotle's study of the embryology of the chick can be traced with some certainty as the seminal work from which all embryological studies, including those of our own day, have been derived.[28]

Aristotle's scientific merit in the biological field is irrefutable. In his mono-graph on this topic, Anthony Preus states:

> Aristotle's work in biology was crucial for the further development of the life sciences in antiquity. As it happened, Theophrastus and others in the Lyceum continued biological study, and Aristotelians carried the tradition to the museum in Alexandria. The Alexandrian school

26. Ibid., p. 51.

27. Rom Harré, *Great Scientific Experiments: Twenty Experiments that Changed our View of the World* (Oxford and New York: Oxford University Press, 1984), pp. 25–32.

28. Ibid., p. 3.

remained the leading center of research in biology and medicine for centuries. This historical development should not be surprising, for Aristotle had developed a comprehensive theoretical system which strongly encouraged biological investigation. . . . Aristotle developed a philosophical foundation for biological research. He also posed many of the problems which later scientists tried to solve. . . . Aristotle is one of the few people who investigated biological phenomena as an essential and central part of his philosophical investigations.[29]

My interest in stressing these aspects of Aristotle's work amounts to more than an apology. I think biological phenomena occupy a central place in nature and that biology is the most important among the natural sciences, and thus a correct worldview should reflect these two facts. I also think that this was already the case at the time of Aristotle, and his worldview contains ideas that still form a good basis and a source of inspiration for natural philosophy.

The systematic development of modern empirical science could not begin with biology, which deals with the most sophisticated natural phenomena. Indeed, biology only reached full maturity in the last part of the twentieth century, when the physicochemical foundations needed to develop a rigorously scientific biology were at hand. Some of the Aristotelian philosophical ideas inspired by the biological realm can be recovered now, with the necessary adaptations and complements. The case of idealistic and romantic modern thinkers is much more difficult, for some of them, like Hegel, intended to substitute his fancies for the empirical science that was already developing. But even in those thinkers we can find interesting ideas that surpass the mechanistic and positivist perspectives and can be included within a rigorous worldview.

The key concept of Jaki's third worldview is that of mathematical patterns. Jaki seriously doubts that this can be considered a final result and concludes his examination of the three worldviews thus:

> The great aim of physical science, the overall synthesis of the scientific understanding of the universe will remain for all practical purposes what it has always been, the ever-remote objective of an intellectual faith.[30]

I would only add that, however remote this objective may always remain, we can make progress in our understanding of nature, we can know that we have progressed, and we can formulate worldviews that are closer to the real features of the natural world. Jaki's works testify that he agrees with this assertion.

---

29. Anthony Preus, *Science and Philosophy in Aristotle's Biological Works* (Hildesheim and New York: Georg Olms Verlag, 1975), pp. 259–260.

30. Jaki, *The Relevance of Physics,* cit. p. 137.

4. The Evolutionary Universe

In 1977 Whitrow outlined the threefold view of nature in a way similar to that of Collingwood. He described the three worldviews as based on three fundamental analogies: the organism, the machine, and human history. The novelty of his analysis lies in the central role that time plays in it:

> The first analogy gave rise to the general idea of *the teleological Universe,* primarily associated with the name of Aristotle, the second to *the clocklike Newtonian Universe,* and the third to *the evolutionary Universe* of modern science. Each of these analogies can be associated with a different view of the nature and significance of *time.* It is the object of the present paper to examine the role of time in the general development of cosmology, as an aid to understanding how our present world-picture has come about.[31]

It is no surprise that time is being considered a central feature. By 1977 cosmology had attracted the interest of the scientific community, and theories about the origin of the universe and cosmic evolution were an important part of the scientific worldview. In addition, other developments in the physical sciences, such as the second principle of classical thermodynamics and Prigogine's development of the thermodynamics of systems far from equilibrium, had also contributed to place time in the focus of attention. Therefore, Whitrow only expresses what the vast majority of scientists consider to be one of the main features of contemporary science: the evolutionary character of nature.

Whitrow emphasizes that progress in the construction of reliably mechanical clocks played a leading role in the development of modern empirical science and greatly contributed to the success of the clock analogy. He recalls that until the fourteenth century the only available ways to tell time were sundials and water clocks. He analyzes the development of mechanical clocks and concludes:

> The invention of a satisfactory mechanical clock had a tremendous influence on the concept of time itself. For, unlike the water-clocks that preceded it, the mechanical clock (if properly regulated) can tick away continually and accurately for years on end, and so must have greatly influenced belief in the homogeneity and continuity of time. The mechanical clock was therefore not only the prototype instrument for the mechanical conception of the Universe, but for the modern idea of time. An ever more far-reaching influence has been claimed for it by Lewis Mumford, who has argued that "it dissociated time from human events and helped create belief in an independent world of mathematically measurable sequences: the special world of science."[32]

31. Gerald J. Whitrow, "The Role of Time in Cosmology," in *Cosmology, History, and Theology,* ed. Wolfgang Yourgrau and Allen D. Breck (New York and London: Plenum Press, 1977), p. 159.

32. Ibid.

The role of time gained in importance as the universe began to be considered under the light of evolution. Although the antecedents of evolutionary views can be traced back to antiquity, only the evolutionary biology of the nineteenth century placed history as a central feature of the universe. Later, several developments in physics, especially those related to the expansion and age of the universe, completed the image of a universe in which history plays a primary role. This evolutionary character of the universe has become one of the main ingredients of the contemporary worldview.

5. THE RELATIVE WORLD OF PROCESS

In *The Search for Certainty*,[33] Wilford Spradlin and Patricia Porterfield analyze the three worldviews, under the headings "The Anthropomorphic World of Words," "The Mechanical World of Form and Function," and "The Relative World of Process." The book aims to show that the ancient quest for certainty is now dead.

This book can be considered representative of an increasingly widespread attitude that is rather critical toward religion and stresses the uncertain character of human knowledge. The analysis of the first worldview ends with a "Benediction" that is quite sarcastic toward Christianity; the last chapter backs the alleged dissolution of Western concepts and the fusing of the results of modern science with Eastern perspectives that leave no room for certainty or other definite ideas. As an example, the authors assert that

> To some degree, the twentieth century relativistic approach to the concept of self resembles the mystical conceptual frames of early Gnostic Christianity in which Christ represented the merger of God and man. With the dissolution of absolutes, we may speculate that old concepts like man and God died in each other or dissolved into each other to form a uniform continuum. From this point of view, the merger of God and man is a conquest of death, which moved from a definitive event or entity to a fluid process in which life and death are relative organisational patterns.[34]

Frankly, I do not understand this view at all. I mention this book because it is completely centered on the threefold scheme of the worldviews and may help one to understand the different interpretations that can be extracted from the analysis of these, while it also alludes to the important role that problems about certainty play in the contemporary context.

---

33. Wilford W. Spradlin and Patricia Porterfield, *The Search for Certainty* (New York-Berlin-Heidelberg-Tokyo: Springer, 1984).

34. Ibid., p. 236.

III. A NEW SCIENTIFIC WORLDVIEW

There is generalized agreement that a new worldview is emerging that is at least as important and powerful as any other worldview in history. Paul Davies and John Gribbin have written:

In fact, as we approach the end of the twentieth century, science is throwing off the shackles of three centuries of thought in which a particular paradigm—called "mechanism"—has dominated the world view of scientists. In its simplest terms, mechanism is the belief that the physical Universe is nothing but a collection of material particles in interaction, a gigantic purposeless machine. . . . The movement toward a "post-mechanistic" paradigm, a paradigm suitable for 21st-century science, is taking place across a broad front: in cosmology, in the chemistry of self-organising systems, in the new physics of chaos, in quantum mechanics and particle physics, in the information sciences and (more reluctantly) at the interface of biology with physics. . . . This monumental paradigm shift is bringing with it a new perspective on human beings and their role in the great drama of nature. . . . We have no doubt that the revolution which we are immensely privileged and fortunate to be witnessing at first hand will for ever alter humankind's view of the Universe.[35]

As I analyze the main features of the new emerging paradigm, I will focus on those features that may help us to appreciate the philosophical and theological relevance of the new ideas. The new worldview can be represented by the metaphor of a self-organization that includes information as one of its main ingredients.

1. A Unified Picture of the World

Although the roots of the new paradigm can be traced back over several centuries, a concrete picture has only been achieved in the last decades of the twentieth century. This new image represents a genuinely important achievement that has deep implications in many fields.

The emerging paradigm is all the more remarkable because it is the first scientific worldview that provides a unified, complete, rigorous, and scientific worldview in which rationality, information, and creativity occupy a central place. When I say that the present worldview is complete I do not mean that it contains all that can be known about our world, but that it includes all natural levels, some of each level's basic features, and the mutual connections between those levels (Figure 3.2).

The microphysical level is well known. The standard model of particles and interactions works very well at the moment. It has repeatedly undergone

35. Paul Davies and John Gribbin, *The Matter Myth* (London: Penguin Books, 1992), pp. 1–3.

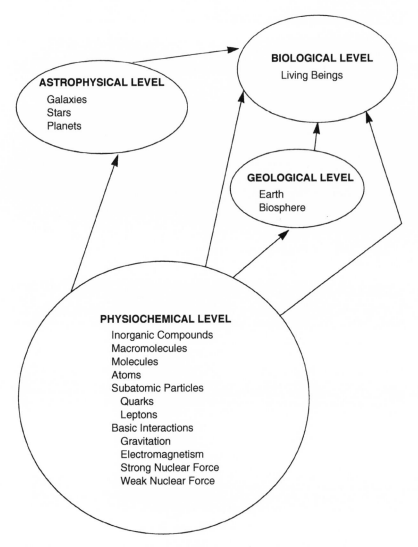

Fig. 3.2   Natural levels. The physicochemical level provides the basis for the other levels. Living beings possess the most sophisticated natural structures, and their existence requires the cooperation of the physicochemical level, which provides the basic components; of the Earth and the entire biosphere, which provide the immediate environment; and also the stars: the Sun provides light and energy for life on Earth, and the heavy atoms were first produced within the stars and were spread when the stars exploded.

rigorous tests and has survived them. In the future a better model may supersede it, but would of necessity include the many well-tested features of the present one. Current microphysics still contains many mysteries: for instance, we do not yet know how to combine the particle–wave duality of the microphysical entities; arguments rage about the significance of Bell's inequalities and about the interpretation of the corresponding experiments such as those of Alain Aspect; and we do not know what will happen when new hypotheses such as the theory of superstrings or the Higgs mechanism can be experimentally tested. In spite of these and other uncertainties, we can safely say that we know to a good approximation what the main constituents of matter are and what the patterns of their activity are. In addition, these uncertainties refer to the most problematic field of subatomic particles, whereas if we consider the more organized levels of atoms, molecules, and macromolecules, we can say with confidence that we know the basic building blocks of the material world.

Modern atomic theory developed during the nineteenth century, and the first subatomic particle, the electron, was discovered in 1897. In the following decades, the structure of the atom and the existence of the subatomic particles that, with the electron, constitute ordinary matter were discovered. Until the 1920s or 1930s, it was impossible to reach a real knowledge of the basic mechanisms that explain the structure and behavior of stars and of living beings. Only the great progress of microphysics at that time made it possible to know the processes of nuclear fission and fusion, and therefore to know that the stars are organized around a nucleus in which nuclear fusion processes take place. The same advances led to the discovery in 1953 of the double-helical structure of DNA, which explained the basic genetic phenomena. The ensuing progress of molecular biology has to be considered as one of the most effective, beautiful, and amazing developments of empirical science in any age, and it has decisively contributed to place biology in the center of the scientific picture of the world.

These examples also show how the links between different levels have been established. A characteristic of the present worldview is precisely that it shows the continuity of the different natural levels; this worldview provides a unified, complete picture of the world. Now we know that everything in the natural world is made of the same basic components, what these components are, and how they work. A unity not only of composition, but also of dynamism exists, as the same basic interactions are present everywhere. One remarkable feature of our world is how much is achieved by applying iterative procedures to a small number of basic elements. This shows the subtlety of the natural processes and constitutes an integral part of the rationality of nature.

Now, for the first time in human history, we have at our disposal a worldview that is both scientifically rigorous and unitary and complete, for it includes the microphysical, mesophysical, and macrophysical levels. This worldview includes both inorganic and biological matter. We know a great deal about the composition of matter and about the behavior of natural systems at the successive physical, chemical, and biological levels; we also know the basic mechanisms that explain the structure and behavior of the stars; and, above all, we have progressed enormously in our knowledge of the mechanisms of life. All natural levels are closely related and constitute a web of mutual interconnections; for this reason I say that we now possess a unified worldview.

Two more points concerning the unitary character of the present worldview are worth noting. One is the existence of theories that unify several previously unconnected fields. Such a unification can only be achieved when we already have several well-developed branches of knowledge, and is a sign of maturity. Some form of unification has always been present as one of the main objectives in science. The new science that was born in the sixteenth century achieved a first and most important unification, by considering earthly and celestial phenomena as subject to the same laws. Other cases of unification can be seen down the centuries; an important example was the unification of electricity, magnetism, and optics under the electromagnetic theory of Maxwell that occurred in the second half of the nineteenth century. In our time, apart from the morphogenetic theories that link different fields, a special relevance may be attributed to the search for the unification of the basic interactions. Here, the electroweak theory shows how the unification of the electromagnetic and the weak nuclear interactions can be achieved; further progress is being made toward the so-called "great unification theories" (GUT), which would add strong nuclear interaction to the unitary picture; and physicists are also working on the difficult task of integrating the gravitational interaction to the other three. A part of the interest of this work lies in the broadening of our worldview implied in it, as true unification of the basic interactions is supposed to have existed in the earliest stages of the universe. Therefore, as these theories progress, we obtain a picture of the world that is more and more unitary, as it includes not only its present features, but also its evolution over billions of years.

This leads to the second point: that the present worldview unifies the analytic and the synthetic perspectives. Empirical science developed systematically from the seventeenth century onward thanks to the analytic method, which breaks up any subject of study into particular components and perspectives. This analytic perspective will always be important, but it may occasionally mislead us if we forget that we are working only in a specific perspective. Scientific progress is now making it possible to recover old concepts that seemed lost and introduce new concepts that refer to the synthetic perspective, especially concepts that represent wholes and tendencies. I will offer some concrete examples of this kind of conceptual progress in the following analysis.

2. Morphogenetic Theories

The new worldview includes both the synchronic and the diachronic perspective. The evolutionary perspective first reached its scientific maturity in the field of biology in the nineteenth century and in the twentieth century also embraced genetics and molecular biology. Cosmic evolution had seriously been proposed as early as the end of the 1920s by the Christian astronomer and priest Georges Lemaître on the basis of Einstein's general relativity and the follow-up work of Friedmann and de Sitter. This became the focus of attention when some of its empirical consequences were successfully tested in the 1960s. If we combine cosmic and biological evolution, we obtain a big global process that supposedly started some ten billion years ago from a primeval state in which all matter and energy were concentrated at enormous density and temperature. We do not know exactly how the different components of our world formed after the Big Bang, but we have plausible accounts that can explain this, at least in principle.

There are many holes in the explanation of the successive steps of that gigantic evolutionary process, and so great attention is devoted to morphogenetic theories that try to explain how new forms of order can emerge from more disordered states. These theories include thermodynamics of irreversible processes, catastrophe theory, synergetics, and deterministic chaos (Table 3.2).

Thermodynamics was a well-established theory as early as the nineteenth century, when it could also be called thermostatics: indeed, to study physical processes, they were reduced first to a succession of states of equilibrium with simple, well-defined properties. Prigogine received the Nobel Prize for chemistry in 1977 for his work on thermodynamics far from equilibrium, a theory that provides the tools to study irreversible processes in which a dissipation of energy occurs. This represents a big step forward for the study of irreversible processes of nature. Among them, a special relevance can be attributed to those processes in which new forms of order emerge. The new thermodynamics provides a clue to explain the emergence of new patterns in some chemical processes, as in Bénard cells and the Belusov-Zhabotinski effect, using nonlinear differential equations. Although the new theory seemed

Theory	Author	Field	Connects
Far-from-equilibrium thermodynamics	Ilya Prigogine	Dissipative structures	Physics and chemistry with biology
Synergetics	Hermann Haken	Cooperative phenomena	All natural levels
Catastrophe Theory	René Thom	Mathematical singularities	
Deterministic Chaos		Sensibility to initial conditions	A great variety of phenomena

Table 3.2 *Morphogenetic theories.*

to challenge the second law of thermodynamics, it has been shown that the emergence of new ordered patterns takes place in open systems that interchange matter or energy with their medium. In those conditions, the system may remain in the same state or it may eventually tend toward a lower state of order, but sometimes new forms of organization can spontaneously emerge. This theory aims to establish links between the biological level and the physicochemical laws, because biological systems are open far-from-equilibrium systems that can be studied using the new tools.

Prigogine claimed that his theory represented a turning point in the history of ideas because it provides a perspective that overcomes the deterministic and mechanistic worldview, which reduced time to an abstract magnitude without real import and reduced natural systems to mere aggregations of their parts. The new perspective emphasizes the dynamic and structural features of nature, and shows the existence of a natural tendential dynamism whose deployment produces natural systems that are real wholes and not merely sums of their parts.[36]

This perspective has been enlarged in the new branch of science called "synergetics" by its founder, Hermann Haken.[37] Its name indicates that what is at stake here are those phenomena that are related to cooperative action. This argument coincides with Prigogine's insofar as both study the formation of new ordered patterns out of less ordered states. But synergetics particularly emphasized the collective behavior of natural elements in the production of new patterns. The paradigmatic case is that of laser, in whose development Haken played an important role. In this case, the collective action is the emission of photons of the same frequency by all the atoms of a system; this enables the production of monochromatic light with great intensity and precision. The classic example to visualize this kind of phenomenon is to think of a choir composed by many voices, all of whom sing in a perfect synchrony and harmony.

Synergetics studies the structural aspects of a great variety of phenomena and tries to link different kinds of phenomena and different natural levels. One of the most interesting developments in this line is the study of the relationship between the microscopic and the macroscopic realms. A useful analogy to illuminate this relationship is that of the letters of the alphabet and the phrases of a language; the structural aspects are crucial because only certain sequences of letters make sense, and once these structures exist, they make possible the formation of other new structures and accordingly make impossible the appearance of others.

Nonlinear thermodynamics and synergetics have opened very interesting perspectives. They show that natural systems possess a dynamism that deploys

36. See Ilya Prigogine, *From Being to Becoming* (San Francisco: Freeman, 1979).

37. See Hermann Haken, *Synergetics. An Introduction* (Berlin-Heidelberg-New York: Springer, 1977); "Pattern Formation and Pattern Recognition: An Attempt at a Synthesis," *Pattern Formation by Dynamic Systems and Pattern Recognition,* ed. Hermann Haken (Berlin-Heidelberg-New York: Springer, 1979), pp. 2–12.

itself according to patterns and produces new structural patterns, and they stress the relevance of many forms of cooperative natural action that lead to different forms of order and organization. In addition, they underscore the unity of nature as they show the connection between its different levels.

Other morphogenetic theories contribute to broadening the scope of those ideas: for instance, catastrophe theory, formulated by René Thom, provides mathematical tools that help in the study of the formation of new patterns. As in nonlinear thermodynamics and in synergetics, catastrophe theory also deals with singularities in which new patterns emerge.

Another item that surely must be added to the list of morphogenetic theories is the so-called deterministic chaos theory. Its origins cannot be traced back to a single author; it is rather the result of some theoretical concepts usually ascribed to Jules-Henri Poincaré at the turn of the twentieth century, taken together with other more modern concepts and with techniques provided by the development of computers. Chaos theory refers to the precision that we can attain regarding the initial conditions of a phenomenon. It is impossible to measure these conditions with infinite precision. However, whereas in classical systems this limitation was not too serious, in chaotic systems this kind of error grows at an accelerating rate. Paul Davies has written:

> The key feature of a chaotic process concerns the way that predictive errors evolve with time. . . . In a typical non-chaotic system, errors accumulate with time. Crucially, though, the errors grow only in proportion to the time (or perhaps a small power thereof), so they remain relatively manageable. Now let me contrast this property with that of a chaotic system. Here a small starting difference between two identical systems will rapidly grow. In fact, the hallmark of chaos is that the motions diverge exponentially fast. Translated into a prediction problem, this means that any input error multiples itself at an escalating rate as a function of prediction time, so that before long it engulfs the calculation, and all predictive power is lost.[38]

Were chaotic systems only to show unpredictability, we would face a complete lack of order and it would be impossible to think scientifically. But this is not the case. Chaotic systems have contributed to uncovering an underlying order of a new kind. Indeed, physicists have labeled the new theories about this subject as deterministic chaos, insofar as they are discovering new kinds of tendencies, much richer than those corresponding to the oversimplified classical deterministic ideas.

3. Natural Dynamism

One of the main features of the new worldview is to rid the concept of matter of some of the connotations it had in the mechanistic picture of the

---

38. Paul Davies, "Is the Universe a Machine?" in *The New Scientist Guide to Chaos,* ed. Nina Hall (London: Penguin, 1992), p. 216.

world. More precisely, the current knowledge of the composition of matter and of its fundamental interactions results in matter not being thought of as something passive and inert, but rather as possessing an inner dynamism at all natural levels. This dynamism is closely related to structure and patterns, insofar as it deploys itself according to temporal patterns and its deployment produces spatial patterns that are the sources of new kinds of dynamism. This scheme, repeated again and again, explains how our world has been built up.

This view does not imply a return to the ancient hylozoism that attributed life to every piece of matter. But it does imply some changes in the usual notion of matter as it has been employed in modern times in the West. Indeed, the dichotomy between inert and living matter interpreted as if inert matter were a merely passive reality cannot be accepted anymore. Of course, the distinction between living and nonliving entities is a very important one, but it cannot be explained only by saying that whereas living beings are self-moving, nonliving matter is completely passive by itself. Defining life only by self-motion does not correspond either to our ordinary experience or to the ancient ideas about life such as those held by Aristotle. Living beings have always been characterized as possessing a complete set of properties that are not present in nonliving beings.

Our present scientific knowledge shows that the idea of matter as something merely passive does not correspond to reality. Dynamism is a basic characteristic of natural entities at all levels of nature. Although we do not have a complete model of the subatomic entities, we can say that all known subatomic particles intervene actively in processes in which some particles are transformed into others, new particles are produced, and energy transfers occur. Those particles are so closely related with energy processes that even their mass is usually expressed in units of energy.

The microphysical level is completely pervaded by dynamism. Stable structures result from equilibriums between different dynamisms. Atoms and molecules react according to specific laws and participate in many different kinds of transformation. Even the so-called inert gases are known not to be inert at all. Therefore, microphysical entities are neither passive nor immutable. The stability of matter is a consequence of dynamic equilibriums and sometimes hides the existence of the underlying dynamism.

At the macrophysical level, natural dynamism also appears to be a characteristic trait of nature, not only at the biological level, but also at the physicochemical one.

Moreover, the components of matter behave in a cooperative way, even at the physical level, producing new structural patterns. Those components behave in a highly sophisticated way rather than simply being passive entities. Dynamism pervades all natural levels and it produces very sophisticated results. This should not come as a surprise to us; in fact, what would be hardly conceivable would be the opposite situation, where the dynamism of living beings would be ultimately based on merely passive entities. We can safely conclude that what appears as inert matter is inert only with respect to some concrete effects, and it can be affirmed that all natural entities possess their own dynamism. I would even add that, in some way, any natural entity, even a single electron, in a metaphorical way "knows" physics in its entirety, as it will act according to its own nature in any circumstance.

Although these ideas are a part of the contemporary worldview, in some respect they were already present in the days of classical science. This is especially the case with Leibniz, who advocated the existence of an "active force" that is an intermediary between the capacity and the action, and which implies a tendency. He said that by virtue of this force matter acts by itself, that the foundation of this force has to be seen in the divine creation, and that all substances possess such an active force.[39]

To say that all natural entities possess their own dynamism is completely consistent with our present scientific knowledge and can also be considered a correct philosophical inference, because a completely passive natural entity would be unintelligible. The idea of such an entity is obscure, and it is hardly understandable how such entities could constitute the basis of the active entities that we know or how they could interact with them. Natural entities do not always develop all their dynamic potentialities, although they possess information about their potential behavior in any circumstance.

4. PATTERNS IN NATURE

If we combine the dynamic character of natural entities with the all-pervasive existence of patterns in nature we can appreciate much better the picture of the world that our present-day science provides us.

Patterns as repeatable structures that can refer to space are usually called "configurations"; when referring to time, they are called "rhythms." These important aspects are closely related, as natural dynamism is deployed according to temporal patterns and produces spatial configurations that, in turn, are a source of new dynamism deployed according to other temporal patterns, and so on. Therefore, we can conclude that dynamism and spatiotemporal patterns are completely intertwined in nature, so that one aspect does not exist without the other.

Science devotes special attention to configurations, but rhythms are also a central focus of scientific research. In fact, laws of motion have occupied a central place since the beginning of modern science and they represent aspects of natural rhythms. Recently the study of rhythms in both the microphysical and the biological world has progressed greatly; this progress is sometimes related to the new studies of chaos. There are good reasons for maintaining that temporal patterns play a central role everywhere in the

---

39. Gottfried Wilhelm Leibniz, "De primae philosophiae Emendatione, et de Notione Substantiae" in *Die philosophische Schriften von Gottfried Wilhelm Leibniz,* vol. 4, ed. C. J. Gerhardt (Hildesheim: Georg Olms, 1965), pp. 469–470.

natural world. As stated in the introduction to a specialized study on this topic:

> Patterns of an almost periodic nature appear all over the place. One sees them in cloud streets, in sand ripples on flat beaches and desert dunes, in the morphology of plants and animals, in chemically reacting media, in boundary layers, on weather maps, in geological formations, in interacting laser beams in wide gainband lasers, on the surface of thin buckling shells, and in the grid scale instabilities of numerical algorithms. This review deals with the class of problems into which these examples fall, namely with pattern formation in spatially extended, continuous, dissipative systems which are driven far from equilibrium by an external stress. Under the influence of this stress, the system can undergo a series of symmetry breaking bifurcations or phase transitions and the resulting patterns become more and more complicated, both temporally and spatially, as the stress is increased.[40]

Patterns are closely tied to the ancient concept of form as it was used to refer to the modes of being of the different entities. The concept of form continues to be present in the development of empirical science. Norma Emerton concluded her historical work about the development of crystallography by saying that the Aristotelian idea of form was the guide that, in a conscious or in an unconscious way, has always inspired the scientific quest.[41] And L. Pearce Williams, in his foreword to that work, wrote:

> This volume attempts to answer the question how brute matter, from whose actions only chaos could be expected, nevertheless is commonly found in an ordered and symmetrical form. . . . The story is a fascinating one. . . . The result is a history that introduces one of the most important and central concerns of modern science.[42]

The present worldview stresses that dynamism and patterns are closely connected and in some way interwoven. Progress in synergetics shows how different dynamisms can cooperate and produce new forms of order. Progress in microphysics shows that huge quantities of microentities collaborate in the production of cooperative patterns. Davies shows his amazement at this fact in this way:

> It is one of the universal miracles of nature that huge assemblages of particles, subject only to the blind forces of nature, are nevertheless

---

40. Alan C. Newell, Thierry Passot, and Joceline Lega, "Order Parameter Equations for Patterns," *Annual Review of Fluid Mechanics,* 25 (1993): 399.

41. Norma Emerton, *The Scientific Reinterpretation of Form* (Ithaca and London: Cornell University Press, 1984), pp. 287–288.

42. L. Pearce Williams, "Preface," in Norma Emerton, *The Scientific Reinterpretation of Form,* cit., pp 7-8.

capable of organising themselves into patterns of cooperative activity.[43]

Recent progress shows, indeed, how synergy works even at the microphysical level. As Davies puts it:

> The unusual property for matter and energy to self-organise into coherent structures and patterns is only very recently becoming appreciated by physicists. . . . Of course, biologists have long studied self-organisation and pattern formation. Today, however, physicists and chemists are joining in, and self-organisation has become a distinctive branch of the New Physics.[44]

Expressions such as "universal miracles" and "unusual property" show the amazement this kind of phenomenon produces in the scientist who reflects on the new achievements of physics. Obviously, microphysical particles know nothing about physics, but they behave in a way that makes possible the formation of increasingly complex patterns.

Patterning is a key feature of the present worldview. The process takes place usually as the production of individual patterns that reproduce a general type that already exists, but in special circumstances it may provoke a new outcome, and a new type of natural pattern is formed and eventually retained and reproduced. Both types of patterning are creative: in the first case because every single developmental process leads to a new individual system that did not exist before, and in the second case because the pattern itself did not exist before. In both cases the phenomenon is really remarkable, especially when we realize that the construction of our world has required an immense quantity of successive processes of patterning, each one of which has opened the door to new potentialities that have later been realized.

Patterning is closely related to the ideas of holism and directionality. Holism implies the existence of properties that correspond to a whole or totality and cannot be reduced to the mere aggregation of the components. Directionality means that a process does not develop in a merely random way but follows a certain tendency. The relationship becomes evident when we consider that patterning always implies the formation of some kind of organization and therefore of a systemic whole, and that the outcome of a process of patterning can be considered as the realization of some potentialities that, in their turn, can be considered tendencies.

The existence of many natural systems that should be considered as wholes is clear in the case of living beings. However, in our ordinary experience we hardly find any other kinds of holistic systems; in fact, the vast majority of the entities that constitute the mesocosmos of our ordinary experience are aggregations that do not possess a unitary characteristic. Nevertheless, on the

43. Paul Davies, "The New Physics: A Synthesis," in *The New Physics,* ed. Paul Davies (Cambridge-New York: Cambridge University Press, 1989), p. 4.

44. Ibid., p. 5.

microphysical level, many of its components are systems possessing a high degree of unity: this is the case of the compounds that are usually called "pure substances" in chemistry. Microphysical entities often exist as parts of larger wholes and in those circumstances they possess a limited individuality, but subatomic particles, atoms, and molecules can also exist separately as holistic systems.

Wholes are formed as the result of the cooperation of different dynamisms. It is understandable that new patterns emerge when a combination of dynamisms occurs for the first time. Furthermore, every new kind of patterning opens new possibilities of further patterning. This leads us to the idea of self-organization.

5. SELF-ORGANIZATION

Self-organization has become the metaphor commonly used to account for the present scientific worldview. In an introductory survey of this topic,[45] Wolfgang Krohn, Günther Küppers, and Helga Nowotny explain that thanks to the scientific developments achieved by Heinz von Foerster, Ilya Prigogine, Hermann Haken, Edward Lorenz, and others, the concept of self-organization began in the 1970s. This concept was thought of as a symbol of a broad new interdisciplinary paradigm extending to the entire worldview and even to the field of the humanities. They trace back the concept to Kant's *Critique of Judgement.*[46]

Kant's problem was how to explain the apparent purposefulness of organic beings, whose parts can be considered at the same time as means and as ends. His solution was to consider organic beings *as if* they were the carriers of real purposes. He goes on to say that we should admit teleology as a regulatory idea that may serve to unify our experience and our investigation, even if we cannot assert that it corresponds to something real. And he adds that self-organization is an exclusive property of living beings, so that we cannot attribute it to nonliving ones; this would amount to an illegitimate kind of hylozoism.

Actually, the idea of self-organization can be traced even further back, for ordinary experience shows that living beings are self-organizing systems. That is why this idea makes it possible to recover some important features of the ancient worldview: holism and directionality. Dislodged by the mechanistic worldview, these concepts reappear under the light of a much broader worldview that results from the enormous progress in our knowledge of the systemic aspects of nature.

45. Wolfgang Krohn, Günther Küppers, and Helga Nowotny, "Introduction," in *Selforganisation: Portrait of a Scientific Revolution,* ed. Wolfgang Krohn, Günther Küppers, and Helga Nowotny (Dordrecht-Boston-London: Kluwer, 1990), pp. 1–10.

46. Immanuel Kant, *The Critique of Judgement* (Oxford: Clarendon Press, 1980), Part II,§ 65.

Self-organization is closely related to patterning. Carsten Bresch speaks of the entire global process of the construction of our world under the heading "Patterns grow in restricted freedom," and tries to explain the existence of directionality in that global process. He explains that, even if we suppose that the process of patterning includes random events, once such an event has happened, the new state will limit the occurence of new random events that can be successfully incorporated into the existing systems:

> We arrive at "historical processes," that is, at processes in which the existing situation can develop, but the probabilities of future random results are dependent upon existing ones (conditional probability, stochastic coupling). Every pattern is the product of such a historical process. This means that, throughout the history of the origin of the pattern, development is possible in various directions, but that the pattern already in existence has a restricting effect, in that certain directions of development are more and others less probable, while yet others are impossible. . . . The essence of pattern growth is *restricted freedom*. . . . What actually happens is determined by chance and is thus indeterminate. But this freedom is subject to constraints that result from the pattern itself and from the patterns surrounding it. That which is new must fit in with that which is already there.[47]

We find here references to chance events. Some authors think that the peculiar combinations of chance and lawfulness provide an explanation for the creativity of nature. In this line, Davies says that

> Chaos seems to provide a bridge between the deterministic laws of physics and the laws of chance, implying that the universe is genuinely creative.[48]

I would say, however, that even if we maintain our argument on the natural level, a third element has to be added to obtain a more complete explanation, and it is related to natural tendencies and cooperativity. There are good reasons to think that many cooperative features of nature have yet to be discovered. Our knowledge of self-organization has probably only just begun.

This is easy to see in the field of evolutionary theories. Despite the claims of orthodox Darwinians who consider natural selection as the chief cause of evolution, other scientists continue searching for new structural laws that may help bridge the many gaps within the evolutionary explanations. Empirical research has found some promising clues in the field of genetics, where the complex combinations of different levels of genetic regulation could explain how a particular mutation can sometimes produce a big and yet viable

---

47. Carsten Bresch, "What Is Evolution?" in *Evolution and Creation,* ed. Svend Andersen and Arthur Peacocke (Aarhus: Aarhus University Press, 1987), pp. 38–39.

48. Davies, "Is the Universe a Machine?" cit., p. 212.

change. Theoretical research, which is more conjectural, provides new hypotheses; for instance, Stuart Kauffman has published two works on this subject: a specialized account[49] and one aimed at a more popular audience.[50] In the first book, first-rate specialists in the field including Manfred Eigen, Stephen Jay Gould, John Maynard Smith, and Richard Lewontin argue that Kauffman's ideas are worthy of serious study. Gould argues that Darwinian theory must be expanded to recognize other sources of order besides natural selection.

Kauffman includes Darwinism in a broader context that contains new sources of order other than natural selection. He centers his work around self-organization, as he tries to show that there must be some sources of spontaneous order that would provide the material on which natural selection could act. Needless to say, the search for these sources of spontaneous order is very difficult at the theoretical level, and it is not easy to test the empirical consequences of the proposed explanations. Kauffman recognizes that the subject of his study is new and not yet completely articulated, but he thinks that some "construction principle" must exist to explain the formation of natural patterns.

One of Kauffman's central ideas is that, given the physical and chemical properties of our world, the probability of life spontaneously emerging was very high; he adds that this is why we are at home in the universe. In this view, holism and directionality play a central role in patterning and self-organization. Even though the controversies about the probabilities of life emerging are far from being settled, it seems indisputable that, since life has actually emerged, the corresponding potentialities have existed since the very beginning and in each one of the successive steps of the global process of self-organization that led to the present state of our world. The basic features of our world are specific enough to serve as the bases of the grandiose process of self-organization that has produced so many increasingly organized outcomes.

Such a process does not refer only to the origins of life. Considered in its entirety, it includes a great number of steps all of which have been necessary to arrive at the level of organization of living beings. This great chain has been produced because the basic steps already contained the potentialities necessary for the formation of the following steps. Moreover, this process cannot be reduced to a historically fortuitous sum of steps: it has produced highly sophisticated results that exist and operate today. Indeed, we may say that one of the most remarkable outcomes of contemporary scientific progress has been that we have begun to know how natural organization works. This can be summarized in a single word: information.

49. Stuart A. Kauffman, *The Origins of Order: Self-Organisation and Selection in Evolution* (New York and Oxford: Oxford University Press, 1993).

50. Stuart A. Kauffman, *At Home in the Universe. The Search for Laws of Self-Organisation and Complexity* (London: Viking, 1995).

6. INFORMATION

Information occupies a central place in the present worldview. Natural scientists speak of information mainly when they refer to the genetic information that contains the basic instructions for the building and working of organisms. This concept can be easily extended to other fields of biology and to nonliving beings insofar as they also contain an entire set of potentialities that are displayed in definite ways according to individual circumstances.

Natural information is stored, coded and decoded, transmitted, and integrated. To illustrate this, I will refer to cell communication (Figure 3.3). The 1994 Nobel Prize for medicine was awarded to professors Alfred G. Gilman and Martin Rodbell for the discovery of G proteins and their role in the transmission of signals in the cells. I quote here from an article by Gilman.[51]

> . . . G proteins are not phantasmagorical entities. Like other proteins, they consist of aminoacids united by peptide bounds. Proteins are organised in large chains of atoms that are folded following characteristic patterns, and they play an important role in organisms; for instance, hormones take part in the regulation of metabolic processes, and enzymes act as catalysts of biochemical reactions.
>
> Roughly speaking, in the human organism there are some ten thousand billion cells, and there are some 250 basic types of them (nerve, muscle, or blood cells, for instance). They are so small that 2.5 cube centimeters could contain a billion medium-size cells. However each one of them is a miniaturised marvel: it contains in its nucleus the entire genetic information, which in human beings is stored in pieces of DNA containing some three billion pairs of nitrogen bases, and it lives, if we can say this, its own life: it receives substances from outside, it transforms these substances in order to get the energy that it needs, it throws away the waste products, it builds up the components needed by the organism and exports them to the right place, it reproduces itself in processes in which the genetic material is duplicated and divided each time. The functioning of a single cell is highly sophisticated.
>
> Cells depend on each other for their existence and functioning, and here we find an entire set of highly specific processes about which it is difficult to speak unless we use an anthropomorphic and metaphorical language. In fact, the cells need to "know" what kinds of molecule exist in their environment so as to let them pass or prevent them from passing through the cell membrane. Once they have permitted some material to pass inside, they need to "know" what to do with it. They also need to "know" the state of the organism to act according to its needs. All this works by using "information." And it is in this area that G proteins play an important role.

As I quote and comment on Gilman here, I will italicize those words that more specifically refer to information. He describes G proteins thus:

51. Maurine E. Linder and Alfred G. Gilman, "G Proteins," *Scientific American,* 267, no. 1 (July 1992): 36–43.

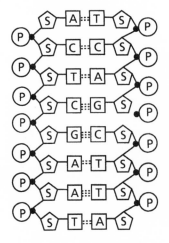

FUNCTIONS OF DNA

REGULATION OF BIOLOGICAL PROCESSES: Particular genes (sequences of DNA) are activated depending on the requirements of the organism and the environment.

REPLICATION of cells: which implies replication of the entire DNA contained in the nucleus of the replicating cell (the DNA of every human cell contains some 3 billion pairs of nitrogen bases).

PLAN OF THE ORGANISM: The entire organism is built up following the information contained in DNA.

HEREDITY: Genetic information is transmitted from parents via their DNA.

Fig. 3.3   Genetic information as "materialized rationality." DNA is structured as a double-helix consisting of a sugar (S), a phosphate (P), and a nitrogen basis (A, C, G, T). Information is stored in the structure of DNA and is deployed in answer to the needs of the organism, according to preestablished plans that include highly sophisticated steps and a remarkable coordination. The storing, coding and decoding, and deploying of genetic information show that dynamism and structure in nature are closely connected and interwoven.

Tucked into the internal surface of the cell's outer membrane, these versatile molecules *coordinate* cellular responses to a multitude of signals that impinge from without.

To make possible our action and even our existence, our cells must communicate with one another, and this communication is performed by chemical *messengers.* However, few messengers need to enter the cell. Gilman explains that

> most of the agents convey *information* through intermediaries. They issue *orders* by binding at the outer surface of target cells to proteins that serve as specific receptors. Then, in a process called *signal transduction,* the receptors, which span the cell membrane, relay the *information* to a series of intracellular *middlemen* that ultimately pass the *orders* to the final executors.

Gilman tells us that many extracellular *messengers* have been already discovered and adds that

> a great many *messengers* rely on just one class of molecules, called G proteins, to *direct* the flow of *signals* from the receptor to the rest of the cell.

The crucial properties of G proteins were identified in the late 1970s at the University of Virginia; Gilman has continued his work at the University of Texas Southwestern Medical Center at Dallas. He states:

We continue to be fascinated by their *machinations,* as well as by the central role they play in an ever increasing array of cellular activities.

It is interesting to note that scientists continue to be amazed by nature. They even speak, as in the preceding quotation of "fascination." Why does this happen? At first sight it seems that scientific progress should diminish our admiration. We are amazed when we do not know how something works; if we know its mechanisms, there would apparently no longer be a reason to feel admiration. But looking at the entire affair from a different perspective, one can see that if the mechanisms discovered in nature are very sophisticated, we may feel admiration when we realize that nature, acting by itself and therefore in a "blind" way, is able to perform so many subtle and complex operations. This is true in the case of G proteins. When scientists describe how these proteins work, they speak of *information, orders, messengers, signals, middlemen, coordination, machinations.* Surely, this talk is anthropomorphic and could partly be replaced by a different language. However, this metaphorical language expresses real facts.

Continuing with Gilman, we examine these phenomena further: At the end of the 1950s the processes of cell *signalling* began to be known; at present:

Scientists now know that many different receptors convey *instructions* of hormones or other extracellular "first messengers" by stimulating one or another G protein. Attached to the inner surface of the cell membrane (the plasma membrane), such proteins in turn act on membrane-bound *intermediaries* called effectors. Often the effector is an enzyme that converts an inactive precursor molecule into an active *"second messenger,"* which can diffuse through the cytoplasm and thus carry the *signal* beyond the membrane. The *second messenger* triggers a cascade of molecular reactions leading to a change in the cell's behavior. For instance, the cell might secrete a hormone or release glucose.

It is worth noting that we are speaking here of a world in which *signals* and *instructions* are transmitted through *messengers* that act as in a relay race, as every messenger participates in part of the process and transmits the signal to the following one. Obviously, first and second messengers, and proteins and effectors as well, are purely physicochemical entities. But they act in a way that could be called "intelligent" when we realize that the very specific, highly coordinated processes that we are considering are the basis for the working of the entire organism. Of course, nobody is directing the flow of information or indicating what must be done in every moment.

The list of discoveries concerning these proteins has grown, as Gilman tells us:

G proteins serve as switches and timers, determining when and for how long signaling pathways are turned on and off. . . . G proteins also amplify signals. In the extremely efficient visual system, for example, one molecule of rhodopsin activates almost simultaneously more than 500 molecules of transducin.

Obviously, G proteins do not think. They have no watches, nor have they studied chemistry or biology. Nevertheless, their action is polyvalent and extremely efficient. Gilman tells us that there are many puzzles still to be solved, an indication that our present knowledge has uncovered only part of the marvels that make the functioning of our organism possible.

In the last analysis, the world of molecular biology is no different from any other field in nature and science, so that the use of terms such as "information," "instructions," and others only corresponds to the need to explain something that in itself is anything but mysterious. However, when scientists explain their discoveries, they may need to use a language full of references that remind us of intelligent behavior.

G proteins are attached to the inner surface of the cell membrane. This membrane consists of a double layer that separates the cell from its environment and makes possible the entrance and exit of appropriate materials and communication with other cells as well. Speaking about this, Gilman writes:

> Clearly, the cell membrane is a *switchboard* of considerable complexity, taking in a diversity of *signals,* assessing their relative strengths and *relaying the summed signals to second messengers* that will assure the cell reacts *appropriately* to a changing environment. . . . Cell membrane is a kind of *switchboard* that can merge varied *signals* or route similar signals down multiple paths, *depending on the needs of the cell.*

Those processes develop depending on the *needs* of the cell. Nature does this by itself. Even though the language that scientists use to describe this is partly metaphorical, the phenomena described are real.

G proteins are only one example among many; the entire field of biology could be considered a collection of information. I only want to show that there are many natural phenomena in which concepts related to information play an important role. The more we discover phenomena of this kind, the more we must face the question of their ultimate explanation. Coding and decoding, transmitting, integrating, performing processes that consist of several consecutive, interdependent steps all manifest behavior that, insofar as it acts to achieve natural goals through sophisticated methods, can be considered a manifestation of rationality.

I dare say that natural information can be called "materialized rationality" because it contains instructions that are stored in material structures and are deployed through natural processes, and these instructions serve as a basis for the construction of highly sophisticated results through equally sophisticated methods. Scientific progress shows that the natural world contains a kind of rationality that is also very effective and sophisticated. I emphasize that this can be considered a plain fact. Of course, it includes some elements of evaluation, which is unavoidable when we try to describe a major aspect of an entire worldview. But my assertion is supported by very accurate scientific descriptions. Even minds strongly opposed to any kind of metaphysics or religions must admit, if they want to be objective, that a great many natural phenomena develop "as if" they had been designed. Scientific progress greatly enlarges the range of such phenomena and provides interesting explanations for them.

Information can be considered one of the most important explanations of many sophisticated natural phenomena. Aristotle spoke of potentialities, and over the centuries people have discussed how these could be interpreted, for instance, in the case of the development of living beings. Preformation seems unacceptable, and mere epiphenomenalism seems to explain nothing at all. Now, information provides a clear account of the preexistence of a plan that makes the existence of something similar to the final result unnecessary but, at the same time, explains how that result is produced.

If the concept of information is closely related to that of "potentiality," it is also linked to that of "plan." In some cases, the plan is so specific that, if the necessary external circumstances exist, the result will be produced, as in the case of the development of living beings. In other cases, potentialities are more open. In general we can say that we live in a world structured in levels of emerging complexity which is always open to the appearance of novelties.

7. An Open Universe

What is most remarkable in the present worldview is that it implies a gigantic process of self-organization in which many novelties have emerged that cannot be understood as a mere sum of their components. The concept of information is helpful in understanding emergence. Information usually includes an entire set of potentialities that will only partially be actualized. Furthermore, different units of natural information can merge, producing a new kind of information; this makes possible the emergence of real novelties.

Seen from this perspective, the universe is full of nonactualized potentialities, and any new integration of information can provoke new outcomes. Actually, technological progress opens new possibilities that refer not only to artificial machines, but also to the introduction of changes in natural beings. This introduces a new factor of openness, because we can use natural laws to modify the spontaneous development of nature. This then would raise ethical questions.

The existence of emergence as a description of the different natural levels seems today a well-established fact. Nevertheless, as the reductionist temptation is always in sight, I will examine the present status of emergence and reduction in the scientific context more closely.

We can speak of emergence and reduction on two levels: the ontological level, in which we consider the real emergence of natural systems (for instance, when we investigate if an atom is something more than a mere aggregation of subatomic particles), and the epistemological level, in which we consider the possibility of deducing theories of a higher scientific level from those of lower level (for instance, if we try to reduce chemistry to physics, or biology to physics plus chemistry).

In the past, the reductionist approach has been an important tool in the hands of supporters of positivist or materialistic views, as it could show that higher level entities or theories would be "nothing but" the sum of entities or theories of lower levels and that, in the last analysis, everything could be reduced to its material components. Thus, in the 1930s reductionism occupied a preeminent place in the neopositivist program, which aimed at unifying science through the reduction of its different branches to a physicalistic language. Although this ideal was soon given up, reduction continued to be treated as the logical deduction of laws or theories of a "reduced" or "secondary" science out of those of a "reducing" or "primary" one. In this line a distinction was made between two types of reduction, "homogeneous" or "unproblematic" reduction, in which all terms of the secondary science were already present in the primary one, and "discontinuous" or "problematic" reduction, in which at least one new term was found only in the secondary science. In this second case, the bridge to relate both sciences could be established by means of a logical connection between the terms, by postulating coordinating definitions, or through factual hypotheses.[52]

Arguments were introduced that pointed toward an increasing skepticism about the possibilities of deductive reductions. With respect to "homogeneous" theories, it could be pointed out that reductions by strict logical derivation seldom occur or that they are impossible because when one or several laws are explained by a new theory, the meaning of basic terms changes. It was admitted that a "weak" or instrumentalist reduction was possible, but this would be merely a partial and approximate coincidence of results. A "strong" reduction between "heterogeneous" theories, in which the reduced theory could be retained and even better corroborated, was said to happen when some correlational laws were empirically well established or when two classes of entities in both theories were identified. The conclusion reached was that it would be convenient to substitute the term "quasi-reduction" or partial explanation, to stress the difficulties of a full reduction.[53]

Nowadays there is a general agreement about the limited value of classical analysis of the problem of reductionism. On the one hand, this analysis depends too much on the deductive model of scientific explanation, which has been improved upon by emphasizing the central role of the conceptual aspects in science. Furthermore, this analysis does not fit well with actual scientific practice. At the thirteenth International Conference on the Unity of Science, whose central topic was the problem of reduction and emergence in the main scientific disciplines, it was stressed that, if actual scientific practice is properly taken into account, what reduction really means is the establishment of partial connections between different epistemological levels, and it was pointed out that those connections may adopt very different modalities.[54]

52. Ernest Nagel, *The Structure of Science* (London: Routledge, 1961), pp. 336–397.

53. Lawrence Sklar, "Types of Inter-Theoretic Reduction," *The British Journal for the Philosophy of Science,* 18 (1967): 109–124; Kenneth Friedman, "Is Intertheoretic Reduction Feasible?" *The British Journal for the Philosophy of Science,* 33 (1982): 17–40.

54. Gerard Radnitzky, ed., *Centripetal Forces in the Sciences,* vol. 2 (New York: Paragon House, 1988).

To sum up, it may be safely said that "derivational reductionism," that is, trying to derive theories of one scientific level from those of other level, corresponds to a philosophical ideal that neither fits well with actual scientific progress nor is practically feasible. Theoretical constructs are formulated with the purpose of solving particular problems in specific scientific areas and are constructed according to the conceptual and instrumental resources available at every moment in time. It seems therefore simpler to replace the traditional problem of reduction between theories with that of establishing relations between fields or areas of investigation, so that epistemological analysis can focus on the great variety of relations between problems and solutions that belong to different natural and scientific levels.[55]

The limits that exist in epistemological reductions imply the limits to the possibility of establishing ontological reductionism. The complete explanation for upper ontological levels resorting only to more basic ones cannot be justified from the scientific point of view. Nevertheless, the quest for the unity of science stimulates the search for relations between the different levels and, in this respect, a kind of partial methodological reductionism finds its proper justification. A similar view can be applied to the unity of nature, which may be considered one of the foundations of the scientific enterprise: the different levels of natural entities and processes are interconnected, but at every concrete level we find specific features that cannot be properly reduced to the mere sum of the properties that belong to other levels. Last but not least, human beings are natural beings who, at the same time, transcend the natural level.

The difficulties of reduction are of such magnitude that the current trends that follow the tradition of reductionism usually avoid using the name reduction and even deny being reductionist, using, for instance, "nonreductive naturalism" or "nonreductive physicalism." In this context, present discussions that follow in some way the reductionist line of thought, mainly in the field of anthropology, usually employ new concepts such as "supervenience."

In any case, it is important to stress that a universe in which there is room for emergence is, by definition, an open universe. This means a universe where there are real novelties and creativity. Such is our world. We are witnesses of the production of novelties in the case of the generation of any new living being and also of the production of nonliving beings, even when their general type already exists. In addition, we know that many novelties have arisen during the long course of cosmic and biological evolution. Many particulars of those processes are as yet unknown and will remain so in the future. But what we already know demonstrates a multilevel world composed of levels of emerging novelties that are based on an astonishing process of self-organization.

In the expression "self-organization" the first part ("self") refers to consistency and power, and the second ("organization") refers to order, direc-

---

55. Lindley Darden and Nancy Maull, "Interfield Theories," *Philosophy of Science,* 44 (1977): 43–64.

tionality, and synergy or cooperativity. Our world possesses a strong consistency and a dynamism whose deployment is able to produce the most sophisticated results at successive levels of organization. We know how information works on the biological level and we can apply this concept at the physicochemical level as well, so that self-organization can be seen at the same time as the source and the result, at different levels, of information that can form sophisticated results by adequately using a small number of components. The 3 subatomic particles (protons, electrons, and neutrons), 92 types of atoms, and 4 nucleotides are enough to account for the basic constitution and properties of our world. What is most worthy of admiration in our present understanding is the sophistication of the methods used and of the results produced. We may realize that this subtlety is closely related to a tremendous power when we notice, for instance, that each one of the subatomic particles must "know" the entirety of physics, and much better than we do, for it will act in an enormous number of circumstances according to the different patterns that correspond to its own mode of being.

The present worldview provides us with a picture of the world that leaves room for novelty and creativity. Paul Davies has written:

> even accepting a strictly deterministic account of nature, the future states of the Universe are in some sense "open." Some people have seized on this openness to argue for the reality of human free will. Others claim that it bestows upon nature an element of creativity, an ability to bring forth that which is genuinely new, something not already implicit in earlier states of the Universe, save in the idealized fiction of the real numbers. Whatever the merits of such sweeping claims, it seems safe to conclude from the study of chaos that the future of the Universe is not irredeemably fixed. The final chapter of the great cosmic book has yet to be written.[56]

This last comment can have a significance much greater than Davies himself thinks if we take into account the Christian faith in a new heavens and a new earth. I will not follow this line because it transcends the perspective that I am now developing. I will focus instead on another aspect of the current worldview stressed by Davies: the relationship between natural creativity and indeterminism.

Many contemporary authors insist on indeterminism as a necessary precondition for creativity. They usually stress that the development of our world does not follow a necessarily predetermined path; otherwise, they think, real novelty and creativity could not exist. Karl Popper, for one, devoted an entire book to this subject.[57]

This kind of argument can show that natural creativity and human freedom should not be considered epiphenomena that ultimately can be reduced

---

56. Davies, "Is the Universe a Machine?" cit., p. 221.

57. Karl R. Popper, *The Open Universe: An Argument for Indeterminism* (London: Hutchinson, 1982).

to necessary physical processes. Of course, if we are able to show that the physical world is indeterministic, we can automatically say that a necessitarian determinism cannot explain the more complex natural levels and also the human realm. Moreover, thanks to the new theories of deterministic chaos, we are now beginning to see how an adequate dose of chance combined with another dose of determinism can provide the basis for an enormous repertoire of possibilities in the natural world, and this repertoire can increase and diversify whenever new potentialities are actualized.

Popper's ideas about propensities represent the building of the universe as the outcome of an open directionality.[58] Scientific progress discovers more and more directionality in the natural world, but the number of combinations of the different dynamisms is so immense that this factor alone can explain the production of real novelties.

The openness of the universe can lead us to pose the question about its uniqueness. We cannot provide a clear answer at the moment. In any case, my argument does not essentially depend on the answer to that question. As I focus on the characteristics of our world that are already known, including its openness, it goes without saying that I do not claim that the present state of our world is the only possible one.

58. Karl R. Popper, *A World of Propensities* (Bristol: Thoemmes Antiquarian Books, 1990).

4

The Intelligibility
of Nature

In our everyday experience we can observe some processes of self-organization, mainly in living beings, such as, for example, the development of
individuals and the regeneration of some parts of their organisms. However,
in the present worldview self-organization is much more than a particular
kind of phenomena: it is a key that unifies our entire representation of natural order. This worldview, centered around self-organization, enriches our
knowledge of the origins of natural order and provides us with an account
of details showing how the different levels of nature are related.

The scientific quest, based on the presupposition that natural order exists
and can be rationally grasped, has been extremely successful so far. As a consequence of scientific progress, our idea of natural order has been enriched
and now provides us with a picture that encompasses the entire process of the
universe since its beginnings and includes the basic features of all natural levels and their mutual relations. Our world appears to be the result of a dynamism whose deployment produces an entire series of increasingly complex
patterns that make our existence possible.

When examining the philosophical and theological implications of the
present worldview we should not forget the methodological gap between the
scientific perspective and the metascientific interpretation of its results. Even
though the progress of science seems quite favorable to metaphysics and religion at the moment, we should always remember that science alone cannot
prove or disprove the existence of metaphysical and spiritual dimensions. Empirical science can provide us with new insights and can help us to formulate
new arguments, but if we desire to obtain metascientific results we must use
metascientific arguments.

The scientific paradigm of self-organization is sometimes used to support the claim that the world is self-contained. As a first step to pave the way for further reflections, I will examine this naturalistic interpretation.

I. A SELF-CONTAINED WORLD?

When scientific progress is seen as disqualifying metaphysical and religious ideas, self-organization seems to complete the naturalistic perspective, because it apparently allows us to explain everything using merely scientific arguments.

A consideration of this naturalistic interpretation as well as the application of that perspective to the problems of origins, in particular the origin of the universe and biological evolution, will lead to an analysis of fallacies usually contained in these naturalistic explanations.

1. Ontological Reductionism

If matter is thought to possess an internal dynamism that could explain the appearance of increasingly complex forms without the intervention of other agencies, self-organization might be regarded as the last step in the process of naturalizing the world and dislodging from it all metaphysical and theological dimensions.

Such a theory is anything but new. For instance, in the eighteenth century, French materialists tried to exploit several discoveries about self-organization to argue that, if matter could organize itself, the recourse to divine action would be redundant. Three discoveries made during the 1740s seemed useful to that purpose, as outlined by John Hedley Brooke:

> In common with other materialists, Meslier argued that matter could organise itself . . . there were three discoveries during the 1740s about which a materialist could get excited. Matter within living systems was shown to have unsuspected powers. One revelation was the evidence for spontaneous generation claimed by the English Catholic priest John Turbeville Needham. . . . Voltaire reported that Needham's results were proving attractive to philosophers who supposed that matter could organise itself. A second revelation came from the Swiss naturalist Albrecht von Haller. Knowing that movement persisted in the hearts of animals that had recently died, Haller inferred the existence of an unknown force in the fabric of the heart. . . . Matter, it appeared, had its own power of movement, independent of an organising soul. A materialist such as La Mettrie, whose *L'homme machine* (1747) was directed against the arguments for an independent soul, welcomed Haller's new force with open arms. . . . A third disclosure was the most astonishing. In the early 1740s, news spread that a freshwater polyp, the hydra, could regenerate itself when cut into pieces. . . . The commotion was not simply caused by matter reorganising itself. If one polyp could become two

by artificial division, then indivisible animal souls surely lost their credibility. It was a delight to the materialists, who wished to have done with souls altogether.[1]

At that time, the issue of preformation versus epigenesis provided further fuel for controversy. Preformationists held that the development of the embryo was the growth of an already organized being that preexisted in a miniaturized form in the egg; their opponents maintained that the new being was formed through a process in which differentiated tissues emerged from less-organized material. Epigenesis, if true, would represent a case of self-organization and could be used as an argument against those who admitted the existence of nonmaterial powers. Some remarked that the processes of self-organization required a deeper explanation; others considered epigenesis a dangerous doctrine because it implied that material forces could produce living beings out of sheer matter.[2]

Because the present worldview extends the concept of self-organization to all levels of the natural world, the temptation of using it to support a naturalistic and reductionist view seems to be much more immediate. An extreme reductionist position, however, faces an obvious difficulty: how can we assume that we possess an ultimate explanation of the world if our knowledge is always incomplete? In more technical terms, how could we claim to have established a complete ontological reduction of the world to natural forces if there are epistemological reasons that clearly suggest the essential incompleteness of any science? In other words, how can someone claim that natural resources are sufficient to explain completely the entire realm of reality if scientific study is always extremely incomplete, even when it is most successful?

Despite these difficulties, self-organization is sometimes interpreted as supporting an ontological reductionism. John Haught, placing himself as spokesman for the supporters of naturalism, proposes on their behalf the following argument:

> In fact, the utter spontaneity of matter's self-organization, a major emphasis in the new science, would seem to render more superfluous than ever the idea of an ordering deity. As it turns out, matter itself is *inherently* self-organizing. Hence there is no need for an extraneous, supernatural designer who would put the stamp of order on chaos. Chaos gives rise to order *spontaneously,* and nature blindly selects those systems that are most adaptive. Self-organization is an irreducible property of matter, so the phenomenon of ordered complexity needs no explanation beyond itself.[3]

1. John Hedley Brooke, *Science and Religion: Some Historical Perspectives* (Cambridge: Cambridge University Press, 1939), pp. 172–173.

2. Ibid., pp. 174–175.

3. John F. Haught, *Science & Religion: From Conflict to Conversation* (New York and Mahwah, N.J.: Paulist Press, 1995), p. 149.

Following this line of argument, naturalists admit that matter is more puzzling than previously suspected, but claim that self-organization supports, at least in principle, a reductionist perspective that admits only natural explanations. For instance, Manfred Stöckler has analyzed the concepts of emergence and reduction to show that the concept of emergence is compatible with a reductionist approach.[4] He shows sympathy toward Fritz Rohrlich's "cognitive emergence," which holds that our cognitive capacity is responsible for the pluralistic nature of our ontology and that a pluralistic approach is compatible with the notion of unity of nature in the sense of a substantive monism.[5]

Stöckler has analyzed the relationship between reductionism and the new theories of self-organization.[6] In a paper on this issue, he refers to Paul Davies, Erich Jantsch, Fritjof Capra, and the editors of *Selbstorganisation* as supporters of antireductionist views.

Stöckler quotes briefly from Paul Davies' *The Cosmic Blueprint,* in which Davies refers explicitly to self-organization and its consequences. Davies says that the emergence of structure and complexity in the universe is the result of an astonishing creativity, and he poses the question of the source of that creative power. He tells us that a part of the answer is provided now by the sciences, whose progress shows that self-organizing processes exist in every branch of science, and he asks whether this implies that the present state of the universe is in some sense predestined; in other words, he asks whether there is a kind of "cosmic blueprint." In this context, Davies asserts that the present worldview is antireductionist:

> For three centuries science has been dominated by the Newtonian and thermodynamic paradigms, which present the universe either as a sterile machine, or in a state of degeneration and decay. Now there is the new paradigm of the creative universe, which recognizes the progressive, innovative character of physical processes. The new paradigm emphasizes the collective, cooperative and organisational aspects of nature; its perspective is synthetic and holistic rather than analytic and reductionist.[7]

Stöckler's interpretation is reductionist but with some qualifications. He distinguishes three kinds of reductionism, which he calls methodological, ontological, and ideological. He is against methodological reductionism, as he thinks that the attempts to reduce scientific theories of one level to theories

4. Manfred Stöckler, "A Short History of Emergence and Reductionism," in *The Problem of Reductionism in Science,* ed. Evandro Agazzi (Dordrecht: Kluwer, 1991), pp. 80, 84.

5. Fritz Rohrlich, "Pluralistic Ontology and Theory Reduction in the Physical Sciences," *The British Journal for the Philosophy of Science,* 39 (1988): 295–312.

6. Manfred Stöckler, "Reductionism and the New Theories of Self-Organisation," in *Advances in Scientific Philosophy,* ed. Gerhard Schurz and Georg J. W. Dorn (Amsterdam and Atlanta, Ga.: Rodopi, 1991), pp. 233–254.

7. Paul Davies, *The Cosmic Blueprint: Order and Complexity at the Edge of Chaos* (London: Penguin Books, 1989), p. 2.

of a more basic level will never be completely successful. Nevertheless, he is in favor of ontological reductionism, which holds that all phenomena of life are processes covered by the laws of physics and that the fundamental laws of physics would be sufficient, at least in principle, for a complete explanation of the whole of nature.

It is extremely important to take note of a brief remark by Stöckler in the midst of his explanations: "The main motive of ontological reductionism is a metaphysical idea of unity of nature."[8] This remark is important for two reasons: first, because he presents ontological reductionism not as a mere consequence of science itself, but as a "metaphysical" idea that, therefore, should be discussed using not only scientific data, but also philosophical arguments; and second, because it demonstrates the underlying reason in favor of ontological reductionism, a "metaphysical" idea of the "unity of nature." Later, Stöckler writes that "the aim of reduction is the unity of science" and argues against adding principles of self-organization, the successors to vital forces, élans vitaux, or entelechies to the laws of physics. He dismisses Davies' arguments in favor of the existence of principles of self-organization as lacking argumentative strength.[9] He leaves us, therefore, with a reductionism motivated by the metaphysical desire to represent nature as a unitary whole in which there is no place for dimensions that could not be studied by empirical science alone.

Stöckler strongly asserts that "the theories of self-organisation are the nonlinear mode of reductionism." He realizes that methodological reduction of scientific theories to more basic ones has limits because our cognitive resources are limited, but he adds that this limitation does not demolish the tenets of ontological reductionism because "the new theories of self-organisation show the connections between different levels of description."[10]

Nevertheless, the existence of connections between all natural levels and the unity of nature do not prove any strong form of reductionism, both because natural causes can always be combined with a divine agency that is not opposed to nature but is rather its ultimate foundation, and because our very arguments about reductionism prove that some dimensions of reality transcend empirical science. Indeed, when we argue about reductionism we use arguments that refer to science itself and therefore do not belong to the realm of science. In this line, William Carroll remarks:

> Whether or not all physical reality (or perhaps all reality) is reducible to the categories of the empirical sciences is a question in the philosophy of nature; it is not a question which is answerable by an appeal to the empirical sciences themselves.[11]

---

8. Stöckler, "Reductionism and the New Theories of Self-Organisation," cit., p. 235.

9. Ibid., pp. 245, 247–248.

10. Ibid., p. 252.

11. William E. Carroll, "Reductionism and the Conflict between Science and Religion," *The Allen Review* (Oxford), 15 (Trinity 1996): 19.

Stöckler asserts that the ontological reductionism he advocates should be distinguished from an ideological reductionism, which he characterizes by the formula "B is nothing but A." This would suppose a reduction in values, Stöckler adds:

> Very often ontological reductionism is attacked because people are afraid of ideological reductionism. I deny that ideological reductionism is a consequence of ontological reductionism, and again, I reject ideological reductionism. But I do not share the opinion of those authors who use the theories of self-organisation as auxiliary troops in the battle against ideological reductionism.[12]

Although Stöckler is right when he rejects ideological reductionism as a negation of the existence of human values and when he emphasizes the unity of nature and the corresponding unity of science as a foundation for the entire scientific enterprise, ontological reductionism is neither a necessary consequence of science nor a defensible position. I would add that, despite intentions to the contrary, ontological reductionism by its very nature cannot be dissociated from antispiritualist positions that represent a real threat to human values. Those values, if they are to have any consistency, should be based on the ontological dimensions of reality.

2. A Self-Created Universe?

The existence of the universe is obviously a necessary condition for natural processes to occur. Since very ancient times, two opposing positions have addressed this issue: one sees the universe as the result of a divine creative act, and the other sees the universe as self-sufficient and self-contained and therefore as infinite, sometimes also as a manifestation of divinity in some kind of pantheism. The real novelty in our times is that a position has been formulated that claims to be based on scientific advances in cosmology and asserts that the universe had a beginning in time but is nonetheless completely independent of any divine act of creation. This means a kind of creation without a creator.

This kind of discussion often refers to a purely physical issue that has no metaphysical or religious connotations in itself; I refer here to the idea that our world originated as a fluctuation of the quantum vacuum, a process that can be explained according to the laws of physics. In this case, it is completely clear that quantum vacuum cannot be equated with the notion of "nothingness." Physicists define different kinds of vacuum; therefore, to say that our world began as a quantum bubble makes sense in physics and is a position that must be argued in scientific terms. The original quantum fluctuation could have been the result of a divine creation, but it is impossible to prove this by

---

12. Stöckler, "Reductionism and the New Theories of Self-Organisation," cit. p. 236.

means of physics alone, for it could also have been the result of prior physical states.

Science alone cannot prove the existence of divine creation. Indeed, from the scientific point of view we can always suppose that some state of the universe, elementary as it may be, was the result of other preceding states. The arguments that can lead us to admit the existence of a divine creation are rather metaphysical and religious. In the thirteenth century Thomas Aquinas argued that, by using rational arguments, we can prove that the world is created insofar as it requires divine action as its foundation, but at the same time we cannot prove by rational arguments that the world has had an origin in time.

In our times, William Lane Craig has argued that, on the basis of scientific cosmology, we could conclude that the universe began to exist:

To recapitulate: since an actual infinite cannot exist and an infinite temporal regress of events is an actual infinite, we can be sure that an infinite temporal regress of events cannot exist, that is to say, the temporal regress of events is finite. Therefore, since the temporal regress of events is finite, the universe began to exist.[13]

Craig provides an extensive argument to support the claim that an actual infinite cannot exist. He speaks in that context of an infinite with a physical character. He does not deny God's existence; on the contrary, he uses the finitude of the universe to support the proof of the existence of a personal God who is the creator of the universe.

Craig seems to be saying that we can infer the temporal finitude of the universe from the Big Bang cosmology. I do not think that this is the case, agreeing with Stanley Jaki when he writes:

Physical science or scientific cosmology is absolutely powerless to show that any stage of material interactions is not reducible to a previous state, however hypothetical. If science is impotent in this purely scientific respect, it is even more impotent with respect to a far deeper problem, a problem of very different nature, namely, that a given physical state must owe its existence to a direct creative act, which brought that physical state into being out of nothing.[14]

Nevertheless, some authors argue that, on this basis, we can assert the temporal finitude of the world and can explain the origin of the universe without appealing to the action of a divine creator. Bizarre as this idea may seem, it has become a commonplace that is sometimes admitted at least as a possibility. Quentin Smith, for example, has developed this kind of argument:

---

13. William Lane Craig, "Finitude of the Past and God's Existence," in *Theism, Atheism, and Big Bang Cosmology*, ed. William Lane Craig and Quentin Smith (Oxford: Clarendon Press, 1993), p. 30.

14. Stanley L. Jaki, "From Scientific Cosmology to a Created Universe," *The Irish Astronomical Journal*, 15 (1982): 260.

there is sufficient evidence at present to warrant the conclusion that
the universe probably began to exist over 10 billion years ago, and
that it began to exist without being caused to do so.[15]

Smith explicitly refers to the absolute beginning of the universe. Though cosmologists speak of the possible origin of the universe as a quantum fluctuation, this cannot be interpreted in a strict sense as a creation "out of nothing" (*ex nihilo*). However, some authors seem to play with those concepts, creating the impression that even if quantum vacuum and its fluctuations cannot be identified with nothingness, they are "almost" nothing at all. But to speak of "almost nothing" is nonsense if we interpret "nothing" rigorously; in that sense, we can say that the concept of "nothing" is a pseudoconcept.

The origin of the universe as a vacuum fluctuation was first proposed by Edward Tryon in 1973. Other models in the same line were then developed and some authors began to emphasize that they could serve to explain the creation of the universe from literally nothing. In 1981, Yacov Zeldovich listed some unsolved questions that would require further work, including:

Does spontaneous birth emerge "out of nothing" or in a space of
more dimensions or as a topological separation from an initially given
empty Minkowskian space?[16]

Indeed, when the spontaneous birth of the universe "out of nothing" is considered as a possibility among other physical explanations, further discussions will result in confusion. The arguments may change depending on current developments of physical theories, but the basic confusion will remain for it consists in attributing to the concepts and methods of physical science a metaphysical meaning they cannot possess. Empirical science deals with processes that can be submitted directly or indirectly to experimental control, and the ultimate foundation of the being of natural entities and processes does not belong to that category. Empirical science presupposes the existence of nature and studies the production of new entities and processes from some preexistent grounding. If a divine agency exists, it cannot be studied by the methods of empirical science. If one denies the legitimacy of approaches other than empirical science to the study of nature, then one must face the self-defeating difficulties of scientism. That denial does not belong to the sciences and therefore becomes meaningless when evaluated by using its own standards.

The ultimate ontological foundation of the universe is a metaphysical

15. Quentin Smith, "The Uncaused Beginning of the Universe," in *Theism, Atheism, and Big Bang Cosmology*, cit., pp. 108–109.

16. Yacov B. Zeldovich, "Spontaneous Birth of the Closed Universe and the Anthropic Principle," in *Astrophysical Cosmology*, ed. H. A. Brück, G. V. Coyne, and M. S. Longair (Vatican City: Pontificia Academia Scientiarum, 1982), p. 578.

problem that must be dealt with using philosophical arguments and cannot be settled through merely physical arguments. As William Carroll puts it:

> Creation, as a proper theological concept, refers to the origin of the universe in the absolute or unqualified senses of origin and of nothing. Such an origin is not, indeed, cannot involve, a change: otherwise we would be referring to a qualified and not to an unqualified origin. . . . The fundamental error in most discussions about creation and the natural sciences is to consider creation as a kind of change. Evolution, whether cosmic or biological, is an explanation of change and is a concern, thus, of the natural sciences. Creation explains the existence of things; it does not explain how natural processes function, no matter how large or ancient these processes are. No theory in the natural sciences can contradict the doctrine of creation, since what creation accounts for is not a process at all, but a metaphysical dependence in the order of being.[17]

This is not to say that scientific cosmology cannot contribute to our understanding of the universe. On the contrary, it provides us with theories that extend the present worldview to a very remote state of the universe and, therefore, helps complete our knowledge of very important features of the world. The present state of the world, and our very existence depends on the properties of the universe in the most ancient stages of its evolution. The study of cosmic evolution therefore plays a central role in the construction of the scientific worldview and in the study of its implications.

3. THE FRONTIERS OF EVOLUTION

Biological evolution is often considered as the main argument in favor of naturalism. Indeed, finality and divine agency had apparently been dislodged from physics, but the realm of living beings posed a serious threat to merely natural explanations for they possess a degree of organization and functionality that seems to require the planning of a superior divine agency. Nevertheless, biological evolution, and more specifically its Darwinist version, apparently explain all biological phenomena through natural causes.

Orthodox Darwinian theory asserts that the existence and characteristics of contemporary living beings can be completely explained by the combination of random genetic variations, which are blind in the sense that they do not follow any particular natural law or any purpose, and natural selection, considered as the organizing mechanism that explains the apparent finality of biological entities. Genetic variations provide the basis of the entire process because they cause the appearance of variations in the organisms, and natural selection is the driving force of evolution as it acts

17. William E. Carroll, "Big Bang Cosmology, Quantum Tunneling from Nothing, and Creation," *Laval théologique et philosophique,* 44 (1988); 68, 70.

as a filter that only permits survival of those organisms best adapted to the environment.

The Darwinian scheme can be further qualified in two ways. First, natural selection, even if itself a blind agency, could, nevertheless, produce highly sophisticated forms of organization. In the long run the effects of natural selection would be similar to those of an intelligent agency, because the repeated elimination of ill-adapted beings would cause the survival of the well-adapted ones. This is how Darwinism can claim to explain the apparent features of living beings by means of a nonintelligent and nonpurposeful agency.

Second, natural selection should be considered a cumulative process and not purely random play. Indeed, when a certain level of organization has been reached, genetic variations and the subsequent natural selection act within the restricted range of possibilities permitted by that present organization. As natural selection progresses, many possibilities will be discarded and new possibilities will arise. As a consequence, the probability of arriving at a highly organized state could not be calculated as a merely random probability based on the listing of the components; it should rather be considered as the much higher probability that arises when many steps have already led to highly organized entities and processes.

This cannot seriously be interpreted as contrary to the existence of divine agency and of the spiritual dimensions of the human being. Human spirituality and divine agency can easily be combined with a process of biological evolution that includes the origin of the human organism. But controversy can arise about two points. First, one may wonder, from the scientific point of view, whether the Darwinian mechanism can completely explain the evolutionary process or whether other causes could also intervene. Second, from the philosophical and theological points of view, conflicts may arise if biological evolution, or its Darwinian version, are interpreted as a complete explanation of everything. This position involves an illegitimate extrapolation of scientific theories outside the limits of science. It is not illegitimate to explore the philosophical and theological implications of evolution, but to use evolution to dismiss philosophy and theology in the name of science.

The doctrine of the major religions does not oppose the scientific doctrine of evolution. For instance, in the official teaching of the Roman Catholic Church there is only one major statement about evolution. In the encyclical "Humani generis" published by Pope Pius XII in 1950, we are told that there is no objection to study the origin of the human body from some other living ancestor provided that the spirituality of the human soul created by God is admitted. In fact, human spirituality cannot be contradicted by empirical science, and we can even say that the development of science can be used to argue that we humans are natural beings who transcend the natural level. References to biological evolution by subsequent popes have usually stressed evolution as a part of God's plan. Pope John Paul II has repeated this idea on several occasions. In 1996 in an address to the plenary meeting of the

Pontifical Academy of Sciences he said that the scientific theory of evolution should be considered today as something more than a hypothesis, adding that a philosophical interpretation of evolution that would not make room for the spiritual dimensions of the human being would collide with the truth about man and would be incapable of providing a foundation for the dignity of the human person.[18]

If we focus on the deepest level of the issue, on the existence of a personal God who is the source of all being and becoming, and also on the existence of spiritual dimensions in the human person who has a unique relationship with God, there cannot be any conflict unless evolution is interpreted in a materialistic way. Some excesses on the part of extremist religious groups that fight against evolution are closely related to contrary excesses of some extremist writers on popular science who interpret evolution as banishing religions; in both cases, however, we are dealing with ideological interpretations both of religion and of science.

Evolution is a major component of the present worldview. However, it should not be used to argue in favor of naturalism by using arguments that, though they appear scientific, are really philosophical and even philosophically unsound.

4. NATURALISTIC FALLACIES

Naturalism is a tricky philosophy containing three fallacies: "the scientific fallacy," "the naturalistic fallacy," and "the fallacy of origins." These fallacies are used today when the present worldview is interpreted in a naturalistic way.

Very often naturalism presents itself as if it were a mere consequence of the scientific method and results, so that the prestige of scientific progress is apparently always on its side. But naturalism is really a philosophy that arbitrarily reduces all problems to those that can be studied using the methods of the empirical sciences and it even reduces them to an oversimplified image that can fulfill its requirements. This could be called "the scientistic fallacy" insofar as it reduces all arguments to those used by empirical science and, at the same time, cannot be supported by scientific arguments.

When we speak of the sciences we must consider them from outside for empirical science cannot completely explain itself. We can study many aspects of the scientific enterprise using methods identical or similar to those used within science, but to study the major issues rigorously we must adopt a different perspective. For instance, the study of the validity of the conceptual constructs and experimental tests that are basic features of empirical science is properly a philosophical question.

Therefore, we should avoid "the naturalistic fallacy," which consists of pre-

18. John Paul II, Message to the Pontifical Academy of Sciences (October 22, 1996), *L'Osservatore Romano,* October 24, 1996, 6–7.

senting a naturalized epistemology as the proper perspective for a serious study of empirical science. A naturalized epistemology studies science in the same way that empirical science studies nature. The naturalistic approach does include an ingredient that should be respected: the need to use as the basis of epistemology a good description of what scientists really do and, therefore, of what the actual practice of science is. However, philosophy is also necessary on that level, because we cannot provide a description of science that includes no interpretation.

We should also avoid "the fallacy of origins" that attempt to explain the synchronic or present features of the world by means of diacronic or evolutionary processes only. An adequate exploration of the present should not consist only in a description of the processes that have led up to it. The explanations of origins are a very important component of this study; progress in this kind of exploration is one of the main achievements of modern science. However, evolution itself poses important problems that cannot be solved by taking into account only their process features. For instance, any process of evolution and each one of its steps require the preexistence of potentialities that can be actualized; therefore, an examination of the self-organizing capacities in our world could not be complete without also examining the question of principles of self-organization. Obviously, if principles of self-organization exist, an account of evolution in terms of blind natural forces could not be considered complete.

These fallacies can act as an obstacle for the progress of science for, by their very nature, they tend to formulate a simplified picture of science that can be matched with the naturalistic prejudices (which are extrascientific); therefore, they tend to consider concrete particular explanations as if they were complete and definitive. Even if we accept that genetic variation and natural selection play a very important role in the explanation of biological evolution, the dogmatic assertion that these two factors alone suffice to explain evolution can easily be an obstacle to discovering other factors that can also play an important role, such as tendencies toward self-organization.

II. UNCONSCIOUS INTELLIGENCE

When seen from the present scientific perspective, the natural world exhibits a rationality that is astonishing in itself and is also astonishing because it provides the basis for our existence as beings who are both part of nature and transcend it. As far as this rationality results from a self-organizing activity, it corresponds to principles that are internal to nature itself.

1. Rationality In Nature

One of the presuppositions of natural science is the rationality of nature, because the scientific quest consists of searching for rational explanations of natural phenomena. The success of the scientific enterprise provides us with new knowledge about the rationality of nature. Certainly we have no guarantees that this rationality exists in any particular case, but scientists always must take the risk and opt in favor of rationality when they extend their research into new fields.

What is really astounding is that, after very many such risks, scientists have not lost yet. Perhaps particular problems cannot be solved at a given moment and every new advance can open new problems. But the overall record is extremely successful and shows a world that is not only highly ordered and rational, but also possesses a specific kind of organization formed by producing successive levels of emergent novelties as the result of an astonishing progress of self-organization.

As a result of scientific progress, the ontological presupposition of science has evolved in a most notable way: order has turned into self-organization. We began with a general idea about natural order as expressing the rationality of nature, and this presupposition of the scientific research has been retro-justified, enlarged, and refined by the present worldview. It has been retro-justified because self-organization is a particularly strong kind of order. It has been enlarged for that very same reason, and also because the whole process of self-organization includes all natural levels and their mutual relations. And it has been refined because we have discovered the internal potentialities of matter in all its levels, so that the idea of purely passive or inert matter has been replaced by the much richer idea of matter as containing active principles of interaction that can produce new kinds of organization.

Self-organization involves a peculiar combination of power and subtleties, a balance between internal sources of activity and synergy, as it consists in the production of successive levels of organization and, therefore, is not a once-and-for-all process. Paul Davies has expressed this as follows:

> The physical world is not arbitrarily regulated; it is ordered in a very particular way, poised between the twin extremes of simple regimented orderliness and random complexity: it is neither a crystal nor a random gas. The universe is undeniably complex, but its complexity is of an *organized* variety. Moreover, this organization was not built into the universe at its origin. It has emerged from primeval chaos in a sequence of self-organizing processes that have progressively enriched and complexified the evolving universe in a more or less unidirectional matter. It is easy to imagine a world that, while ordered, nevertheless does not possess the right sort of forces or conditions for the emergence of complex organization.[19]

Certainly, self-organization implies the existence of an intrinsic, spontaneous source of organization within material entities. A basic feature of natural entities, living and nonliving, is their spontaneous dynamism, which is

---

19. Paul Davies, "The Unreasonable Effectiveness of Science," in *Evidence of Purpose: Scientists Discover the Creator,* ed. John Marks Templeton (New York: Continuum, 1994), p. 45.

deployed according to temporal patterns so that it produces new spatial patterns, which are the source of new kinds of dynamism, and so on. This does not mean that the distinction between living and nonliving beings should be blurred, nor that panpsychism is correct. Nevertheless, the label of "inert matter" that is usually applied to nonliving beings is inadequate, because it falsely suggests that those entities do not possess an inner principle of activity. One of the most important findings of contemporary science is precisely to have shown that the basic interactions responsible for physical phenomena are already present at the microphysical level, so that all physical systems contain the microphysical sources of these interactions. Natural dynamism is a ubiquitous property often hidden by the equilibriums that exist between different dynamisms.

Natural entities possess a highly sophisticated dynamism. I dare say that all subatomic particles know the entirety of physics and chemistry much better than we do. The reason is very simple: a single electron can be found in a great variety of circumstances, and in every one of them it will act according to its nature.

Moreover, electrons have a built-in principle of self-organization that plays a highly important role in our world. By virtue of the Pauli exclusion principle, which reflects the fact that two fermions cannot occupy the same quantum state in the same system, microphysical systems are structured according to definite patterns. Fermions (protons, neutrons, and electrons) are the basic components of all atoms. Atoms that contain an increasing number of protons in their nucleus also contain an equal number of electrons around the nucleus, so that the peripheral electrons are structured according to the Pauli exclusion principle to form the characteristic patterns of each kind of atom. These patterns are responsible for the physical and chemical properties of atoms and of the larger systems formed by them (Figure 4.1).

The case of the Pauli exclusion principle is important because it shows how an extremely simple "principle of organization" works. That principle is a physical law that accounts for the existence of a great variety of natural patterns. Self-organization doubtless proceeds according to natural laws and it should therefore be possible to know the principles that govern it.

Paul Davies has examined this issue in *The Cosmic Blueprint.* He poses the question in a provocative way when he speaks of a general theory of organization (TOO) and says that:

> (it) will undoubtedly lead to major revisions of known physics. . . .
> (it promises) to uncover entirely new principles that will challenge
> the scope of existing physics. . . . The central issue facing the seekers
> of TOOs is whether the surprising—one might even say unreasonable—propensity for matter and energy to self-organize "against the
> odds" can be explained using the known laws of physics, or whether
> completely new fundamental principles are required.[20]

20. Davies, *The Cosmic Blueprint,* cit., pp. 138–139.

Elements	Atomic number	Distribution of electrons										
		K	L		M			N			
		1s	2s	2p	3s	3p	3d	4s	4p	4d	4f
H	1	1									
He	2	2									
Li	3	2	1								
Be	4	2	2								
B	5	2	2	1							
C	6	2	2	2							
N	7	2	2	3							
O	8	2	2	4							
F	9	2	2	5							
Ne	10	2	2	6							
Na	11	2	2	6	1						
Mg	12	2	2	6	2						
Al	13	2	2	6	2	1					
Si	14	2	2	6	2	2					
P	15	2	2	6	2	3					
S	16	2	2	6	2	4					
Cl	17	2	2	6	2	5					
Ar	18	2	2	6	2	6					

Fig. 4.1   Organizing principles. The exclusion principle formulated by the Nobel Prize winner Wolfgang Pauli holds that two fermions cannot be found in an identical quantum state within the same system. As a consequence, electrons in all atoms are distributed in different levels following characteristic patterns. The result of this distribution is that atoms possess well-defined internal structures, which determine their chemical interactions and the physical properties of bigger systems. Therefore, the Pauli exclusion principle, an ordinary physical law, acts as a kind of organizing principle. Such organizing principles are internal to the natural world and can be, at the same time, the intended result of divine creation.

Davies asserts that:

If we accept that there exists a propensity in nature for matter and energy to undergo spontaneous transitions into new states of higher organizational complexity, and that the existence of these states is not fully explained or predicted by lower level laws and entities, nor do they "just happen" to arise for no particular reason, then it is necessary to find some physical principles additional to the lower level laws to explain them. . . . We seem to be on the verge of discovering not only wholly new laws of nature, but ways of thinking about nature that depart radically from traditional science.[21]

Davies does not provide examples of such principles that are generally accepted. This is hardly surprising, since he refers to radically new ways of thinking that do not exist as yet. He distinguishes different possible organizing principles and analyses several proposals that he considers too strong. These include some encompassing the entire cosmos, such as Roger Penrose's hy-

21. Ibid., p. 142.

pothesis about the initial smoothness of the universe, which according to Penrose should emerge from a time-asymmetric fundamental law, and the so-called "perfect cosmological principle" proposed by Herman Bondi, Thomas Gold, and Fred Hoyle in connection with their steady-state theory about the universe as a whole; others refer to the microphysical level, such as Ilya Prigogine's proposal to modify the laws of dynamics, and David Bohm's suggestion to modify quantum physics so that new explanations of natural order may be obtained.

In contrast to Davies, Manfred Stöckler sees little evidence in favor of new specific principles of self-organization. Dismissing Davies' arguments, he asserts:

> processes of self-organisation can be understood without adopting special principles. In this sense they give evidence for the program of reductionism.[22]

The differences between these two authors are probably due to Stöckler's emphasis on reductionism and Davies' emphasis on emergence, novelty, and creativity. Perhaps Davies and Stöckler are not too far apart. Both emphasize that the principles of self-organization pertain to the scientific realm, although Davies stresses the difference between those principles and the science that exists now.

It is hard to predict whether new principles of self-organization will be discovered but it seems likely. For example, in the field of developmental biology it is likely that new discoveries will be made in the line of homeotic genes and gene regulation, which will increase our understanding of development and evolution.

In any case, many laws already exist that, in a broad sense, may be considered principles of self-organization. The Pauli exclusion principle is such a law, showing that a scientific law need not have any distinctive feature to be considered a self-organizing principle. In some ways, all scientific laws can be considered as such. The Pauli exclusion principle, like any other law of physics, merely describes a behavior. However, this behavior automatically provokes a type of organization that affects all electrons of all atoms, and therefore many other types of organization and most properties of matter; this is why it can be considered a principle of self-organization. Insofar as all scientific laws intervene as conditions for the existence of a world that has been formed through a huge process of self-organization, every one is a principle of self-organization. Obviously, when one or several laws are responsible for the regular production of a well-determined, organized result, they should be considered self-organizing principles in a stronger sense.

We should not represent principles of self-organization as having a consistency of their own. Scientific laws and principles do not have a separate existence; they are abstract formulations that express in a symbolic and approx-

---

22. Stöckler, "Reductionism and the New Theories of Self-Organisation," cit., p. 248.

imate way the behavior of natural systems. In our search for principles of self-organization, we should not imagine them as different or independent from the behavior of natural systems. They are either built-in tendencies of natural systems or they do not exist at all, because if they were superimposed from outside we would no longer be dealing with self-organization.

The distinctive trait of self-organization is, precisely, the combination of an inner dynamism ("self ") that produces a functional result ("organization"). If we conceptualize the laws in a quasi-Platonic way as if they had a semi-independent existence, then we should ask, following Stephen Hawking in *A Brief History of Time:* "What is it that breathes fire into the equations and makes a universe for them to describe?"[23] and we could find it most natural, as Kitty Ferguson did, to write a book entitled *The Fire in the Equations.*[24] Surely, Hawking and Ferguson would agree that equations do not have an independent existence and are only an approximate account of what happens in the real world. The real problem is to explain the existence of that world, composed of systems capable of combining themselves to produce an astonishing range of new patterns.

Where do new natural patterns come from? Or, in other words, how can we explain the emergence of novelties in the natural world? John Haught attributes great importance to this question. Speaking of the new science of complexity, Haught attributes to the supporter of contact between science and theology (presumably himself) the following interesting assertions:

> The new sciences (if we may call them that) focus our attention in a fresh way on the pervasive fact of patterning. In doing so they are dealing with something as fundamental as being itself, and not with just another gap that could conceivably be filled in by fresh scientific discoveries. After all, can we really separate the deep question of a thing's existence or "being" from the fact of its patterning? For anything to exist at all would it not have to possess some degree of organized structure? Without at least some internal ordering of its components could anything even have actuality? Our position, as articulated by Whitehead, is that things simply cannot exist without being ordered in a definite way. Indefiniteness would be equivalent to non-existence.[25]

Haught adds that science presupposes the existence of patterning and that the question about the existence of patterning has some metaphysical connotations:

> Thus, the question scientists are asking today about *why* there is complexity in the universe is only a hair's breadth away from the

---

23. Stephen Hawking, *A Brief History of Time* (New York: Bantam, 1988), p. 174.

24. Kitty Ferguson, *The Fire in the Equations: Science, Religion & the Search for God* (Grand Rapids, Mich.: Eerdmans, 1995).

25. Haught, *Science & Religion,* cit., p. 151.

theological question concerning why anything exists at all. . . . The very possibility of doing science in the first place *presupposes* the fact of patterning as science's field of exploration . . . science cannot by itself explain the naked fact of patterning. True, it is *discovering* complex designs that it never noticed before. . . . But can scientists ask the very deep question as to why there is any patterning at all and pretend that they are not thereby steering perilously close to metaphysics? And when they wonder why complex patterning has the features of diversity, emergence, adaptability, and interactivity, can they pursue such inquiry to the very end without making contact to theology?[26]

The scientific quest is centered around the search for patterns. Science presupposes that patterns exist and that they can be explained on the grounds of other natural patterns. The present worldview shows that nature displays an impressive array of patterns pertaining to different levels that are interconnected in a big system full of functionality that makes the existence of truly rational beings possible.

Seen under the present worldview, the world is highly rational because it is the result of a great process of self-organization in which new patterns emerge that can be integrated in a series of progressively organized systems that provide the basis for the existence of rational human beings. Nature is rational insofar as it has been formed according to rational principles, and because it provides the basis for the existence of rational beings.

Nature is rational because it includes a huge series of processes that are integrated in a very sophisticated way. One may wonder, indeed, how it is possible to reach so many varied results with so few elements. The basis of most natural phenomena can be described as a small number of components combined in successive levels using recursive methods so that they finally produce highly organized systems. Thus, three subatomic particles are the basic constituents of ordinary matter; 92 atoms are the components of a great variety of natural systems; 4 nucleotides are the elements of the highly sophisticated genetic information; some 20 amino acids are the components of proteins. Subtlety in the methods and sophistication in the results are the rule in nature.

Davies refers to the process of self-organization with these words:

The fact that this rich and complex variety emerges from the featureless inferno of the Big Bang, and does so as a consequence of laws of stunning simplicity and generality, indicates some sort of matching of means to end that has a distinct teleological flavor to it.[27]

In fact, the rationality of nature points toward problems related to finality or teleology in nature.

---

26. Ibid.

27. Davies, "The Unreasonable Effectiveness of Science," cit., p. 46.

2. TELEOLOGICAL BRIDGES

Even if empirical science by itself cannot be used for or against metaphysics and teleology, some bridges exist that may connect both fields. The development of science since the seventeenth century seemed to undermine the foundations of the bridge related to natural finality or teleology, but the new worldview seems to have restored it in a new and most interesting way.

2.1. UPDATING THE TELEOLOGICAL AGENDA

Teleological thinking, which discovers in the physical world some kind of purpose, has throughout human history been a source of metaphysical and religious inspiration. Indeed, the workings of nature show a rationality that, insofar as it is displayed by irrational beings, seems to require a superior rational cause that can account for it. The rationality of nature is clearly perceived in living beings, which possess a high degree of functionality, but it can also be perceived in the cooperativeness of physical elements and forces that produces the conditions necessary for the development of life and, finally, of human, rational life.

Teleological thinking is a component of all traditional cultures, whatever their particular religious ideas may be. From its very beginning, Christianity has used the teleological arguments developed by ancient thinkers such as Plato, Aristotle, and the Stoics, and has added new arguments to them. This kind of reasoning, which is based on the sense of awe, wonder, and mystery that arises from the contemplation of nature, can be understood by everyone, as it is based on facts that can be known through everyday experience.

However, the seventeenth-century birth of empirical science was accompanied by a strong opposition to teleology, an opposition that has been increasing ever since. This opposition is usually presented as a consequence of scientific progress, so it is extremely interesting to analyze the situation created by recent progress in the sciences, which provides new elements for a reintroduction of a teleological worldview.

Indeed, the challenges to teleology in the name of science seem to have been removed by the scientific developments of the second half of the twentieth century. Even if the new worldview centered around self-organization does not in itself have a univocally determined philosophical meaning, it clearly indicates that teleological dimensions in nature exist that can be investigated by empirical science.

The present worldview underscores the existence of holism, functionality, morphogenesis, information, tendencies, and synergy or cooperativity, which are dimensions closely related to teleology. Therefore, antiteleological arguments can no longer be presented as supported by the prestige of empirical science.

To clarify this issue further, we should note that natural teleology presents us, not with a single problem, but with many closely interconnected though not identical problems. We can speak about teleology in the physical and in the biological world, in the field of rational purposes and in that of natural tendencies, on a small scale and on a global one, at the natural level and as a search for the ultimate explanation of nature outside nature itself, considering God as the end that confers value to human actions and asking for the purpose of God in the creation. To tackle the problem of natural teleology with any guarantee of success, it is necessary to introduce some order into the multiplicity of issues involved.

First of all, I will differentiate between four mutually connected levels of teleology: teleology considered as the end of processes, as the goal of tendencies, as a value for subjects, and as the purpose of plans (Figure 4.2).

On the first level, teleology refers to the "end" of a "process." Sometimes we can distinguish particular stages in a process and consider the conclusion of any one of them as an end. We can speak about ends in a spatial sense, but when we talk about teleology we are primarily interested in the ends of processes that develop in time. This meaning of "end" is at the same time something real and completely neutral from the philosophical point of view. However, it is a necessary component of the remaining three levels.

The second level contains a stronger finalist meaning, as it refers to the "goal" of a "tendency." This meaning presupposes the first and adds something, the existence of a tendency toward a determined end. This is no longer

---

> 1. END of a PROCESS
>
> "The End" of a film, of a journey, of an exam
> Final stages of any process
>
> 2. GOAL of a TENDENCY
>
> Attractive or repulsive physical forces
> Multiple tendencies of living beings
>
> 3. VALUE for a SUBJECT
>
> Something good or bad for the subject who acts
>
> 4. PURPOSE of a PLAN
>
> There are known aims and designs

Fig. 4.2   Four levels of teleology. These four meanings of finality are mutually connected. The first is always present in the second; both are present in the third; and the first three are present in the fourth. Something can be the end of a process without being the goal of any tendency, a value for any subject, or the purpose of an intelligent plan. In contrast, if the purpose of a plan exists, there must also exist, as its necessary conditions, a value for a subject, a goal of a tendency, and the end of the process. Every level presupposes the previous ones and adds something new.

a neutral issue from the scientific or philosophical points of view, and it poses two problems: how we can determine the existence of tendencies and how we can explain them.

On the third level a new qualification is introduced: we say that particular ends have a "value" for some "subject." Here, "value" means that something is convenient or inconvenient, good or bad, for a particular subject or kind of subject. Discussions about teleology sooner or later refer to values.

These three levels exist in both natural and human activity. But on the fourth level there is a new kind of teleology that belongs only to the purposeful activity of intelligent beings: to reach a "purpose" as a consequence of a "plan." This is the level on which we can properly speak of purposeful actions and of design.

Intelligent purposeful action is teleological because, by its very nature, it is directed toward something that can be considered to be the end of the action. This end is a goal, as far as it is reached as the result of a tendency, and is also a value, because otherwise the subject would not desire it. Natural activities are not so clearly teleological because it may be difficult to determine whether they are directed toward determinate goals, and because it may be even more difficult to determine whether these goals, if they exist, can be considered real values.

The problem of natural teleology has a double aspect: first, to determine whether natural tendencies toward goals that can be considered values exist, and then, if these goals exist, to determine whether they require the existence of some intelligent plan that governs the activity of nature.

2.2. NATURAL TELEOLOGY: THE FACT

The status of teleology at present is somewhat paradoxical. On the one hand, the progress of science clearly shows that natural finality is a real dimension of nature; on the other hand, the repetition of antifinalist arguments makes it difficult to accept that, or, at least, to recognize its true relevance.

The existence of natural teleology can be considered, from the perspective of the present worldview, to be a well-corroborated fact. There is little doubt that the biological world is full of teleological phenomena that are a characteristic feature of living beings. Francisco Ayala has argued that teleological explanations are indispensable in biology and cannot be reduced to nonteleological explanations without loss of explanatory content, and he has proposed a notion of teleology close to the notion I have used. According to Ayala, teleology primarily refers to the goal or purpose toward which we direct our activity, and then it is extended "to describe actions, objects or processes which exhibit an orientation towards a certain goal or end-state." Ayala characterizes teleology by means of functionality and distinguishes three kinds of biological phenomena that can be labeled teleological:

> There are at least three categories of biological phenomena where teleological explanations are appropriate. . . . These three classes of teleological phenomena are established according to the mode of re-

lationship between the object or process and the end-state or property that accounts for its presence. . . .
(1) When the end-state or goal is consciously anticipated by the
agent. This is purposeful activity and it occurs in man and probably in
other animals. . . .
(2) In connection with self-regulating or teleonomic systems,
where there exists a mechanism that enables the system to reach or
to maintain a specific property in spite of environmental fluctuations. The regulation of body temperature in mammals is of this
kind. In general the homeostatic reactions of organisms belong to
this category. . . .
(3) In reference to structures anatomically and physiologically designed to perform a certain function. . . .[28]

Ernst Mayr also asserts that on the biological level there are many goal-
directed processes:

Goal-directed *behavior* (in the widest sense of this word) is extremely
widespread in the organic world; for instance, most activity connected with migration, food-getting, courtship, ontogeny, and all phases
of reproduction is characterized by such goal orientation. The occurrence of goal-directed processes is perhaps the most characteristic feature of the world of living organisms.[29]

This amounts to recognizing that, in the biological realm, the existence of
natural finality is a plain fact. In this context, Mayr uses the term "teleonomy," which he defines thus:

A teleonomic process or behavior is one which owes its goal-directed-
ness to the operation of a program.[30]

Then, Mayr distinguishes "open" and "closed" programs:

The programs which control teleonomic processes in organisms are
either entirely laid down in the DNA of the genotype (closed programs) or are constituted in such a way that they can incorporate additional information (open programs), acquired through learning,
conditioning, or other experiences. Most behavior, particularly in
higher organisms, is controlled by such open programs.[31]

Although others use different terminology or propose different classifications
of teleological phenomena, there is a general unanimity in recognizing that finalist phenomena exist and play a most important role in the biological world.

---

28. Francisco J. Ayala, "Teleological Explanations in Evolutionary Biology," *Philosophy of Science,* 37 (1970): 8–9.

29. Ernst Mayr, *Towards A New Philosophy of Biology* (Cambridge, Mass.: Harvard University
Press, 1988), p. 45.

30. Ibid.

31. Ibid., p. 49.

But such unanimity does not exist in the search for finalist phenomena in the nonliving world. For example, Mayr speaks of "teleonomic" processes only in the biological world and asserts that in inanimate nature we find only "teleomatic" processes, mere consequences of natural laws.

Of course, biological systems possess distinctive finalist features and a kind of "strong" teleology or teleonomy, as many processes are directed toward well-defined, concrete goals. Directionality in the inanimate world is much more "open." Nevertheless, the entire natural world, also in the nonliving realm, possesses many directional dimensions, and when we consider the physicochemical world as a necessary condition for the living world, it can be considered in its entirety as a functional part of a greater whole. I do not intend to revive an organicistic worldview in either its ancient form or some other form, such as the one proposed by the Romantics or the Gaia hypothesis proposed in the contemporary scene. I limit myself to that which, in my opinion, can be safely asserted on the basis of present scientific knowledge.

The world is full of teleological dimensions. When we search for them, we can easily see that virtually any of the main aspects of our world can be taken as a particular case of teleology. Although this holds especially for living beings, the physicochemical world also exhibits many directional features that acquire a special meaning when seen as necessary conditions for the existence of living beings.

Directionality indicates the existence of tendencies toward goals, which is the hallmark of natural teleology. When different components of nature cooperate in the production of a unitary result, we deal with a kind of directionality that can be called "cooperativity."

It is not difficult to find examples of directionality and cooperativity. If we begin with the most elementary components of the world, we find out that subatomic particles and the four basic interactions behave according to well-known specific patterns and collaborate to build up successive levels of organization—atoms, molecules, macromolecules, and the bigger inorganic and organic beings. The entire construction of our world is the result of the deployment of tendencies that collaborate to make up unitary systems.

The existence of tendencies means that selective channels of behavior exist. It is easy to perceive that natural entities, on both the biological level and the physicochemical level, display a tendency-like behavior. Moreover, tendencies often favor the cooperation of different elements to form higher levels of organization.

Natural systems occupy a central place in nature. Many of them are unitary systems organized according to regular patterns. Doubtless, a great part of the world consists of aggregations, but they also are made up of natural unitary systems that possess, in different degrees, functionality and cooperativity.

To establish the existence of tendency-like behavior in the natural world, it is not necessary to present a collection of specific scientific results for we would need to include the entirety of present scientific knowledge. Any scientific advance helps us to know how natural dynamism is deployed following privileged channels. The present worldview is very important in this context because, for the first time in history, it includes the basic components of all natural levels and also their mutual relations; therefore, it provides us with a picture of the world that clearly demonstrates the ubiquitous existence of holism, tendencies, and cooperativity.

The ubiquity of teleological dimensions in nature should not be a surprise, because any kind of "stabilized organization" implies the existence of such dimensions. A stable organization implies the existence of holism, for some kind of unity will be present among the components of the organization. It also implies the existence of some kind of functionality and cooperativity, because the components will perform their role jointly with each other in the unity of the whole. Our world certainly possesses a high degree of stabilized organization, so the fact that it exhibits many teleological features is not surprising.

Holism, functionality, and cooperativity are finalist dimensions because they imply that different components collaborate to reach a common goal. These dimensions were present in the ancient teleological worldviews, because they were easily perceived in living beings. They suffered an eclipse when the mechanistic worldview triumphed and have been rehabilitated in the present worldview, attaining greater importance than they had before. Indeed, we now understand them much better.

Moreover, as a consequence of recent progress, information has emerged as a new finalist dimension that plays a specially relevant role in nature. The well-known case of genetic information clearly shows not only that finality exists, but also demonstrates how it works. Indeed, the existence of teleological dimensions was a mystery until we reached an understanding of how it works through information. Stored information is a program that includes potentialities that will be actualized according to the circumstances. If we generalize this concept and apply it to other fields of nature, we realize that every natural system, even a single subatomic particle, contains a huge amount of information about its possible behavior in different circumstances. Therefore, our understanding of information allows us to see that the behavior of natural systems is very selective, that it is partly programmed in advance, and that it can be displayed in a great variety of specific behaviors depending on a practically indefinite number of possible circumstances.

We can conclude that, from the point of view of the present scientific worldview, the existence of teleological dimensions in our world—not only in the biological level, but also in the physicochemical—is a plain fact. Until now the state of the sciences did not provide sufficient grounds for it; only the scientific progress of the last decades of the twentieth century has made it possible to reach this vantage point.

But what about values? Even if we admit the all-pervasive existence of teleological dimensions in nature, what has this to do with values? After all, if we cannot show that the ends reached through natural tendencies are values, the existence of teleological dimensions would not be too important. As Mark Bedau puts it:

There is a certain essential conceptual link between teleology and value, and the specific contour exhibited by the theory of teleology will depend on the specific shape possessed by the view of value to which it is connected.[32]

To develop a value approach to natural teleology will be impossible unless some kind of absolute value exists. Indeed, there are many potential beneficiaries in nature and it is impossible to harmonize all of their interests.

Even though I may be accused of anthropocentrism, I will argue that absolute value that exists in the natural world is the specifically human values, for we human beings are natural beings who, at the same time, transcend the natural level. If human beings are seen as a mere product of blind natural forces, human life becomes accidental and not transcendent. But there are strong reasons to support the opposite view. The progress of science shows that we are endowed with creative and argumentative capacities that are related to the pursuit of truth and the service of mankind as ethical goals. Therefore, the more the sciences progress, the more we should realize that our intellectual and ethical dimensions place us above all other natural beings.

Seen from this perspective, the huge process of natural self-organization that led to our existence can be considered as the deployment of many coordinated tendencies that have made possible the creation of a new world of intellectual and ethical values that transcends the material level even as it is rooted in the natural world. This is not to say that we can know the role that every element plays in the overall plan. Nevertheless, we can note the existence of such a plan and recognize our central role in it.

2.3. NATURAL TELEOLOGY: THE EXPLANATION

That the natural world exhibits different kinds of teleology should be considered a well-established fact in the present worldview. The next problem is how to explain that fact.

A standard answer runs this way: our world possesses a high degree of teleology as a consequence of a very long process of evolution in which many innovations have been brought about in an accidental way and only the best adapted have survived. No wonder, therefore, that when we look around or even look within us we find so many contrivances that apparently seem to suggest the existence of a purposeful plan.

Sometimes this explanation is taken to be opposed to the existence of a divine plan and incompatible with it. It is not too difficult, however, to realize that such incompatibility does not exist at all, but it is only a manifesta-

---

32. Mark Bedau, "Naturalism and Teleology," in *Naturalism: A Critical Approach,* ed. Steven J. Wagner and Richard Warner (Notre Dame, Ind.: University of Notre Dame, 1993), p. 44.

tion of a mistaken view that places natural explanations and divine agency in opposition.

We are obviously correct when we search for natural explanations of teleology, and adaptation resulting from evolution is a good candidate. However, the very existence of evolution leads to a different type of question: is it reasonable to attribute the highly sophisticated rationality that exists in the natural world, including all its finalist dimensions, to the action of natural forces only?

The standard answer to this new question runs this way: even if natural forces are in some sense blind, they can nevertheless cause goal-directed effects that seem to be the result of an intelligent plan. Specifically, natural selection is a force of that kind. It has no purpose in mind, as it has no mind at all, but its action in the long run produces teleology-like effects. Richard Dawkins, a vehement proponent of this view, has designed a kind of experiment that may help to visualize the plausibility of his claim. This is how he poses his experiment:

> I don't know who it was first pointed out that, given enough time, a monkey bashing away at random on a typewriter could produce all the works of Shakespeare. The operative phrase is, of course, given enough time. Let us limit the task facing our monkey somewhat. Suppose that he has to produce, not the complete works of Shakespeare but just the short sentence "Methinks it is like a weasel," and we shall make it relatively easy by giving him a typewriter with a restricted keyboard, one with just the 26 (capital) letters, and a space bar. How long will he take to write this one little sentence?[33]

On this basis, Dawkins assumes that the monkey tries once and again in a series of discrete trials, each consisting of 28 bashes at the keyboard. This can be simulated by a computer program. The probability of producing the desired phrase by a series of independent tries would be almost completely negligible. Here, Dawkins introduces an apparently small change in the program. The first random-produced phrase is duplicated repeatedly but with a certain random change in the copying, and then:

> The computer examines the mutant nonsense phrases, the "progeny" of the original phrase, and chooses the one which, *however slightly,* most resembles the target phrase, ME THINKS IT IS LIKE A WEASEL.[34]

The procedure is repeated time and again. The target was finally reached in generation 43 the first time, and in generation 41 the second time. Dawkins uses this simulation to conclude that natural selection, when understood not

---

33. Richard Dawkins, *The Blind Watchmaker: Why the Evidence of Evolution Reveals a Universe without Design* (New York and London: Norton, 1987), p. 46.

34. Ibid., p. 47.

as a collection of independent once-for-all mutations but as a process of "cumulative" selection that takes as the point of departure the outcomes already reached, can easily account for the adaptations and apparent teleology of our world, making divine agency redundant.

Dawkin's argument is tricky, because he introduces a teleological component in his monkey computer game when he inscribes in the program the instruction to "choose(s) the one which most resembles the target phrase." It is difficult to formulate a statement that is more teleological, for it includes the existence of a target and the selection of the phrase closest to it. In pure Darwinism supported by Dawkins, natural selection is supposed to be blind and to have no purposes at all. Although the result of natural selection will be the survival of the fittest, each step of that kind is unique and should not be considered as forming a progressive series that tends toward an increasingly perfect goal. The example is, therefore, completely deceptive.

A more important problem exists concerning the concept of natural selection. I refer to one aspect of the discussion: the "passive" character of selection. This amounts to recognizing that selection should not be considered the real source of innovations. Mayr has written:

> natural selection is strictly an a posteriori process which rewards current success but never sets up future goals. No one realized this better than Darwin, who reminded himself "never to use the words higher or lower." Natural selection rewards past events, that is the production of successful recombinations of genes, but does not plan for the future. This is, precisely, what gives evolution by natural selection its flexibility. With the environment changing incessantly, natural selection—in contradistinction to orthogenesis—never commits itself to a future goal. Natural selection is never goal oriented. It is misleading and quite inadmissible to designate such broadly generalized concepts as survival or reproductive success as definite and specified goals.[35]

This is pure Darwinism. To explain evolution, we must examine what the sources of innovation are.

From the scientific point of view, these sources are genetic variation and recombination. If we consider the world such as it exists now, the conditions necessary for the kind of evolution that has led to human beings are enormously specific. Therefore, we can be sure that a huge number of successive specific potentialities have existed that were necessary for our existence, and even others that we do not yet know. Evolution implies the existence of many successive potentialities whose actualization depends on particular contingent facts, and those potentialities should be extremely specific.

That there must exist some positive source of self-organization indepen-

---

35. Mayr, *Towards A New Philosophy of Biology,* cit., p. 43.

dent of natural selection is stressed by several authors. Referring to Stuart Kauffman, John Haught asserts:

> Creativity in evolution takes place primarily in the self-organization that occurs *prior* to selection. Thus natural selection by itself cannot account for all the creativity in evolution.[36]

Some authors attribute to natural selection an active role in evolution. It is easy to find in the literature statements in which natural selection appears as the subject of actions that play an important role in evolution. For instance, the very same Mayr who speaks of natural selection as an *a posteriori* process that cannot have any future goal, criticizes Jacques Monod because "he totally ignores natural selection as a creative process and ascribes all evolution to pure chance."[37]

Natural selection is a metaphor that originates in the purposeful artificial selection used by human beings. In any case, we should admit that the present state of our world, as the result of a huge process of self-organization, is the result of the actualization of many successive potentialities that have served as the basis for each of the successive steps that have brought it about. Not only the initial potentialities, but also the basic physical laws and constants, and the successive kinds of systems that have been formed along the process of evolution, must have been enormously specific.

Mayr strongly criticizes any attempt to introduce final causes as an explanation of evolution; he criticizes any explanation of evolution, even if antifinalist as in the case of Monod, because he thinks they have been unable to integrate natural selection into their thinking. Nevertheless, he asserts that "development constraints" are "an important evolutionary factor," and he also attributes an important role to "development potentiality."[38] The evolutionary relevance of this kind of factor is apparently related to finality, but Mayr strongly asserts:

> There are severe constraints on the evolutionary potentialities of a given line, but this is, of course, something entirely different from a final cause.[39]

And he closes any door that could lead to teleology by saying emphatically:

> Finalism is no longer part of any respectable philosophy.[40]

Mayr himself provides the clue to understanding his antiteleological position in a discussion entitled "What led to the Decline, if not Demise, of Fi-

36. Haught, *Science & Religion,* cit., p. 158.

37. Mayr, *Towards A New Philosophy of Biology,* cit., p. 243.

38. Ibid., pp. 246–247.

39. Ibid., p. 241.

40. Ibid., p. 248.

nalism?"[41] Mayr argues that if final causes existed, they should produce a steady progress in evolution and that, as science is unable to detect them, they should be attributed to metaphysical or supernatural causes, which have no place either in science or in philosophy. He also argues that mechanistic explanations for evolution eliminate evidence in favor of final causes. Moreover, he adds that, if final causes exist, future evolution could be predicted, which is not the case. Furthermore, Mayr says that the existence of rectilinear trends, of trends in nonutilitarian characters, and of trends in deleterious characters, all of which have been used as arguments against natural selection, can be explained in a nonteleological way. Mayr finally adds that the existence of directive final causes should cause far more perfection in nature than actually exists.

This rejection of teleology seems to be rooted in prejudices against final causes that would disappear if we could observe that final causes should not be the subject of scientific research, that they do not necessarily have to lead to steady evolutionary progress, and that they not only are compatible with explanations in terms of efficient causes, but also require them. Finality and efficiency are not opposed but complementary: the one supposes the other, and neither can exist in isolation.

The mechanisms of evolution provide explanations for natural teleology that should be interpreted, from the philosophical perspective, as the successive actualization of potentialities, in a huge process that includes an immense variety of highly sophisticated events and results. This philosophical point does not interfere with scientific explanations; rather, the existence of potentialities should be taken as a condition for the possibility of the actual events.

Another objection to the teleological perspective holds that our world is only one of the many outcomes of the natural process of evolution. No wonder then, the objection continues, if among the many results there is one like our world in which there is so much order. This criticism has been used routinely against a book about "the anthropic design argument"; the reviewer does not argue against the divine creation of the world, but dismisses the anthropic arguments this way:

> However, he (the author) presents no evidence that there isn't a huge number of universes that have irrupted into existence, do not interact, may not include all possible ones, and whose existence makes the chance occurrence of this universe unremarkable. So, he can't conclude that this universe has been rigged by God. Corey might counter that universes can't come into being without the act of a creator but that would be a different argument, one that, if successful, renders the anthropic design argument otiose. For eliminating our statistically inspired astonishment at being alive, a necessarily existing creator is no better than a host of spontaneous universes. Indeed, if

41. Ibid., pp. 248–251.

we apply Occam's Razor to kinds of entities and not mere numbers, the latter is preferable.[42]

I must confess that I am not very impressed by this kind of argument. In fact, we know that many billions of places exist that are very different from ours, and we can conjecture that different physical laws may hold for many of them. However, this does not diminish the fact that, as the result of an immense evolutionary process of self-organization, our world has the high degree of organization we perceive. Actually, our world is so specific that we could even think that God, wanting to form it according to natural principles, created a self-organizing universe so immense that our little world could be formed. As Joseph Zycinski puts it:

> Cosmologists for a long time have been intrigued by the question of why life appeared so late in a universe which has been expanding for 20 billion years, and why the density of matter in the universe is so small that successive generations continually relive Pascalian anxiety in their experience of the emptiness of infinite spaces. Modern cosmology supplies a partial explanation. Even if life were to develop in only one place, a large and old universe would have been required. Billions of years of cosmic evolution are necessary for the appearance of carbon producing stars, an indispensable element for the rise of known forms of life.[43]

The present worldview does not by itself prove any metascientific thesis. It cannot be used, under the form of anthropic principles, as a substitute for metaphysical and theological reasoning. It does, however, show that our world is full of directional dimensions, of tendencies and synergy, of rationality. It introduces information, which is a kind of materialized rationality, as a concept that plays a central role in explaining our world. It represents our world as the result of a gigantic process of self-organization, where successive specific potentialities have become actualized and have produced a series of increasingly organized systems that have culminated in the human organism, which provides the basis for a truly rational existence. Therefore, the present worldview amplifies the basis for teleological reasoning, which is one of the main bridges that may connect the natural and the divine.

3. TELEOLOGICAL PUZZLES

A number of problems with teleological thinking have often been formulated in the name of science. I will consider also the main difficulties posed in the past as far as they continue to be influential now.

42. Brian Zamulinski, "Review of M. A. Corey, 'God and the New Cosmology: The Anthropic Design Argument,'" *Australasian Journal of Philosophy,* 72 (1994): 405.

43. Joseph M. Zycinski, "The Anthropic Principle and Teleological Interpretations of Nature," *The Review of Metaphysics,* 41 (1987): 318.

The consequences of scientific progress for teleological thinking can be classified in three successive steps, which reflect three great scientific revolutions and their corresponding worldviews: (1) the birth of modern physics in the seventeenth century, which was accompanied by the mechanistic worldview; (2) evolutionary theory in the nineteenth century and the process worldview; and (3) the self-organization paradigm and the corresponding present worldview.

3.1. PHYSICS AND TELEOLOGY

Mechanics, the study of physical phenomena related to the motion of matter, was the first branch of mathematical physics which reached its full scientific status in the hands of Kepler, Galileo, Newton, and other pioneers of modern science. One of the great achievements of mechanics at that time was the unification of the phenomena of the heavenly bodies and the earthly ones under the same laws. The success of the new mechanical physics was tremendous in both the theoretical and practical realms.

These scientific developments were accomplished by nonscientific ideas that were not completely adequate. The mechanistic worldview reduced nature to the motion of pieces of matter that collide and eventually become united. Mechanism was considered in the seventeenth century to be a real advance; indeed, mechanical models were useful for the new physics, and therefore mechanism could seem a real part of science itself. The confusion was partly due to the controversial birth of modern empirical science, which intended to replace the ancient natural philosophy, one of whose main tenets was precisely teleology. In this context, a critical attitude toward teleology seemed to be a necessary ingredient of the new physics.

A detailed analysis of the different arguments for and against teleology in the seventeenth and eighteenth centuries would exceed the limits of my present purpose but it will be sufficient to mention some of the criticisms that have persisted until today, such as are contained in the synthesis of the teleological arguments elaborated by physicists John Barrow and Frank Tipler. Referring to Francis Bacon (1561–1626), they write:

> Although Bacon certainly did not wish to deny that Nature may both possess and display some divine purpose, he objected to the use of this belief in generating teleological "explanations" which then became intermingled with the empirical investigations of the physical sciences. . . . For Bacon, final causes have a role to play only in metaphysics. In physics, experience guides us to exclude them. With Bacon's ideas we see the beginning of a trend that has continued to the present day with most scientists *qua* scientists ignoring "ultimate" questions; and instead, concentrating on more limited local problems and the interconnection between material and efficient causes.[44]

---

44. John D. Barrow and Frank J. Tipler, *The Anthropic Cosmological Principle* (Oxford: Clarendon Press, 1986), p. 51.

Bacon's problem referred only to physical science, in which teleology was seen as a useless concept. According to Bacon, the new science should provide explanations that would serve as predictive tools so as to obtain an increasing control over nature. These explanations were related to material causes (namely, the composition of matter) and efficient causes (namely, the causes of motion). No place remained for formal and final causes, which were seen as part of the sterile discussions of the Scholastics that should, therefore, be abandoned. In addition, it was difficult to make room for teleological reasoning in the inductive procedures that Bacon felt should guide scientific activity and eventually lead to the discovery of natural laws.

Bacon was partly right. Indeed, it is difficult to determine what role teleology could play in a physics based on mathematics and experiment. Nevertheless, because the laws of physics indicate the existence of directionality in nature the new science contained teleological features. The perspective adopted by mathematical physics does not permit us to explicitly study the teleological dimensions, which remain as a presupposition of scientific research whose existence is corroborated by the progress of science. Therefore, the new physics did not exclude the existence of teleology in nature; rather, it could be used as a tool to further develop teleological considerations. In any event, these considerations should not be sought in the explicit formulations of mathematical physics but in reflections on its ontological presuppositions and implications.

In the mechanistic thought of René Descartes (1596–1650), teleology did not find a better place. Descartes was the champion of a mechanistic philosophy in which the study of nature should be based on mathematics, so that there was no room for final causes. Descartes' position is described by Barrow and Tipler this way:

> Like Galileo and many other renaissance scientists he was convinced that the primary qualities of the Universe were mathematical in nature. This led him firmly to reject final causation as a useful scientific concept because it was associated with an anthropocentric and subjective view of the world, reflecting little more than our presumption in supposing we could unravel the purposes of God. Things have many ends, Descartes says, but most of these have no interaction with Man at all.[45]

Descartes added a further difficulty when he said that searching to know finality in nature would amount to investigating God's purpose in the creation, which is not the task of science and would furthermore be completely impossible. This argument has also been transmitted to posterity and is sometimes used by the supporters of antiteleological views. Nevertheless, it is not difficult to see that using natural teleology to know God's existence and plans cannot lead to a knowledge of his plans in detail.

---

45. Ibid., p. 53.

More arguments against teleology were presented by Spinoza and Hume. Although not as closely related to the development of empirical science as the arguments of Bacon and Descartes, their antiteleological arguments have a deep impact on the discussions about teleology today.

Benedict de Spinoza (1632–1677) devoted an entire appendix in his *Ethics* to accumulating proofs against final causes. This overview of them is borrowed again from Barrow and Tipler:

> Such (teleological) notions, he claims, have only arisen because of our ignorance of mechanical laws of Nature and our gullibility regarding the prejudices of anthropocentric philosophy. Far from being in a position to determine the causes and effects of most things we tend to react in amazement, thinking that however these things have come out, they cannot but be for our benefit. . . . Those who employ finalistic reasoning simply confuse causes with effects. . . . Also, if the doctrine of final causes is correct, he argues, then those most perfect things we are seeking as irrefutable evidences of the "perfect principle" must, by definition, lie in the unobservable future. . . . Spinoza claims that our deductions of final causes are probably nothing more than mere wish-fulfillment; expressing, not the nature of the real world, but the nature we hope it has.[46]

David Hume (1711–1776) criticized, in his *Dialogues Concerning Natural Religion,* a variety of teleological arguments. Barrow and Tipler summarize his criticism:

> The principal objections which Hume allows to surface during the course of the discussion are threefold: Firstly, the Design Argument is unscientific; there can be no causal explanation for the order of Nature because the uniqueness of the world removes all grounds for comparative reference. Secondly, analogical reasoning is so weak and subjective that it could not even provide us with a reasonable conjecture, never mind a definite proof. And finally: all negative evidence has been conveniently neglected. Hume maintains that a dispassionate approach could argue as well for a disorderly cause if it were to concentrate upon the disorderly aspects of the world's structure. His aim is not so much to refute the Design Argument as to show that it only raises questions that are undecidable from the evidence available.[47]

Whereas Bacon and Descartes were religious believers who objected against teleology primarily on allegedly scientific grounds, Spinoza's pantheism and Hume's skepticism provoked more extensive attacks and the antifinalist arguments multiplied. Hume's ideas had a great impact on Immanuel Kant (1724–1804), who partly accepted the empiricism at the base of Hume's attacks on teleology but, at the same time, intended to supersede Hume's skepticism. Ac-

---

46. Ibid., pp. 59–60.

47. Ibid., p. 70.

cording to Kant, we cannot know the true nature of real things and therefore we cannot assert the existence of natural teleology or use it as the basis for a proof of the existence of God. Nevertheless, Kant recognized the relevance of natural order, especially as displayed by living beings, in itself and also when used as the basis for the teleological proof of the existence of God. He concluded that, even if we cannot speak of teleology as a true feature of reality, teleological thinking is most useful in our attempts to study the natural world, which, mainly in the biological realm, behaves "as if" it were teleologically ordained. This is why, in spite of his opposition to teleology as a philosophically valid concept, Kant's ideas about teleology as a regulative principle could foster scientific research along teleological lines. As Barrow and Tipler put it:

> Kant's notion of teleology had an enormous influence on the work of German biologists in the first half of the nineteenth century. Like Kant, for the most part these biologists did not regard teleology and mechanism as polar opposites, but rather as explanatory modes complementary to each other.[48]

This overview shows the kind of difficulties that were raised against teleology in the seventeenth and eighteenth centuries. Teleology is useless for science, is the result of an illegitimate anthropomorphic perspective, implies a presumptuous attempt to understand the purposes of God, is unknowable, implies an illegitimate translation of purposive human activity into the ambit of natural beings.

These objections notwithstanding, teleology was not completely dismissed in the epoch of classical physics. Actually, the new science was used extensively as the basis of new teleological arguments for the existence of God. Many people, when they considered the universe from the perspective of the new science, saw it as a highly ordered world ruled by laws, which seemed to require a divine author. In the English-speaking world, for instance, William Paley (1743–1805) published his famous *Natural Theology,* in which he widely used teleological reasoning to prove the existence of God. After Paley, the *Bridgewater Treatises* continued the line of teleological reasoning in favor of natural theology. Nevertheless, criticisms against teleology were widespread and have exercised a strong influence ever since.

The present worldview shows that many teleological features exist in nature and in empirical science as well, but the use of the scientific method excludes an explicit reflection on them, for that is a philosophical task. We also know now that mechanical models have a restricted applicability and that a mechanistic perspective can capture only some traits of the natural world. In addition, although the analytic way of thinking is very important in scientific work, the accumulation of knowledge obtained using that perspective enables us to know qualitative features of nature that correspond to the synthetic perspective and are often related to teleology.

48. Ibid., p. 74.

Other antiteleological arguments are mostly related to purely philosophical and theological problems. In fact, one could guess that difficulties raised against the existence of final causes in nature often arise because it seems that, if we admit final causes, we would also be obliged to admit the existence of God as the only true ultimate explanation for them. This kind of difficulty, already present in these earlier arguments, acquired a great relevance when modern theories of evolution were developed in the nineteenth century.

3.2. BIOLOGY AND TELEOLOGY

Although the theory of biological evolution existed long before Charles Darwin (1809–1882), it acquired far-reaching relevance after he published in 1859 *The Origin of Species*. The main novelty of Darwin's theory was that he proposed hereditary variation and natural selection as the mechanisms responsible for evolution. Darwin himself added a reference to the Creator at the end of his book. Nevertheless, it was apparent that the theory of evolution could be seen as a substitute for teleological thinking, for it could provide natural explanations of facts hitherto considered to be finalist.

In spite of some particular conflicts, it can be said that most religious authors consider evolution to be compatible with divine agency, and to provide a more adequate understanding of a divine plan than the idea of a special creation for every species. Most scientists declare evolution and religion to correspond to fields that are different and compatible, even complementary, but some see evolution as incompatible with religion. Of this latter group, two have exercised a strong impact in the second half of the twentieth century as opponents of religion in the name of evolutionary science: the French Nobel Prize-winner Jacques Monod and the Oxford biologist Richard Dawkins. Both Monod and Dawkins target teleology (or the doctrine of final causes) and intend to show that scientific progress leaves no room for teleology and, therefore, for a divine plan. I find their arguments defective because they conflate evolutionary science into an entire natural philosophy, which in its turn is conflated into an entire explanation of the world. I have already analyzed some aspects of their doctrines, but here I will examine some methodological defects that make their positions quite deceptive.

Monod argues that empirical science is based on the postulate of objectivity, which precludes any talk about final causes, and concludes that, in consequence, the old alliance between man and nature, which permitted us to see the world as a way toward the divine and to find a meaning for our lives, has been broken. His style becomes rather pathetic at the end of his book:

> Man knows at last that he is alone in the universe's unfeeling immensity, out of which he emerged only by chance.[49]

Monod's arguments are completely misleading, as no such a thing as his postulate of objectivity, which would preclude teleology, exists. An elementary

---

49. Jacques Monod, *Chance and Necessity* (New York: Alfred A. Knopf, 1971), p. 180.

epistemological reflection shows that in empirical science we require that theories may be checked by experiments and, therefore, it is we who limit the possible subjects of our study and omit those dimensions of reality that cannot be studied in that way. Obviously, this does not mean that those dimensions do not exist. If we adopt Monod's standards we should reject his philosophical statements as meaningless because they do not follow the requirements of empirical science. His work refers to the philosophy of modern science; if we reject teleology because it cannot be studied using the method of empirical science, philosophy in its entirety, including Monod's work, should also be rejected.

As a matter of fact, the evidence for teleology in the biological realm is so clear that Monod merely renames it and speaks about "teleonomy," a word that seems to be free of possible theological implications. However, teleonomy is simply a kind of teleology or finality. The existence of teleology in a wide spectrum of biological phenomena should be considered as a plain fact, and Monod himself acknowledges this.

Dawkins has articulated a strong antitheist argument whose principal merit is the brilliance of the metaphors he uses. The main metaphor is the title of his book—*The Blind Watchmaker*—whose aim is very well expressed in the subtitle: "Why the evidence of evolution reveals a universe without design." His argument, although presented in a brilliant language full of clever scientific explanations, is poor from the philosophical point of view. Indeed, Dawkins tells us that he is only interested in a certain kind of explanation; namely, to find out what the components of the object that we try to explain are and how they work. In answer to charges of reductionism, he names his approach "hierarchical reductionism," adding that he admits the existence of different levels of organization and that the only reductionism worth being against would be that which tries to explain complicated things directly in terms of their smallest parts, even as the sum of the parts.[50] But this is only a deceptive argument that, dismissing one extreme form of reductionism, seems automatically to justify a more sophisticated one. If we only ask what things are made of and how they behave we will never have to face philosophical or religious questions, but this will be only due to a deliberate simplification of our quest.

The "blind watchmaker" refers to natural selection, which, acting as a purely natural blind force, enables us to account for all the subtleties we find in the biological realm. Of course, Dawkins knows that the biological level is built on the base of the physical level and that, therefore, we could continue our quest by asking for an explanation of the existence and laws of that more basic physical level. But he tells us that, as a biologist, he is not competent in this matter and adds that, in any case, the physical chemist Peter Atkins has provided a possible explanation of the self-creation of the universe according to physical laws, so that a divine creation would not be needed to explain the

---

50. Dawkins, *The Blind Watchmaker,* cit., pp. 11–13.

existence and basic features of the physical world. Indeed, Atkins' book on the creation is overtly provocative and paradoxical, as is the conclusion that Dawkins draws from his brief incursion in physics:

> The fundamental original units that we need to postulate, in order to understand the coming into existence of everything, either consist of literally nothing (according to some physicists), or (according to other physicists) they are units of the utmost simplicity, far too simple to need anything so grand as deliberate creation.[51]

I would only comment that this conclusion has nothing to do with physics. Indeed, physics will never tell us that the fundamental physical components of the world consist of literally nothing, or that they are too simple to need a deliberate creation. Of course, some physicists (like Atkins himself) may say and even publish things like these; nevertheless, in this case they cannot speak in the name of physics, but only as ordinary people who use arguments that lie outside physics.

Dawkins himself cannot be accused of lack of sincerity, as he warns us in the preface of his book:

> Explaining is a difficult art. You can explain something so that your reader understands the words, and you can explain something so that the reader feels it in the marrow of his bones. To do the latter, it sometimes isn't enough to lay the evidence before the reader in a dis-passionate way. You have to become an advocate and use the tricks of the advocate's trade. This book is not a dispassionate scientific treatise. . . . Far from being dispassionate, it has to be confessed that in parts this book is written with a passion which, in a professional scientific journal, might excite comment.[52]

I have nothing against passionate arguments. Only, the readers should not for-get it, and Dawkins leaves to his readers the onus of completing the argu-ments if they want to reach a balanced view. This task is not easy, since Dawkins, even though not too strong at philosophy, is a professional biologist and an expert in communication.

I would like to add one more thing about evolution and teleology. Books require people who can write and read them—people who can use a mean-ingful language that possesses a means of written expression and syntactical rules. If we take the classic example of the monkey writer usually used against evolution and used by Dawkins in favor of evolution, we can easily ascertain that the main problem if we want to have a written text does not consist of winning against the chances of random typing; after all, this could be over-come, as Dawkins aptly remarks, by introducing a rule favorable to cumula-tive selection (even if this rule has a distinctive teleological flavor). The main

51. Ibid., p. 14.
52. Ibid., p. x.

problem is that, in the case of the monkey, we have no language, no alphabet, no syntax, no understanding of what a human language does mean.

In a similar vein, evolution presupposes the existence of an alphabet, of an entire collection of words, of a syntax, of acceptable rules of formation of sentences. In this case, the alphabet and the words are subatomic particles, atomic nuclei, atoms, molecules, macromolecules, and other composites, and the syntax and the rules of formation are the laws of physics, chemistry, and biology at the successive levels of composition. Therefore, the primary problem is that evolution implies a whole set of elements and rules that are as rational as those of human language if they are to produce the highly sophisticated series of organized systems that leads to human beings.

The basic problem is whether rationality must exist in advance if rational outcomes are going to be produced, or whether rationality can be the outcome of automatic blind forces. This problem is not just a scientific one. However, as far as scientific progress helps us to know the rationality of nature and its teleological dimensions, it may also help us to decide for the absolute primacy of rationality.

3.3. SELF–ORGANIZATION AND TELEOLOGY

The self-organization worldview helps address the traditional objections to teleology, which can be classified under four headings: uselessness, impossibility, unknowability, and illegitimacy.

Uselessness refers to the utility of teleology in science. Although teleology is not explicitly included in scientific reasoning (even though teleological reasoning is sometimes used in science), it is certainly included in its results: indeed, self-organization is seen in the holistic, functional, and directional features of nature. Some of the most relevant advances of contemporary science have occurred in molecular biology, where functionality, organization, directionality, and rationality are the rule. The relevance of teleology for science has remained unseen because early progress in modern science first occurred mainly in mechanics and then in other branches of physics, but the enormous progress of physics and chemistry has made possible the present progress of biology, where teleological dimensions play a central role.

Impossibility refers to the alleged action of the future on the present. One of the most important drawbacks of teleological thinking appears to be that it requires such unintelligible action. Nobody can imagine how a future goal can influence processes that develop in the present. Nevertheless, the concept of information has changed the entire situation. In a strict sense, genetic information includes a program that guides the course of future action. In a wider sense, information can be seen as a set of possibilities that will develop according to the circumstances, as a kind of open program whose end is not completely predetermined because it depends on the integration of different pieces of information. In either case the future is already planned, in a more rigid or more plastic way, and is contained in the encoded information, which can be conceptualized as materialized rationality.

The problems related to *unknowability* are partly solved by the same argument we have used for information. But in addition, as far as unknowability refers to divine plans, the present worldview permits us to understand how divine plans can include both very sophisticated processes and accidental coincidences. Natural teleology can be a road to God because it shows that natural tendencies produce highly rational results, providing the basis for the existence of truly rational beings, but this is also compatible with the existence of contingent elements and partial drawbacks. Of course, arguments based on natural teleology cannot provide a detailed knowledge of God's plans. Although teleology is sometimes seen as unknowable because divine plans are identified with perfectly deterministic and linear processes, this is an arbitrary assumption that derives from an anthropomorphic idea of God.

Illegitimacy refers to the very possibility of the existence of nonintelligent purposes, which would apparently be a categorical error, for purposes can only be attributed to rational beings. Nevertheless, functionality, directionality, cooperativeness, and all teleological dimensions exist wherever a situation of stabilized organization exists. As our world is full of stabilized organization and has been formed through a huge process of self-organization, it is completely legitimate to use teleological categories to study the world and to talk about it.

III. A DIVINE ART

The preceding reflections are most coherent with the existence of a truly divine agency, a personal God who has conceived natural dynamism and uses it to produce, according to natural laws, a world of successive levels of emerging innovation, which ultimately makes possible the existence of truly rational beings.

1. THE WAYS OF DIVINE ACTION

Analogy is very useful when we try to speak about God. On the one hand, God's action on nature should be seen as completely different from natural causality. God cannot simply be a first cause as the mere beginning of a series of causes. God's causality, as the source of all being and becoming and activity, cannot be represented by using the categories that we apply to created causes. We should admit an essential difference between God and creatures, for otherwise we would not really be speaking about God. On the other hand, divine and natural causality must have something in common, insofar as in both cases we are dealing with causes that produce effects. In this context, analogy means that we apply the concept of cause both to God and to creatures, partly in the same way and partly in a different way.

To be more specific, in our context (which is limited here to natural theology, and so does not explore divine revelation, supernatural grace, and related items) divine action refers to the ultimate foundation of the being and activity of created causes. This has been traditionally conceptualized by speaking of the "First Cause" and the "secondary causes," using the capital letters and the singular to express the essential difference between the two types of causality. Ian Barbour refers to this issue this way:

> Some theologians have developed the thesis of Thomas Aquinas that God as primary cause works through the matrix of secondary causes in the natural world. God endows each creature with intrinsic properties and empowers it to express them. This differs from deism by asserting that the world does not stand on its own but needs God's continual concurrence to maintain and uphold it. It also differs from deism in acknowledging the emergence of radically new forms of life and mind in evolutionary history. There are no gaps in the scientific account on its own level; God's action is on a totally different plane from all secondary causes.[53]

This clarification does not by itself solve all mysteries about divine action; however, it prevents some frequent misunderstandings and helps us understand better the relationship between God and nature. When applied to the present worldview, it means that the deployment of natural dynamism following specific temporal patterns (rhythms) and creating new spatial patterns (configurations) can be considered both a natural process and an effect of divine action. No dichotomy exists between the two: they refer to different but complementary levels.

This perspective is consistent with a divine agency that not only respects the created causes, but also fosters them. Even though an omnipotent God can produce any effect directly, leaving aside the created causes, we can easily understand that God would enhance the created causes because it is God himself who has given them their being and their powers. Therefore, scientific progress does not contradict God's plan; on the contrary, the more we know how created causes behave, the more we should admire the greatness of a God who communicates to creatures the capacity to collaborate with him to achieve goals that represent both the fulfillment of God's plans and the perfection of the created agents.

According to John Haught, the present worldview underscores God's respect toward the agency of created causes:

> The universe of complexity and chaos suggests an understanding of God's power as gentle and persuasive rather than coercive. A world which, as a whole, is so sensitive to the initial conditions from which it has evolved is one that seems to be guided more by tenderness than by brute force. . . . the universe does exhibit, from its very beginning, the character of being influenced by some gentle, non-coercive quali-

---

53. Ian G. Barbour, "Experiencing and Interpreting Nature in Science and Religion," *Zygon*, 29 (1994): 475.

ty of self-ordering that allows it to proliferate into an amazingly creative diversity of adaptive systems. . . . There is a great deal of freedom in the unfolding of the story. But we cannot help speculating that there is nevertheless a gentle constraining of the initial conditions, so that the cosmos will at least tilt in the direction of becoming more and more interesting.[54]

We should not represent the effects of divine action too mildly. Respect toward natural agency also means that natural causes will deploy their potency regardless of side effects that eventually may be contrary to the tendencies of other natural beings. Big and small catastrophes enter this kind of plan as natural components. Diversity means that different tendencies often cannot be reconciled. Nevertheless, all this can help us to understand better the role that physical evil can play in God's plan. Disorder may actually play an important role in the overall progress of nature, and thus God may permit different kinds of relative disorder as a way to foster further progress.

Haught also aptly remarks that the developments in the theories of chaos and complexity have enabled us to realize that simple causes may produce highly ordered states of affairs:

Chaos theory, furthermore, shows that exceedingly complex patterning can arise out of the simplest laws of nature and that order is latent even in the most aimlessly meandering and apparently random of processes.[55]

This is perhaps one of the most interesting consequences of the present worldview. We are beginning to know how highly sophisticated results can be obtained using simple elements and rules.

John Polkinghorne has explored the theological implications of the scientific theories of deterministic chaos in several of his writings. These are some of his conclusions:

The concept of divine action through information input into a world made open to such agency through the dynamic flexibilities of chaotic systems is one which is already being explored. The following consequences flow from such a picture:

(1) God's action will always be hidden. It will be contained within the cloudy unpredictabilities of what is going on. It may be discernible by faith, but it will not be exhibitable by experiment. . . .

(2) Although much of the physical world is cloudy and unpredictable, there are also clockwork and predictable parts of what is going on. This regularity will be to the believer signs of divine faithfulness. . . .

54. Haught, *Science & Religion,* cit., p. 156.

55. Ibid., p. 157.

(3) The picture given is of an open future in which both human and divine agency play parts in its accomplishment. . . .
(4) Petitionary prayer can be exercised with scientific integrity. . . .[56]

The present worldview also stresses the contingency of nature. Natural order should not be seen as a rigid, predetermined collection of events but rather as a story that includes real novelty. This perspective, as Haught also stresses, opens new routes for the relations between science and theology, as science is seen no longer as a timeless body of knowledge but includes historical dimensions that can be related to divine action in human history.

A contingent world that includes unforeseen events (which, in any case, do not escape divine knowledge and power), after all, matches the Christian teaching much better than a deterministic necessitarian view. Christian doctrine has always taught that God is completely free with respect to all creatures, so that the universe might not have existed at all or God may have created different worlds. The Archbishop of Paris, Stephen Tempier, condemned contrary opinions held by Latin Averroists on May 7, 1277. This date, Pierre Duhem wrote, could be considered the foundation day of modern empirical science; it seriously fostered in university communities such as Paris and Oxford a way of thinking in which empirical research about the contingent world and new ideas about other worlds made sense. Three of the 219 condemned propositions run this way: "Nothing happens by chance, but everything happens by necessity . . . nothing happens in a contingent way" (21); "the first cause cannot make more than one world" (34); "God cannot move something in an irregular way, namely in a way different from the present one" (50).[57] Edward Grant has written:

> Until 1277, the possibility of other worlds had not been seriously entertained by Christian authors. . . . On the issue of one world, Aristotle and his Christian followers were in harmony. But if He wished, could God create other worlds? Prior to 1277, such a hypothetical question would not have been discussed seriously. After 1277, the intellectual context was dramatically altered and the question about other worlds, as well as a host of other unusual and striking questions, was not only raised but its consideration became commonplace. . . . Seventy-five to one hundred years later authors of such stature as John Buridan, Nicole Oresme, and Albert of Saxony discussed the possibility of a plurality of worlds with the condemna-

56. John Polkinghorne, "Chaos Theory and Divine Action," in *Religion & Science. History, Method, Dialogue,* ed. W. Mark Richardson and Wesley J. Wildman (New York and London: Routledge, 1996), pp. 248–250.

57. Henricus Denifle, *Chartularium Universitatis Parisiensis,* Paris, 1891, Tomus I (Bruxelles: Culture et Civilisation, 1964), pp. 543–558.

tion of 1277 clearly in mind. Going beyond the mere presentation of new cosmological ideas, they even sought to resolve hypothetical physical problems which posed a serious challenge to Aristotelian physics.[58]

The present worldview underscores the relevance of contingency, because every particular outcome in nature is seen as a result of many coincidences. Novelty and diversity are not an exception, but rather a rule. Unpredictability has entered even into the most classical scientific issues. Of course, when we speak of unpredictability we do not refer to God, whose knowledge lies outside our categories of space and time and whose omnipotence encompasses everything as its primary cause.

Speaking about contingency, it is interesting to refer to the emphasis Thomas Torrance places on "contingent order" as one of the Christian ideas that fostered the development of empirical science,[59] and to the emphasis Wolfgang Pannenberg places on the role played by contingency as a bridge between nature and divine action in history. Pannenberg remarks that what we call laws of nature do not reflect exact regularities, because the natural occurrences are never repeated in exactly the same way.[60] The introduction to a book of Pannenberg's essays states:

> The continuity of this creation can be characterized as the continuity of a history of God being engaged in with his creation. This historical continuity adds to the continuity that is expressed in the regularities of natural processes: while the description of those regularities in the form of "natural laws" abstracts from the contingent conditions of their occurrence, historical continuity comprises the contingency of events together with the emergence of regularities. Thus the category of history provides a more comprehensive description of the continuous process of nature.[61]

Natural order is contingent, for it is the result of singular circumstances. However, nature is full of organization, directionality, synergy (cooperativeness), and sophisticated activities. All this is most coherent with the "continuous" activity of divine wisdom.

This discussion of contingency leads us to a question that deserves specific attention: how to combine the existence of a divine plan with the huge process of evolution that includes a great amount of chance.

58. Edward Grant, *Physical Science in the Middle Ages* (Cambridge: Cambridge University Press, 1977), p. 74.

59. Thomas F. Torrance, *Divine and Contingent Order* (Oxford: Oxford University Press, 1981).

60. See Wolfhart Pannenberg, *Towards a Theology of Nature: Essays on Science and Faith* (Louisville, Ky.: Westminster John Knox Press, 1993), especially the essay "Contingency and Natural Law," pp. 72–122.

61. Ted Peters, "Editor's Introduction: Pannenberg on Theology and Natural Science," in Wolfhart Pannenberg, *Towards a Theology of Nature*, cit., p. 22.

2. CONTINGENCY AND A DIVINE PLAN

The problem is usually posed in the following straightforward way: is there a direction in evolution? If the scientific answer is negative, the immediate following questions is: how can we combine this lack of directionality with the existence of a divine plan that governs the natural world?

Biologists tend to stress that evolution cannot have a predetermined direction, because it necessarily includes many random events as the raw material for selection. It is undeniable, however, that there has been progress toward more sophisticated kinds of organization; evolution exhibits a development of increasing complexity.

There should be no problem in combining evolution and the existence of a divine plan, as God completely transcends our categories and is not limited to acting in any particular way. Difficulties on this topic are usually due to the mistaken idea that a divine plan should produce a chain of events of such a kind that we could recognize the necessary links between them. The existence of a divine plan is presented as linked to the determinism formerly admitted in classical physics, as if a divine plan meant a deterministic account of nature, which obviously would collide with contingency. Ernst Mayr, in an essay on the concept of finality, states:

> A finalistic world view is largely if not entirely deterministic. . . .
> That something in the world could be due to chance was unacceptable for a theist, and chance was therefore largely ignored in the writings of the theistic thinkers. What arguments there were about the interpretation of creation concerned almost entirely the "necessity" component.[62]

Nevertheless, the existence of a kind of natural contingency compatible with a divine plan is anything but new in theology. In his commentary on Aristotle's *Metaphysics,* Thomas Aquinas argued against those who say that everything in nature happens according to necessity. He said that it is not possible for all future events to have a proper cause and added that nevertheless this is compatible with the existence of a divine providence governing the natural world. The reason is that God is the primary cause from which everything depends in its being, but this does not impose the same kind of necessity on all created effects: God makes some effects happen in a necessary way, whereas others may happen in a contingent way. The same effect can be considered contingent compared to its immediate causes and included at the same time within a divine plan that cannot fail.[63] Aquinas remarks that everything is subject to God's plan but adds that this does not mean that all happens with the same degree of necessity; he clearly asserts that God wants some things to be made in a necessary way and other things to be made in a contingent way:

---

62. Mayr, *Towards A New Philosophy of Biology,* cit., p. 233.

63. Thomas Aquinas, *In duodecim libros Metaphysicorum Aristotelis Expositio* (Torino-Roma: Marietti, 1964), book 6, chapter 3: lecture 3, nos. 1191–1222.

therefore, he concludes, God prepares necessary causes for some things and contingent causes for others, so that the universe may be more complete.[64]

Obviously, Aquinas was not thinking about evolution when he examined this problem, but his idea is important for our present purpose. In fact, God's action is the action of the First Cause, which extends its influence, as the foundation of being itself, to all creatures under every aspect. Therefore, for God the contingency of any particular event makes no difference; rather, it is He who makes possible the occurrence of contingent events. We tend to conceive of God's plans and activity by comparison with ours, but this analogy has its limits. Everything depends on God's activity, but this does not mean that everything possesses the same kind of necessity.

That God rules the world does not mean that nature behaves in a completely ordered way according to our own criteria. Therefore, it cannot be argued that the existence of random evolutionary events and the patchwork character of evolutionary adaptations are incompatible with the existence of a divine plan. On the contrary, the existence of many contingent events fits well with a God who respects the mode of being and acting of his creatures because He himself has planned and wanted them.

The new discoveries about chaos and complexity may help us to understand that a highly sophisticated organization can result from very simple causes that include randomness. Referring to the physicist Joseph Ford and to Edward Lorenz, one of the founders of the new physics of chaos, James Gleick has written:

"Evolution is chaos with feedback," Joseph Ford said. The universe is randomness and dissipation. But randomness with direction can produce surprising complexity. And as Lorenz discovered so long ago, dissipation is an agent of order. "God plays dice with the universe," is Ford's answer to Einstein's famous question. "But they're loaded dice. And the main objectives of physics now is to find out by what rules were they loaded and how can we use them for our own ends."[65]

Indeed, even from our limited point of view, we can understand that the chance contained in evolution operates within a strict set of conditions that impose a kind of directionality. Christian de Duve comments that

chance did not operate in a vacuum. It operated in a universe governed by orderly laws and made of matter endowed with specific properties. These laws and properties are the constraints that shape the evolutionary roulette and restrict the number that it can turn up.[66]

64. Thomas Aquinas, *Summa Theologiae* (Torino-Roma: Marietti, 1952), part 1, question 19, article 8.

65. James Gleick, *Chaos: Making a New Science* (New York: Viking, 1987), p. 314.

66. Christian de Duve, *A Guided Tour of the Living Cell* (New York: Scientific American Books, 1984), p. 357.

In a similar vein, Carsten Bresch analyses the different steps of evolution as a process of pattern growth in restricted freedom and concludes:

> Has evolution, growing out of innumerable random events (conditional chance, with restriction by that which already exists) a steady direction? The answer is an unambiguous "yes."[67]

Bresch remarks that human beings are not a necessary outcome of evolution. The processes that have led to our existence are full of coincidences that, even if they were included as part of God's plan, are contingent. In this sense, Stephen Jay Gould is right when he stresses that the evolutionary path that has led to the existence of human beings includes many accidental events.[68] Nevertheless, this does not mean that evolution is incompatible with the existence of a divine plan.

De Duve adds some interesting remarks regarding this point. A Nobel Prize winner himself, de Duve proposes an intermediate way between two other Nobel Prize winners: the determinist Einstein and the hazardist Monod. De Duve explains the neo-Darwinian account of evolution, says that change operates within a range of limiting conditions, and adds:

> Faced with the enormous sum of lucky draws behind the success of the evolutionary game, one may legitimately wonder to what extent this success is actually written into the fabric of the universe. To Einstein, who once said: "God does not play dice," one could then answer: "Yes, he does, because He is sure to win." In other words, there may be a design. But it started with the "big bang."
>
> Such a view is shared by some, not by others. The French scientist Jacques Monod, one of the founders of molecular biology and the author of the celebrated book *Chance and Necessity,* published in 1970, argued eloquently in favor of the opposite view. "Our number," he wrote, "came out in the game at Monte Carlo." And further: "The Universe was not pregnant with life, nor the biosphere with man." His final conclusion reflects the stoically (and romantically) despairing existentialism that greatly affected his generation of intellectuals in France: "Man now knows that he is alone in the indifferent vastness of the Universe from which he has emerged by chance."
>
> This is nonsense, of course. Man knows nothing of the sort. Nor does he have any proof to the contrary, either. What he does know, however—or, at least, should know—is that, with the time and amount of matter available, anything resembling the simplest living cell, let alone a human being, could not possibly have arisen by blind chance were the universe not pregnant with them.[69]

67. Carsten Bresch, "What Is Evolution?" in *Evolution and Creation,* ed. Svend Andersen and Arthur Peacocke (Aarhus: Aarhus University Press, 1987), p. 56.

68. Stephen Jay Gould, "The Evolution of Life on the Earth," *Scientific American* 271, No. 4 (October 1994): 64, 65, 69.

69. De Duve, *A Guided Tour of the Living Cell,* cit., pp. 357–358.

De Duve concludes, from the point of view of the scientist who also thinks as a natural philosopher, that evolutionary thinking is compatible with the existence of a divine plan and suggests that there are pointers that lead us to admit the existence of such a plan.

The present worldview offers a new understanding of the ways followed by evolution, because it completes the classical account of evolution with the perspective of self-organization. This new perspective is still in its beginnings, but it has already opened new vistas that possibly will be enlarged by further scientific progress. The combination of chance and necessity, of variation and selection, jointly with the potentialities for self-organization, can be easily seen as the way used by God to bring about the process of evolution. Loaded dice, a universe pregnant with life and human beings, specific potentialities—these are concepts and metaphors that show the possibility of combining God's gentle agency with the action of the natural causes planned by God himself. Bresch provides another useful metaphor: he imagines a pilot in his plane at the North Pole who decides his route in a random way using a roulette wheel; no matter what direction he follows, one day he will arrive exactly at the South Pole (provided he does not turn back).[70] This comparison shows again that limiting conditions can explain the directionality of evolution (Figure 4.3).

We can conclude, on the one hand, that evolution can be combined with a divine plan even if the process of evolution includes progress and drawbacks, because there is no reason why a divine plan should necessarily be characterized as linear and always progressive. On the other hand, we can add that the existence of chance events in the evolutionary chain is compatible with the existence of directionality in evolution.

3. NATURAL AND DIVINE CREATIVITY

That natural order is a presupposition of empirical science, and that the present worldview underscores the creativity of nature in a new way, has been expressed by Langdon Gilkey with these words:

> Modern scientific knowledge about the process is based itself—as its own precondition—on the presupposition of order . . . What has become the "wonder" of modern cosmology is that in natural process order combines with change and with novelty and yet remains order. . . . The modern scientific vision of a changing evolutionary process exhibiting continually new forms, and yet illustrating precisely in these changes a universal order—this vision is *new*.[71]

The existence of a dynamic order is an essential feature of the present worldview. We tend to think about order as a static arrangement, in which

70. Quoted by Rainer Isak, *Evolution ohne Ziel? Ein interdisziplinären Forschungsbeitrag* (Freiburg: Herder, 1992), p. 380.

71. Langdom Gilkey, "Nature as the Image of God: Reflections on the Signs of the Sacred," *Zygon,* 29 (1994): 497.

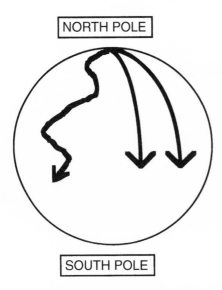

Fig. 4.3 Teleology and predictability. A future outcome can be predicted even though there are in principle many different paths that can be chosen, every one of which would apparently lead to different results, provided the paths are located within a stable organization. Thus an airplane moving off the North Pole will always reach the South Pole exactly, whatever particular route it may take, provided it always moves South.

different parts occupy a well-determined place in the whole. What is really new is the knowledge that these formations are the outcome of spontaneous natural processes and that the present state of our world is the result of an entire series of such processes. The present worldview includes a general perspective and some detailed explanations of a few particular processes. Future advances will surely provide more details.

Patterning, the production of new spatiotemporal patterns, is therefore one of the main features of the cosmic process of self-organization. Patterning is the result of interactions, new combinations, new arrangements; in this sense, it should not be considered mysterious. However, we face an enormous series of successive processes of patterning in which increasingly organized systems are produced that finally make possible our existence as human beings. Therefore, it is not the lack of knowledge about the processes and their mechanisms, but rather the new kind of knowledge that leads us to think about finality and divine agency. The more the sciences progress, the more they provide us with knowledge of the process of self-organization that clearly suggests the existence of a divine source of power and perfection.

This perspective is most coherent with the Christian doctrine of a universe that has been created unfinished and has been given to human beings so that they may collaborate with God in carrying this world to its ultimate end, finding their own fulfillment in the effort spent to humanize and divinize the world. The natural sciences now place before us an open future. This not only means that we, by exercising our freedom, are responsible for the future of humankind, but also that nature itself enters this project as an essential element. The evolution of nature has played a central role in the production of the present state of affairs. Now, natural evolution has been replaced by an evolution based on science and in the use of the powers of nature by man.

These two kinds of evolution are not self-contained; they point toward the divine source of power, order, creativity, and meaning.

In his introduction to the book *Evidence of Purpose,* John Marks Templeton has written:

> There is here no knockdown argument for design and purpose, but certainly there are strong hints of ultimate realities beyond the cosmos. . . . One of the strongest hints, in our opinion, relates to the new understanding of the creativity of the cosmos, its capacity for so-called self-organization . . . current science leads us to look for a new paradigm, a universe fraught with creativity in the direction of cooperative and organizational processes . . . there appears to be a continuity of organization into novel and increasingly complex structures and relationships throughout the spectrum of transitions from stardust to thinking man. . . . From a theological perspective it is indeed tempting to see this remarkable self-organizing tendency as an expression of the intimate nature of the Creator's activity and identification with our universe.[72]

Indeed, unless one endorses some kind of pantheism, which would be full of conceptual difficulties, the present worldview clearly provides new strength for the arguments that point to a Creator who is different from the world and transcends it. But, at the same time, a Creator who as the source of all being and power is most intimate to the created world, so that we could say that He governs the world not only "from without," but also "from within."

Regarding the cogency of teleological arguments to prove the existence of God I would add that, of course, no argument is so compelling that it may be used as an automatically effective tool for conversion. Nevertheless, I think the present worldview enlarges the basis of arguments such as that proposed by Thomas Aquinas in his famous fifth way.

In fact, the fifth way does not suppose that a linear divine plan that can be known and predicted by us in all detail exists. Rather, it intends to show that the purposeful activity of natural beings requires a cause which, since it must have imbued the natural beings with their own tendencies, must be the author of nature: this must be God. This argument is based on the existence of goal-directed activity in nonrational beings that leads to optimal results, and therefore on the existence of goals achieved as the result of natural tendencies. Moreover, it includes a reference to values that is usually bypassed and that, in my opinion, constitutes the core of the argument. Indeed, Aquinas refers to the activity of natural beings that, as a consequence of their natural tendencies (not by accident), reach an end that is described as "what is best." The Latin original sentence, *id quod est optimum,* clearly shows that Aquinas uses the superlative of "good." Putting all this together, this argument asserts that through the activity of natural beings many goals that are "very good"

72. John Marks Templeton, "Introduction," in *Evidence of Purpose: Scientists Discover the Creator,* ed. John Marks Templeton (New York: Continuum, 1994), pp. 11–12.

are reached. If we see the natural world as the basis that makes possible the existence of human beings and the development of their activity, we can conclude that the present worldview amplifies that argument.

Another text of Aquinas is most relevant in the context of the present worldview. It belongs to Aquinas' commentary on Aristotle's *Physics,* book 2, chapter 8, whose topic is the existence of finality in nature. After an examination of the Aristotelian arguments in favor of teleology, Aquinas offers a solemn definition of nature:

> Nature is nothing but the plan of some art, namely a divine one, put into things themselves, by which those things move towards a concrete end: as if the man who builds up a ship could give to the pieces of wood that they could move by themselves to produce the form of the ship.[73]

I find this text breathtaking, as it represents a thirteenth-century approximation of the present worldview. In this text nature is seen as God's handiwork, which progresses toward its full-shaped form driven by an interior principle, a natural tendency that is the result of God's action. The example used by Aquinas required a lot of imagination, but corresponds literally to the kind of self-organization that today we study scientifically.

Aquinas' anticipation was possible because self-organization is already visible in ordinary experience, through some essential features of living beings and also through the cooperation of the different parts of nature that makes possible our existence. Very little was known in ancient times about the details, and the ancient organicistic worldview also included other elements that were superseded by the new science of the seventeenth century. The modern mechanistic worldview threw the baby out with the bathwater and the analytic perspective prevailed until the second half of the twentieth century, when the enormous body of information accumulated about the details of natural phenomena made possible the emergence of a new worldview in which the self-organizing features are presented as a consequence of scientific progress.

The new worldview alone does not lead to metaphysical or theological consequences. However, reflection upon it paves the way for a kind of "comprehensive naturalism" in which the role of natural agency is fully recognized and, at the same time, is seen as supported by a founding divine action that does not oppose nature but rather provides it with its ultimate foundation. This perspective stresses that God usually acts to respect and protect the natural capacities of His creatures, as He has provided them with great and marvelous potentialities so that they may cooperate with God's plans in a great variety of ways. These potentialities are never exhausted, so that new results can always be produced or expected. Now this is possible through the use of the knowledge provided by scientific progress.

---

73. Thomas Aquinas, *In octo libros Physicorum Aristotelis Expositio* (Torino-Roma: Marietti, 1965), book 2, chapter 8: lectio 14, no. 268.

Scientific Creativity
and Human Singularity

Scientific creativity is proof of our singularity. It shows that we possess dimensions that transcend the natural ambit and can be labeled as spiritual. A purely materialist view leads to an image of the human being that cannot explain the unity of our experience and our scientific achievements.

5

Reading the Book
of Nature

If science is to exist, natural order is not enough. Another necessary condition is required: the existence of specific human skills enabling us to know that order. In natural science we seek for a knowledge of nature that goes far beyond the limits of our ordinary experience; we must therefore develop methods that also transcend those used for everyday knowledge.

How do we use our cognitive abilities in empirical science? Scientific progress is most relevant in this context: the more the sciences progress, the more we can know about our capabilities, because any creative progress in empirical science means that we develop skills that previously existed as potentialities. Therefore, the analysis of scientific progress can contribute to the formation of an adequate picture of the human being. Also on this level there is a feedback from scientific progress on the epistemological presuppositions of science, which are concerned with our ability to propose theoretical explanations and to submit them to empirical tests.

If we consider the overall progress of the different scientific disciplines since the birth of empirical science in the seventeenth century, we can conclude that since then we have developed astonishing abilities that have evolved in highly sophisticated ways. This sophistication is so rich that it is difficult to provide a unitary explanation of the achievements of empirical science. No wonder, then, that there is no unanimity among philosophers of science, as each one of them usually stresses different specific features of the scientific enterprise. I will analyze below some of the proposals of the most influential contemporary authors in the philosophy of science and shall then develop my own account.

I. THE RATIONALITY OF SCIENCE

The feedback from scientific progress on the epistemological presuppositions of science can be considered under the heading of "rationality," because these presuppositions are mainly concerned with our argumentative capacity. We can reach explanations that remain far away from our ordinary experience because we can use arguments to prove and disprove our theories. Moreover, the topic of scientific rationality occupies a central place in contemporary epistemology.

The different accounts of scientific rationality try to explain how science works, or better yet, how scientists do science. That is why these accounts may provide new information about our own capacity for knowledge. My analysis intends to extract from the main epistemological perspectives of the twentieth century what helps to represent our own cognitive abilities; we can always learn something, even from mistakes.

1. The Scientific Conception of the World

Empiricism was one of the main theses of the philosophy proposed by the Vienna Circle, whose programmatic manifesto, *The Scientific Conception of the World,* was published on the occasion of a conference of the Ernst Mach Society (Vienna) and the Society for Empirical Philosophy (Berlin), held in Prague on 15–16 September 1929.[1] The publication of this manifesto marked the birth of the Vienna Circle, a group of scientists and philosophers gathered around Moritz Schlick, who in 1922 was appointed to the chair of Philosophy of the Inductive Sciences at the University of Vienna. That name gives an idea of the role induction was supposed to play in the empirical sciences, which for a long time had been named "inductive sciences." Empirical science allegedly proceeded by generalizations from empirical data, according to the ideal proposed by Francis Bacon. Many people followed Bacon, believing that induction was the only way to reach sound knowledge about nature while avoiding useless speculation.

The empiricist account of science, in its inductivist version, was considered by the members of the Vienna Circle to be a central feature of the scientific method. They thought that the new developments in logic made it possible to show that only knowledge obtained following the empiricist rules should be considered legitimate; any other claim to knowledge could be shown to be meaningless by applying the so-called "empiricist criterion of meaning," which would allegedly permit us to classify all statements as "meaningful" or "meaningless." Meaningful statements would refer only to states of affairs that could be empirically verified, and these statements could be true

---

1. Rudolph Carnap, Hans Hahn, and Otto Neurath, *The Scientific Conception of the World: The Vienna Circle,* reproduced in Otto Neurath, *Empiricism and Sociology,* ed. Marie Neurath and Robert Sonné Cohen (Dordrecht: Reidel, 1973), pp. 298–318.

or false. Meaningless statements would be statements badly constructed from the logical point of view; they would not correspond to any empirically discernible state of affairs and, therefore, could neither be true nor false. Empirical verification would consist in a logical reduction to sensory data, which were considered to be "the given" in experience. For instance, Schlick, the leader of the Circle, wrote:

> The justified unassailable nucleus of the "positivistic" tendency seems to me to be in the principle that the meaning of every proposition is completely contained within its verification in the given.[2]

Schlick complained that this principle had frequently been mixed with many untenable propositions; therefore, he wrote: "a logical purification is necessary." In any case, he left little doubt about the meaning of his attempt:

> The act of verification in which the path to the solution finally ends is always of the same sort: it is the occurrence of a definite fact that is confirmed by observation, by means of immediate experience. In this manner the truth (or falsity) of every statement, of daily life or science, is determined. There is thus no other testing and corroboration of truths except through observation and empirical science. Every science (in so far as we take this word to refer to the content and not to the human arrangements for arriving at it) is a system of cognitions, that is, of true experimental statements.[3]

In the Vienna Circle's manifesto, Ernst Mach, the physicist, philosopher, and historian of science, was praised because of "his investigations of the construction of scientific concepts from ultimate elements, namely sense data." We can also read there that the statements of science, the only meaningful ones, can be reduced "to the simplest statements about the empirically given." The authors presented themselves as empiricists and positivists, asserting that "there is knowledge only from experience, which rests on what is immediately given," and that "the meaning of every statement of science must be statable by reduction to a statement about the given."[4]

Arguing that the new logic was the instrument that would make it possible to achieve the proposed intellectual revolution, Rudolf Carnap wrote:

> The analysis of the concepts of science has shown that all these concepts, no matter whether they belong, according to the usual classification, to the natural sciences, or to psychology or the social sciences, go back to a common basis. They can be reduced to root concepts which apply to the "given," to the content of immediate experience.[5]

2. Moritz Schlick, "Positivism and Realism," in *Logical Positivism*, ed. Alfred J. Ayer (Glencoe, Ill.: The Free Press, 1960), p. 106.

3. Moritz Schlick, "The Turning Point in Philosophy," in *Logical Positivism*, cit. p. 56.

4. Carnap, Hahn, and Neurath, *The Scientific Conception of the World*, cit., pp. 302, 306–307, 309.

5. Rudolph Carnap, "The Old and the New Logic," in *Logical Positivism*, cit., pp. 143–144.

Nevertheless, the attempt at reducing scientific statements and theories to sense data repeatedly led down blind alleys. Indeed, because the concepts, statements, and theories of science cannot be reduced in a purely logical way to sensory experiences, the empiricist account of science acts as a straitjacket that cannot explain the achievements of science, and, if taken seriously, would suffocate further progress. The primitive position of the Vienna Circle was completely mistaken, and it soon met severe criticism. As a result, the neopositivists felt obliged to change their views. For instance, Carnap formulated a new version of them in his 1937 article "Testability and Meaning." The successive attempts at reconstructing the sciences according to empiricist requirements always led to new difficulties. Years later, Carl Hempel described those difficulties and finally recognized that:

> A closer study of this point suggests strongly that, much like the analytic–synthetic distinction, the idea of cognitive significance, with its suggestion of a sharp distinction between significant and non-significant sentences or systems as such, has lost its promise and fertility as an explicandum.[6]

In the meantime, some of the most prominent neopositivists emigrated to the United States of America and exercised a strong influence on the development of philosophy of science in their new positions. One of them, Herbert Feigl, said that the spirit of logical empiricism was flexible and capable of evolving, adding that it consisted basically of the "scientific worldview" or "scientific outlook," which continued in the twentieth century the spirit of the Enlightenment. According to Feigl, this scientific outlook constituted a wide movement that could include different pragmatist and naturalist approaches that, in any case, would coincide in their rejection of metaphysics and theology as prescientific.[7]

The essay by Feigl just quoted was published in 1953 in the anthology *Readings in the Philosophy of Science*. The false problems created by the neopositivists have not completely disappeared from the epistemological scene. Actually, in a much larger anthology published some 40 years later, we read:

> Our model for this anthology was Feigl and Brodbeck's *Readings in the Philosophy of Science*. . . . During the 1950s and early 1960s, when sophisticated developments in logical positivist philosophy of science dominated the field, Feigl and Brodbeck's anthology represented an almost ideal collection of readings for any serious introductory philosophy of science course. . . . As we know from our experience with it as students and teachers, Feigl and Brodbeck was a marvelous textbook.[8]

6. Carl G. Hempel, "The Empiricist Criterion of Meaning," in *Logical Positivism,* cit., p. 129.

7. Herbert Feigl, "The Scientific Outlook: Naturalism and Humanism," in *Readings in the Philosophy of Science,* ed. Herbert Feigl and May Brodbeck (New York: Appleton-Century-Crofts, 1953), pp. 4, 9–10.

8. Richard Boyd, Philip Gasper, and J. D. Trout, eds., *The Philosophy of Science* (Cambridge, Mass.: The MIT Press, 1991), p. xi.

The old anthology was the product of a brief period of positivist consensus in the philosophy of science, according to the editors of the new anthology, and they feel that now a new consensus has emerged. One may wonder, however, how an anthology that included many essays written by positivist-minded philosophers can be considered "almost ideal" and "marvelous." The answer may be that there is a kind of continuity between the two anthologies regarding some basic issues: as the neopositivists clearly emphasized their antimetaphysical and antitheological intention, so in the new work we find several references to the success of the materialist perspective. We are told that one of the main points of agreement in the new consensus in the philosophy of science is that "materialist conceptions of both biological and psychological matters are well confirmed"; the editors also refer to "the current conception of the possibility of nonreductionist materialism" and to "recent antireductionist treatments of materialism," as if nonreductionism could suffice to endow materialist ideas in the philosophy of mind with respectability.[9]

The neopositivists presented their antimetaphysical and antitheological attitude as the new "scientific conception of the world." This was one of the main ideas of the programmatic manifesto of the Vienna Circle. In fact, the manifesto explicitly alludes to the antimetaphysical and antitheological character of the scientific outlook, which is opposed to metaphysics and theology as "the opposite spirit of enlightenment and antimetaphysical factual research" and the "spirit of a scientific conception of the world."[10] The manifesto describes the birth of the Circle around Schlick as the gathering of members who, even though they held different opinions, coincided in the direction of "a scientific conception of the world," so that:

> It became increasingly clearer that a position not only free from metaphysics, but opposed to metaphysics was the common goal of all . . . The Vienna Circle does not confine itself to collective work as a closed group. It is also trying to make contact with the living movements of the present, so far as they are well disposed toward the scientific world-conception and turn away from metaphysics and theology.[11]

Antimetaphysical and antitheological views, however, have nothing to do with science, and when presented as if they were a consequence of scientific progress, they represent a pseudoscientific doctrine. The picture of science that must be built up to support that pseudoscientific ideology is based on arbitrary grounds and, as I have said, if it were put into practice, would act upon science as a paralyzing straitjacket, because the methods of empirical science are much richer than their empiricist or positivist substitutes. A friend of some

9. Ibid., p. xiii.

10. Carnap, Hahn, and Neurath, *The Scientific Conception of the World,* cit., p. 301.

11. Ibid., pp. 304–305.

members of the Vienna Circle and an agnostic himself, Karl Popper noted in his 1934 book *The Logic of Scientific Discovery,* that

> positivists, in their anxiety to annihilate metaphysics, annihilate natural science along with it.[12]

In fact, the difficulties of the empiricist and positivist perspectives do not lie only in some particular details. The whole approach is mistaken. We cannot build a single concept of empirical science following the requirements of empiricism. Observation and logic play a central role in empirical science, but the scientific enterprise includes in every one of its steps a strong dose of creativity and interpretation that cannot be reduced to mechanical operations or formal logic alone.

According to the official records, neopositivism has long been dead. Apparently its proponents soon changed their mind, and other approaches very different and even opposed to positivism occupied the central place in epistemology. Nevertheless, we cannot forget it if we want to understand the contemporary scene. On the one hand, the evolution of neopositivism was not a complete retreat from the primitive positions. For instance, Carnap, one of the leaders of the Vienna Circle who emigrated to the United States, wrote in 1961, in the introduction to a new edition of his classic work *The Logical Structure of the World* that he still agreed with the philosophical orientation of that book, especially with the problems posed and the methods employed, and he reminded the reader that the main problem was the possibility of a rational reconstruction of the concepts of any field of knowledge on the basis of concepts that refer to the immediately given.[13]

The new doctrines that originated from the evolution of neopositivism had a tremendous impact that is still being felt today. Therefore, our present problems can only be understood and solved if we keep in mind the main shortcomings of the positivist position. These shortcomings concern the relationship between theoretical constructs and empirical evidence, a relationship that is much more complex than previously thought and can be adequately represented only if we capture the role of creativity and interpretation in empirical science. At the same time, the failure of neopositivism clearly shows that metaphysics and theology cannot be demolished in the name of an empiricist philosophy whose main theses do not survive when critically examined in light of their own standards.

2. The Critical Attitude of Karl Popper

Karl Popper has been one of the most influential philosophers of science in the twentieth century. His philosophy centers around rationality and has

---

12. Karl R. Popper, *The Logic of Scientific Discovery* (Boston: Unwin Hyman, 1990), p. 36.

13. Rudolph Carnap, *The Logical Structure of the World and Pseudoproblems in Philosophy* (London: Routledge, 1967), p. V.

been labeled "critical rationalism." According to Popper, a close relationship exists among the "critical attitude," the "scientific attitude," and the "rational attitude."

Although he never participated in the meetings of the Vienna Circle and cannot be considered a member, Popper was a friend of some members, published his first book in a collection directed by them, and shared with them a common interest in the logical analysis of science. There were strong similarities between the idea of verification proposed as a criterion of meaning by the positivists and the idea of falsification proposed as a criterion of demarcation by Popper. No wonder, then, that Popper has too often been considered a neopositivist.

Popper's ends and means were, nevertheless, different from those of the Vienna Circle, and in some important respects were completely opposed. Popper made a great effort to clarify this issue, especially in his "Replies to My Critics," published in the two volumes devoted to his philosophy edited by Paul Schilpp.[14] It is important to bear this in mind because otherwise it would be impossible to understand Popper's contribution to the problem of scientific rationality. Nevertheless, Popper is often presented, even now, as a neopositivist, as for example, in the work of Nancey Murphy.[15] Certainly, she distinguishes "logical positivists" from "neopositivists," but to list Popper under any "positivist" heading is seriously misleading.

This confusion may arise from several sources. In the United States a positivist-oriented epistemology was preeminent until the 1960s, and it was logically oriented such as Popper's epistemology was (although it is difficult to find Popper's texts in the anthologies widely used as the basic reference works for philosophy of science in those years). In addition, Marxist authors, in their frequent controversies with Popper, would often accuse him of being a positivist, a cliché that was repeated as a kind of *ad hominem* argument. Moreover, Larry Laudan, one of the most influential authors in epistemology, repeatedly links Popper with the positivists in a confusing way, and he eventually speaks of him as a positivist.[16]

Strictly speaking, "positivism" refers either to its founder, the French nineteenth-century philosopher Auguste Comte, or to the members of the Vienna Circle, such as Moritz Schlick, Rudolf Carnap, Otto Neurath, and Herbert Feigl, and those sympathetic to the Circle such as Hans Reichenbach.

Central to Comte's ideas, as a consequence of his antimetaphysical attitude, was the reduction of empirical science to the task of establishing relations between observable facts. This cannot explain even the most elemen-

14. Karl R. Popper, "Replies to My Critics. I. Introduction," in *The Philosophy of Karl Popper,* ed. Paul A. Schilpp (La Salle, Ill.: Open Court, 1974), pp. 961–976.

15. Nancey Murphy, *Theology in the Age of Scientific Reasoning* (Ithaca and London: Cornell University Press, 1990), pp. 55, 82.

16. See Larry Laudan, *Beyond Positivism and Relativism: Theory, Method, and Evidence* (Boulder, Colo.: Westview Press, 1996), pp. 4, 7, 15, 16, 18, 20, 21, 23.

tary parts of modern empirical science, and Popper strongly opposed such a view; he rather sees science as an adventure that progresses because we formulate bold conjectures that go far beyond the realm of our experience. Another characteristic idea of Comte's positivism is the so-called "law of the three stages," which ascribes religion and theology to a mythical stage that has been superseded by metaphysical abstract thinking, which, in its turn, has been superseded by positive science. Certainly Popper was an agnostic, but he never had an antitheological attitude, and even though his metaphysics are not as strong as classical metaphysical doctrines, he attributed a great relevance to metaphysics and was involved in openly metaphysical discussions. Therefore, Popper cannot be called a positivist in Comte's sense.

Neither can Popper be considered a neopositivist in the sense of the members of the Vienna Circle, for central to their position was a strong antimetaphysical and antitheological attitude. Popper proposed falsification as a criterion of demarcation between the empirical sciences and metaphysics, but he did not conceive it as a weapon against metaphysics; rather, falsificationism can easily be interpreted as expressing that empirical science, because it studies spatiotemporal natural patterns, can submit its theories to repeatable empirical tests, whereas metaphysics studies problems that transcend the limits of empirical science. This is why Popper repeatedly says that metaphysical problems cannot be settled by empirical tests but can be discussed in a fully rational way.

The main ideas of Popper's epistemology can be summarized in the title of one of his books, *Conjectures and Refutations.* In Popper's view, science progresses by formulating hypotheses that go far beyond the available data and by submitting them to empirical tests. Because he emphasizes the logical impossibility of attaining conclusive results using the hypothetico-deductive method, Popper stresses that no theory can be definitively verified, but that a single contrary instance suffices to falsify a theory. Hence he concludes that all our knowledge is conjectural, so that the quest for certainty is completely mistaken. He admits the existence of objective truth, which would act as a regulative idea for the entire scientific enterprise, but adds that even if we eventually could reach true knowledge, we could never be sure of its truth:

> Thus the concept of truth plays mainly the role of a regulative idea. It helps us in our search for truth that we know there is something like truth or correspondence. It does not give us a means of finding truth, or being sure that we have found it even if we have found it.[17]

In empirical science, then, if the results of the test contradict the theory, we have learned something and can formulate a better theory because we are able to eliminate previous errors.

Popper strongly stresses the role of creativity in the scientific enterprise. He asserts that scientific theories cannot be logically derived from or reduced to

---

17. Karl R. Popper, *Objective Knowledge: An Evolutionary Approach* (Oxford: Clarendon Press, 1989), p. 318.

empirical data. Theories are the result of the creative activity of scientists, and their empirical control always includes interpretations and decisions. When he proposed falsification as the criterion of demarcation between science and metaphysics, Popper carefully noted that it is we who *decide* to accept some particular statement as a potential falsifier of a theory, and it is we who *decide* to consider a theory as falsified or corroborated. Accordingly, this criterion of demarcation does not imply that statements can be classified as either meaningful or meaningless. He clearly acknowledged the meaningfulness of metaphysical ideas and discussed many of them. His epistemology is linked not to the rejection of metaphysics, but of pseudoscience. The roots of his philosophy are closely related to a humanist outlook that intends to show the drawbacks of pseudoscientific theories that, even as they present themselves as scientific, should rather be considered intellectual traps that have led to massive disasters in the twentieth century. Marxism and Nazism are two of these.

I do not share Popper's radical diffidence toward certainty, which is probably due to a too narrow conception of certainty, as if certainty required completely logical proofs that do not exist, even in mathematics. Speaking of the philosophical doctrine of realism, Popper says:

> Realism like anything else outside logic and finite arithmetic is not demonstrable.[18]

Of course, if we define demonstrability this way, and we recognize as certain only that which can be demonstrably proved, we must conclude that there is no certainty outside logic and finite arithmetic. I think this is Popper's idea. But Popper could agree to a broader idea of certainty. Indeed, in spite of his strong accent on fallibilism, he clearly speaks of the hope that our theories may be true, proclaims himself as a scientific realist, and thinks that scientific progress leads us closer to the truth.

The fallibilist account of science, even though it rightly underscores the provisional character of a great part of our scientific knowledge, should be complemented with a positive recognition of the possibility of attaining truth and certainty.

Popper rightly stresses the elements of creativity and interpretation present in every step of the scientific method, not only in the formulation of new hypotheses, but also in the formulation and acceptance of the empirical statements that serve to test those hypotheses and in the evaluation of the hypotheses under the light of the available evidence. The role that these elements play in Popper's epistemology is strongly highlighted if we consider the ethical roots of Popper's epistemology. Hubert Kiesewetter, a former disciple and a close friend of Popper, has written:

> Since studying at the London School of Economics and Political Science in 1967–68 the question of the ethical roots or moral sources of

---

18. Ibid., p. 38.

Popper's philosophy has never ceased to occupy my mind. . . . In recent years I extensively discussed with Sir Karl the issue of the ethical foundations of his philosophy . . . it is my intention to demonstrate that *all* his (Popper's) thinking is deeply rooted in ethics. . . . Karl Popper's methodology of falsificationism or critical rationality has been formed in its nucleus long before he studied mathematics, physics and natural philosophy at Vienna University. Therefore, it is my hypothesis that Popper's method of trial and error . . . is inseparably interwoven with ethical of moral principles.[19]

The ethical roots of Popper's epistemology are closely related to his rejection of pseudoscientific theories. His 1919 experiences made Popper aware of the pseudoscientific character of Marxism, which presented itself as based on laws of history that could allegedly be established in a scientific way. According to Popper, the supporters of pseudoscience desire for their theories the prestige of science while avoiding the rigor of the scientific method: they search for verifications of their theories and manipulate contrary evidence so their theories can be preserved from any change. The scientific attitude, on the other hand, leads its adherents to empirically test scientific theories in order to improve or replace them with better theories.

Evaluations of Popper's epistemology are usually centered, however, on logical elements such as the asymmetry between verification and falsification, and on the problem of induction. One can hardly overestimate the relevance of these logical problems in Popper's epistemology. They are of primordial importance. However, they are linked to wider and deeper problems that involve the ethical responsibility of the entire human person.

Popper considers rationality mainly as an attitude: the attitude of reasonableness; of openness to reexamining our theories in the light of new data and arguments; of searching for counterexamples to detect errors in our theories and thus to improve them; of settling our differences through dialogue and not by force. Popper clearly presents his "critical rationalism" as part of his "moral articles of faith." In *The Open Society and Its Enemies,* Popper's most explicit characterization of his critical rationalism says:

I use the word "rationalism" in order to indicate, roughly, an attitude that seeks to solve as many problems as possible by an appeal to reason, i.e., to clear thought and experience, rather than by an appeal to emotions and passions. . . . We could then say that rationalism is an attitude of readiness to listen to critical arguments and to learn from experience. It is fundamentally an attitude of admitting that *"I may be wrong and you may be right, and by an effort, we may get nearer to the truth"* . . . In short, the rationalist attitude, or, as I may perhaps label it, the "attitude of reasonableness," is very similar to the scientific attitude, to the belief that in the search for truth we need co-operation,

---

19. Hubert Kiesewetter, "Ethical Foundations of Popper's Philosophy," in *Karl Popper: Philosophy and Problems,* ed. Anthony O'Hear (Cambridge: Cambridge University Press, 1995), pp. 275–276.

and that, with the help of argument, we can in time attain something like objectivity.[20]

Popper explicitly stresses that his rationalism is rooted in a kind of "faith in reason" and, therefore, is based on a choice that is a moral decision.[21] This cannot be considered a secondary element in Popper's philosophy.

Popper openly supports a realistic stance. He considers empirical science to be the search for truth, although he thinks we can never know for certain that we have reached true knowledge. Science is, as he puts it in the title of his intellectual autobiography, an "unended quest" for truth.

I shall argue later that we obtain true knowledge in empirical science and that we may know when we have obtained it. Moreover, I shall examine in more detail Popper's fallibilism, distinguishing a weak kind of healthy fallibilism and a strong kind that may lead to seriously misleading consequences. My attitude toward Popper's epistemology, and even more toward his metaphysical and religious ideas, is very cautious.

Nevertheless, I think that Popper rightly stresses some points that are important for the purposes of my argument. Popper fought for intellectual modesty and rejected any kind of pseudoscientific theory that enslaved men in the name of science. Also, he insisted on the role of human creativity and the corresponding human singularity. In this approach, creativity plays a central role. We are no longer considered to be observers who register empirical data or use them in a mechanical way to formulate or verify our hypotheses. Rather, we are active subjects who pose problems, formulate tentative theories, evaluate them, and decide if they survive our systematic criticism. Popper is right to emphasize the role of creativity in science and when he underscores the ethical roots of a rational attitude that plays an important role in the progress of science.

3. Paradigms and Revolutions: Kuhn's Psychosociohistorical View

Little attention has been paid to the ethical features of Popper's epistemology, which has usually been considered only as a study of the logical relations between scientific statements. An epistemology centered around logic was generally dominant when in 1962 Thomas Kuhn published *The Structure of Scientific Revolutions,* which became one of the most influential works in the twentieth-century literature on science. His account highlighted the historical, psychological, and sociological factors in the development of science. Kuhn's explanation of this development centered on the behavior of the scientific community. This work served as a stimulus for several attempts at harmonizing the logical and the sociohistorical approaches. However, Kuhn's in-

---

20. Karl R. Popper, *The Open Society and Its Enemies,* vol. 2 (London: Routledge, 1977), pp. 224–225.

21. Ibid., pp. 231–232.

spired epistemology has come in for sharp criticism because it seems to concede too much to irrationalism.

The success of *The Structure of Scientific Revolutions* was partly due to the apparent simplicity of its argument. In Kuhn's account, scientific progress can be understood as the result of alternating between two kinds of scientific activity: in periods of "normal science" scientists concentrate on the routine activity of puzzle-solving within a shared framework or paradigm; then, when too many or too important anomalies exist that cannot be solved by the accepted paradigm, scientists seek for new theories leading to the emergence of a new paradigm and its acceptance by the community. This latter activity Kuhn called "extraordinary science" and would mean that a "revolution" is produced.

One major feature of Kuhn's theory is that the triumph of a new paradigm is not the consequence of arguments based on logic and facts; rather, it is a kind of "gestalt-switch," which could be compared to a religious conversion. Thus, Kuhn seemed to accept that new theories do not triumph until the old-fashioned scientists die. Therefore, scientific progress does not follow a rational pattern, and it is even dubious whether we can seriously speak of progress at all; at least, if the new theories are "incommensurable" with the old ones, the usual idea of cumulative progress should be abandoned. That is why Kuhn's work has been considered to provide arguments in favor of irrationalism.

We can ask whether this view concedes too much to the role creativity in science. Apparently, it is completely opposed to the empiricist view held by the neopositivists. It may seem, therefore, paradoxical that *The Structure of Scientific Revolutions* was published at the same time as an independent book and also as a part of the *Encyclopedia of Unified Science,* a project of the Vienna Circle in the 1930s that aimed at a synthesis of the entire field of the sciences in a unified body of knowledge that could be reduced, in the last analysis, to a physicalist language.[22]

Among the members of the Vienna Circle, Otto Neurath was a strong advocate of the cause of the unity of science. He was also the author of a paper about unified science, sociology, and physicalism. Neurath held that the language of unified science is the language of physics and declared his preference for the title "Vienna Circle for Physicalism." He advocated a kind of empirical sociology that could be exemplified by Marxism:

> Marxism is, to a higher degree than any other present-day sociological theory, a system of empirical sociology. The most important Marxist theses employed for prediction are either already formulated in a fairly physicalistic fashion (so far as traditional language made this possible), or they can be so formulated, without the loss of anything essential. We can see in the case of Marxism how sociological

---

22. Thomas S. Kuhn, *The Structure of Scientific Revolutions,* 2d enlarged ed. *International Encyclopedia of Unified Science,* vol. II (Chicago: The University of Chicago Press, 1970), n. 2.

laws are sought for and how relations conformable to law are established.[23]

It must be immediately added that, even though Otto Neurath was a pre-eminent figure in the Vienna Circle, his emphasis on unified science and physicalism, and even more on Marxism, was not necessarily shared by other members of the Circle. In any event, it is not clear to see the connection between Kuhn's essay and Neurath's old project.

We may conjecture that in both cases there was a common interest in the sociology of science. It is also possible to discover a more subtle connection between Kuhn's ideas and those of the Vienna Circle.

In fact, in contrast with the usual presentation of Popper as the intermediate link between the Vienna Circle and Kuhn, Derek Stanesby has presented Popper as a most welcome figure between the extremes represented by neopositivism (the Vienna Circle) and relativism (Kuhn). He analyzes the position of the neopositivists, closely linked to the first epoch of Ludwig Wittgenstein and centered around a rigid and univocal criterion of meaning that excluded as meaningless all propositions except those of everyday experience and of the empirical sciences. Then he examines the position of Kuhn, which would correspond to the second epoch of Wittgenstein, and he says that Kuhn's relativist conclusions are due to the fact that he also accepts, like the neopositivists and the first Wittgenstein, a rigid idea about meaning. According to Stanesby, having realized that the positivist criterion of meaning is untenable, Kuhn concluded that there are as many meanings as languages and that every language corresponds to a way of living, so that all we can do is play language games. In this case, we cannot establish a rational discussion between the different ways of living, paradigms, or languages, because they are holistic and untranslatable. Popper represented fresh air between these extremes, because he was preoccupied not with meanings and languages but with real problems.[24]

I do not agree with Stanesby's positive evaluation of Popper's philosophy as an instrument for theology. Stansby borrows the relationship between the two extremes from Dudley Shapere,[25] who asserted that the thesis of the theory-dependence of meanings (held by relativists) and its opposite, the condition of meaning invariance (held by positivists), derive from the same mistake (or excess). If this appreciation is correct, Kuhn's "irrationalism" could be understood as a reaction against the rigid correlation established by the neopositivists between concepts and sense data. Moreover, this reaction could be seen as a continuation of the corrections introduced by the neopositivists, who proposed what Shapere has labeled the "contextual theory of meaning."

23. Otto Neurath, "Sociology and Physicalism," in *Logical Positivism,* cit., p. 309.

24. Derek Stanesby, *Science, Reason and Religion* (London: Routledge, 1988).

25. Dudley Shapere, "Meaning and Scientific Change," in *Scientific Revolutions,* ed. Ian Hacking (Oxford: Oxford University Press, 1981), pp. 28–59.

According to Shapere, Kuhn and Feyerabend moved in the late 1950s and early 1960s in the direction opened by the neopositivists. The meaning of theoretical concepts depends on a "context" (a theory, a family of theories, or even the whole of science as a web, according to different versions of the contextual interpretation). Therefore, different meanings could not be translated, as they are defined within different contexts. For the same reason, new theories could not be logically compared with the old ones, which implies the thesis of the "incommensurability" of theories. Relativism seems unavoidable, as far as we could not use logical arguments in order to evaluate scientific theories.

Actually, the simplicity of Kuhn's scheme may be misleading, as a closer analysis shows that the interpretation of his thought may be a truly difficult task. In the famous 1965 London International Symposium of Philosophy of Science, Margaret Masterman noted that Kuhn had given his key concept of "paradigm" in *The Structure of the Scientific Revolutions* at least 21 different meanings.[26] Kuhn later provided further reflections on this subject,[27] and his thought has also been reconstructed by Paul Hoyningen-Huene in a way that is anything but simple.[28]

In *The Structure of Scientific Revolutions,* Kuhn pays too little attention to knowledge and truth in his explanation of science. Years later, in his Presidential Address at the 1990 Meeting of the Philosophy of Science Association, he presented his latest views in a historicist perspective that was "a sort of post-Darwinian Kantianism,"[29] in which the notion of truth as correspondence with reality was in the main abandoned:

> what is fundamentally at stake is rather the correspondence theory of truth, the notion that the goal, when evaluating scientific laws or theories, is to determine whether or not they correspond to an external, mind-independent world. It is that notion, whether in an absolute or probabilistic form, that I'm persuaded must vanish together with foundationalism. What replaces it will still require a strong conception of truth, but not, except in the most trivial sense, correspondence truth.[30]

Kuhn gives up the very notion of truth as correspondence. Given that truth plays an important role in science, such thinking could easily result in a

26. Margaret Masterman, "The Nature of a Paradigm," in *Criticism and the Growth of Knowledge*, ed. Imre Lakatos and Alan Musgrave (Cambridge: Cambridge University Press, 1990), pp. 61–65.

27. Thomas S. Kuhn, "Second Thoughts on Paradigms," reprinted in Kuhn's book *The Essential Tension* (Chicago: The University of Chicago Press, 1977), pp. 293–319.

28. See Paul Hoyningen-Huene, *Reconstructing Scientific Revolutions: Thomas S. Kuhn's Philosophy of Science* (Chicago: The University of Chicago Press, 1993).

29. Thomas S. Kuhn, "The Road Since Structure," in *Science and the Quest for Reality*, ed. Alfred I. Tauber (Washington Square, N.Y.: New York University Press, 1997), p. 244.

30. Ibid., p. 236.

misinterpretation of the behavior of the scientific community. In fact, the sociology of knowledge that developed in the last decades of the twentieth century has sometimes clashed with the scientific community, because some scientists feel that this interpretation undermines the prestige of empirical science and the social support that science needs.

Nevertheless, Kuhn's psychosociohistorical explanations of science, linked to the behavior of the scientific community, are important in some respects, for those aspects must be taken into consideration if we desire to obtain a complete representation of the scientific enterprise. They also provide some interesting clues regarding the image of man. Indeed, the behavior of the scientific community, as Kuhn describes it, is highly sophisticated: scientists do not follow standard rules and yet they cope quite successfully with very difficult problems, combining theoretical and empirical reasoning in a complex way. Even the apparently routine activity of puzzle-solving, which is presented by Kuhn as characteristic of the periods of normal science, presupposes the existence of an entire set of human abilities that are necessary to learn the state of the art and to manage the new problems that arise in the normal practice of science. Kuhn does not elaborate in detail a theory of human knowledge; but his explanation of science supposes that such a theory may exist and include the existence of highly developed human abilities.

4. PROGRAMS OF SCIENTIFIC RESEARCH: IMRE LAKATOS

Kuhn's emphasis on the role of history as a clue for understanding science found an echo in Imre Lakatos, who had a training in dialectical historicism in communist Hungary. He then fled to England and, after becoming a disciple and then a colleague of Popper in the London School of Economics, tried to make an original synthesis of Popper's and Kuhn's approaches. He considered this task to be a most important one, as can be easily perceived from the paper in which he first outlined his new proposal:

> The clash between Popper and Kuhn is not about a mere technical point in epistemology. It concerns our central intellectual values, and has implications not only for theoretical physics but also for the underdeveloped social sciences and even for moral and political philosophy. If even in science there is no other way of judging a theory but by assessing the number, faith and vocal energy of its supporters, then this must be even more so in the social sciences: truth lies in power. Thus Kuhn's position vindicates, no doubt, unintentionally, the basic politic *credo* of contemporary religious maniacs ("student revolutionaries").[31]

In spite of the last claim, Lakatos retained Kuhn's idea of history as the

31. Imre Lakatos, *The Methodology of Scientific Research Programmes,* Philosophical Papers, vol. I, ed. John Worrall and Gregory Currie (Cambridge: Cambridge University Press, 1984), pp. 9–10.

field in which epistemology must decide its problems. Rationality is no longer viewed mainly as an attitude, as in Popper; it is rather considered as the rational explanation for the process of scientific change. Now, to be rational means to explain how we can proceed in a logical way when we choose or reject competing theories. Lakatos tried to extend and articulate Popper's ideas so that they could be applied to explain the historical record of scientific progress and, eventually, to reconstruct it in a rational way; he tried to combine Kuhn's interest in the history of science with an expansion of Popper's ideas.

The move was simple and intelligent. Lakatos proposed that the units submitted to falsification are not theories, but "Programmes of Scientific Research"; entire sets of theories that can be considered as a large unit, as for example, Newton's gravitational theory or the development of atomic theory in the nineteenth century. Lakatos also distinguished two different parts of those programs: a "negative heuristics" that is the "hard core" of the program, which in principle is considered valid and not subject to revision, and a "positive heuristics" constituted by "auxiliary hypotheses" that are submitted to tests and get adjusted, readjusted, or even completely replaced. The auxiliary hypotheses form the "protective belt" around the hard core. To complete the picture, Lakatos said that "a research programme is successful if all this leads to a progressive problemshift; unsuccessful if it leads to a degenerating problemshift."[32]

Lakatos defined problemshifts thus: If we have a series of theories, each of them resulting from adding auxiliary hypotheses to the previous one to accommodate some anomaly, and each theory has at least as much content as the unrefuted content of its predecessor, such a series is "theoretically progressive" (and we will have a theoretically progressive problemshift) if each new theory predicts some novel, hitherto unexplained fact. Such a series is also "empirically progressive" (and we will have an empirically progressive problemshift) if some of those predictions are corroborated. Lakatos uses these ideas to propose a new criterion of demarcation:

> we *"accept"* problemshifts as "scientific" only if they are at least theoretically progressive; if they are not, we *"reject"* them as "pseudoscientific." . . . progress is measured by the degree to which a problemshift is progressive, by the degree to which the series of theories leads us to the discovery of novel facts. We regard a theory in the series "falsified" when it is superseded by a theory with higher corroborated content.[33]

This proposal provides a simple framework that enables us to judge whether a research program is scientific or pseudoscientific, and if it is scientific, whether it is progressive or degenerative, replacing the "instant ratio-

32. Ibid., p. 48.

33. Ibid., pp. 33–34.

nality," which is required to judge all this in a moment, with an appreciation that takes into account many factors over a long period.

As an account of scientific rationality, Lakatos' proposal contains interesting features that like Kuhn's account of science, are expressed through a simple scheme. That partly explains why it also has been quite successful. Lakatos strongly stresses the role creativity and interpretation play in the development of empirical science, for he provides a highly sophisticated image of empirical science and of epistemology. In fact, Lakatos intended to supersede epistemological views that he considered too dogmatic or naive, putting in their place a truly "sophisticated" falsificationism. This falsificationism takes into account the logical features of science and the psychosociohistorical dimensions, combines a sophisticated version of Popper's falsificationism with Kuhn's main ideas, and provides a new research program that acted as a stimulus to the study of historical cases in the history of science. Soon thereafter, in 1976, a collective work was published:

> This volume constitutes the first collected edition of work so far done in illustrating an important new development in the philosophy of science, "the methodology of scientific research programmes," with case studies drawn from the history of the physical sciences.[34]

With his proposal Lakatos intended to illuminate serious human problems that have great theoretical and practical relevance. Therefore, whether we agree with his proposal or not, we can safely conclude that it underscores once more the specificity of the human being who is able to work successfully in the highly sophisticated fields of empirical science and epistemology.

5. PAUL FEYERABEND'S CRITIQUE OF SCIENTIFIC REASON

Paul Feyerabend, who had been close to Popper, was years later the head of an "epistemological anarchism" that strongly opposed the prevailing views on scientific rationality. Due to Feyerabend's idiosyncrasy, it is not easy to know for sure what he really meant in the writings of his anarchist epoch. I shall concentrate on a single point that is most relevant for my argument: his rejection of scientism.

Feyerabend correctly perceived that, underlying many epistemological accounts, scientism played the role of an implicit presupposition that often proved an insurmountable obstacle to posing the right questions and finding the right answers. He denounced this situation, usually in a provocative and ironic way, but sometimes more seriously. Thus, in a paper entitled "On the Critique of Scientific Reason," he wrote:

> There are two questions that arise in the course of any critique of scientific reason. They are (i) *What is science?*—how does it proceed,

---

34. Colin Howson, ed., *Method and Appraisal in the Physical Sciences: The Critical Background to Modern Science, 1800–1905* (Cambridge: Cambridge University Press, 1976), editorial preface.

what are its results, how do its procedures, standards and results differ from the procedures, standards and results of other enterprises? (ii) *What's so great about science?*—what makes science preferable to other forms of life, using different standards and getting different kinds of results as a consequence? What makes modern science preferable to the science of the Aristotelians, or to the ideology of the Azande? Note that in trying to answer question (ii) we are not permitted to judge the alternatives to science by scientific standards.[35]

I think that Feyerabend is right when he describes empirical science, in question (i), as a human enterprise, and that he is wrong when, in question (ii), he considers it as a "form of life" that competes with other forms of life. It is impossible to live scientifically. Empirical science always consists of particular objectifications, and it cannot be used as a real orientation for practical purposes in ordinary life. A mistake on this point may lead us to identify science, considered as a form of life, with scientism, instead of seeing scientism as an unjustified extrapolation of science. One can understand, then, that Feyerabend says:

> In the history of thought answers to question (ii) are often taken for granted. For example, it is taken for granted that Truth is something quite excellent and that all we need to know are the detailed features of this Excellent Thing. This means that one starts with a *word* and uses the enthusiasm created by its *sound* for the support of questionable ideologies (cf. the Nazis on Freedom).[36]

Nevertheless, if we do not take seriously the issue of scientific truth, we cannot correctly identify the real roots and meaning of scientism.

Feyerabend's position is interesting because it shows the difficulties faced by someone who reacts against scientism but does not have the necessary means to propose a valid alternative. Our contemporary culture suffers from the same defect, often in an unconscious way, and this explains the existence of many forms of irrationalism linked to skeptical, relativist, and pragmatic positions.

6. PROBLEM SOLVING AND LAUDAN

Larry Laudan presented himself as the new patron saint of the philosophy of science and has been successful in his attempt. In the preface to his 1984 book *Science and Values,* he enthusiastically praised Thomas Kuhn but then made it clear that he intended to go far beyond Kuhn:

> Indeed, for more than two decades, the views of Thomas Kuhn—and reactions to them—have occupied center stage in accounts of scien-

---

35. Paul K. Feyerabend, "On the Critique of Scientific Reason," in *Method and Appraisal in the Physical Sciences,* cit., p. 310.

36. Ibid.

tific change and scientific rationality. That is as it should be, for Kuhn's *Structure of Scientific Revolutions* caused us all to rethink our image of what science is and how it works. There can be no one active today in philosophy, history, or sociology of science whose approach to the problem of scientific rationality has not been shaped by the Gestalt switch Kuhn wrought on our perspective on science. This debt is so broadly recognized that there is no need to document it here.

Less frequently admitted is the fact that, in the twenty-two years since the appearance of *The Structure of Scientific Revolutions,* a great deal of historical scholarship and analytic spadework has moved our understanding of the process of scientific rationality and scientific change considerably beyond the point where Kuhn left it. Indeed, we are now in a position to state pretty unequivocally that Kuhn's model of scientific change, as developed in *Structure* and elaborated in *The Essential Tension,* is deeply flawed, not only in its specifics but in its central framework assumptions. . . . But just saying so is not enough. The decanonization of a discipline's patron saint is always a slow and arduous task, and one demanding that the case be carefully constructed and that it cut to the heart of the matter. This book is a contribution to that effort.[37]

Laudan had already begun to gain his place in the list of first-rate authors in contemporary philosophy of science in 1977; in his book *Progress and Its Problems,* he had summed up his proposal in few words:

I propose that the rationality and progressiveness of a theory are most closely linked—not with its confirmation or its falsification—but rather with its *problem-solving effectiveness.*[38]

He expressed the same idea with a slight difference in a 1981 paper:

My own proposal . . . is that the aim of science is to secure theories with a high problem-solving effectiveness.[39]

In working out this idea, Laudan distinguishes different kinds of problems (empirical and conceptual) and of problem solving, proposes a methodology that could be applied to appraise scientific progress, applies his ideas to concrete historical case studies, and proposes a kind of metamethodology that may serve to choose among different methodologies of science.

Laudan refers to other philosophers of science, mainly to Popper and Kuhn, in an attempt to show that his position is far better than theirs; however, one cannot avoid the impression that his ideas are partly an expanded rewriting of Popper, Kuhn, Lakatos, and Feyerabend. For instance, the idea

37. Larry Laudan, *Science and Values* (Berkeley: University of California Press, 1984), pp. xii–xiii.

38. Larry Laudan, *Progress and Its Problems: Towards a Theory of Scientific Growth* (Berkeley: University of California Press, 1977), p. 5.

39. Laudan, *Beyond Positivism and Relativism,* cit., p. 78.

of focusing on problem solving can hardly be considered a new one. Feyer-abend, in a review to *Progress and Its Problems,* expressed his complaint when, referring to Laudan's criticism of current views, he wrote:

> His arguments against them often have the following interesting pat-tern: a philosopher (historian) is introduced as holding a view, or making a suggestion S. S is examined, demolished and replaced by Q which is shown to be a natural consequence of Laudan's model. The model obviously is vastly better than its alternatives. Yet the poor philosopher never proposed S; he held Q, the very ideas that Laudan presents as his own. On such occasions—and they occur rather fre-quently—Laudan sounds like a thief who chides his victims for lack-ing the items he has just taken from them. This is a very clever ruse and one would like to congratulate Laudan on it but unfortunately he has borrowed it from Lakatos.[40]

Feyerabend illustrated his critique stressing that the problem-solving model, which is the general framework of Laudan's philosophy, is a triviality for any-one who has spent even a few days with Popperians.

I cannot help thinking that, in fact, Laudan's epistemology is, in some re-spects, a complex expansion of already well-known ideas. For example, re-garding the problem of demarcation, Laudan concludes that:

> there is no fundamental difference in kind between scientific and other forms of intellectual inquiry. All seek to make sense of the world and of our experience . . . the quest for a specifically scientific form of knowledge, or for a demarcation criterion between science and nonscience, has been an unqualified failure . . . our central con-cern should be with distinguishing theories of broad and demonstra-ble problem-solving scope from theories which do not have this property—regardless of whether the theories in question fall in areas of physics, literary theory, philosophy, or common sense.[41]

I would agree with Laudan's view insofar as it means that there can be seri-ous knowledge claims in any area of human experience. Nevertheless, I feel that Laudan moves in the path marked by Kuhn, as he seems to leave aside the very notion of truth. Indeed, when he discusses the aims of science, he says that there has been a tendency to characterize them in terms of such tran-scendental properties as truth or apodictic certainty, and he adds that we lack the necessary criteria to judge how these aims would be achieved, conclud-ing that it is preferable to set goals for science that can be achievable in prin-ciple; at this point, he introduces his proposal to characterize the aim of sci-ence in terms of problem-solving effectiveness.[42]

---

40. Paul K. Feyerabend, "More Clothes for the Emperor's Bargain Basement. A Review of Lau-dan's *Progress and Its Problems,*" reprinted in Paul K. Feyerabend, *Problems of Empiricism,* Philo-sophical Papers, vol. 2 (Cambridge: Cambridge University Press, 1981), p. 233.

41. Laudan, *Beyond Positivism and Relativism,* cit., pp. 85–86.

42. Ibid., p. 78.

Laudan analyzed the doctrine of underdetermination, trying to demystify "the assaults on methodology which have been mounted in its name,"[43] and he quotes the great physicist, historian, and philosopher of science Pierre Duhem, who wrote at the beginning of the twentieth century:

Pure logic is not the only rule for our judgements; certain opinions which do not fall under the hammer of the principle of contradiction are in any case perfectly unreasonable.[44]

Underdetermination means that empirical data, however abundant, are never sufficient to determine univocally which theory explains them. Underdetermination has been used in favor of relativism and skepticism, against the very existence of scientific methodology, and in a number of other ways. Laudan offers vivid examples of a variety of uses of underdetermination in the contemporary scene.[45]

Underdetermination is closely related to the fact that science is not a matter of pure logic. In science we always begin with a problem and propose a tentative hypothesis to solve that problem. But we do not have purely logical rules that may lead us from our problem situation to the right hypothesis; therefore, we must take a risk when we formulate and accept (even tentatively) our hypotheses. Moreover, once we have formulated a hypothesis, we have no purely logical methods to establish it, owing to the simple reason that, even if our hypothesis enables us to explain the original problem, we may always suppose that another, better explanation exists. If we know that a statement is true, we also know that its consequences must be true; but in our case we only know the consequences, and no logical rule exists that may allow us to establish a particular explanation of them as the only possible explanation or the right one. Therefore, the connection between empirical data and scientific theories is not too rigid.

Under these circumstances, any attempt to explain the rationality of science using a simple scheme is faulty from the very beginning. Laudan apparently identifies rationality with progressiveness, and both of them with problem-solving effectiveness (at least, he considers these three concepts to be very closely related). In some way, this identification is a trivial matter, because in science we always try to solve problems by using arguments. If we leave aside scientific truth, as Laudan seems to do, it will be very difficult to provide a satisfactory account of scientific rationality.

In any case, Laudan's epistemology contains a large number of problems and suggestions. Reading his works, one cannot help feeling that both empirical science and epistemology are very complex enterprises that require powerful skills and cannot be treated in a routine way. Scientific progress re-

---

43. Ibid., p. 29.

44. Pierre Duhem, *The Aim and Structure of Physical Theory* (Princeton, NJ: Princeton University Press, 1951), p. 217.

45. Laudan, *Beyond Positivism and Relativism*, cit., p. 30.

quires creativity, and epistemology requires interpretation. Laudan's episte-mology takes seriously the complexity of science and of epistemology itself, and thus it is a new testimony of the singularity of the human skills that are involved in those activities.

7. RATIONALITY: AN OVERVIEW

Epistemology, considered as the study of the nature and value of scien-tific knowledge, is a young discipline. For a long time after modern empiri-cal science came of age in the seventeenth century, philosophy of science was only an occasional occupation of individual scientists and philosophers. Around 1930 it became a discipline cultivated in a truly systematic way, but it was very difficult to propose an objective view about the reach of science. Indeed, the fathers of modern epistemology were mainly the neopositivists of the Vienna Circle, who, moved by a strongly antimetaphysical attitude, de-veloped an empiricist epistemology that was inadequate as an objective ac-count of empirical science.

The failure of the empiricist program clearly showed that the methods of empirical science cannot be reduced to induction and verification, but in-clude creativity and interpretation as essential ingredients. These features were underscored by Popper, who combined the specific character of empirical science with the respectability of metaphysical arguments. The perspectives inspired by Kuhn stressed the relevance of the history of science in episte-mological arguments as well as the role of creativity and interpretation. In the debate on scientific rationality, Feyerabend strongly criticized scientism as an important cause of misunderstanding. On the other hand, Lakatos and Lau-dan have proposed more and more sophisticated ideas to evaluate scientific progress, combining the logical aspects of empirical science with historical and sociological ones. Debates about scientific rationality continue and have led to new perspectives, which are presented as a "naturalization" of episte-mology, where "naturalize" means to study science by using the very same method used by empirical science.

The positions mentioned disagree on many particular subjects. Neverthe-less, all of them clearly stress that empirical science cannot be explained as the result of applying automatic methodological rules or algorithmic decision procedures.

A complete account of scientific progress should include an analysis of the logical dimensions of science, and of the historical and sociological dimen-sions as well. In the last decades, epistemology has got rid of the burden orig-inally imposed on it by the neopositivists, and, even if there is no general agreement regarding many epistemological issues, a wide range of studies have developed in the fields of logic, history, and sociology of science, so that we have reached a vantage point that enables us to determine the main char-acteristics of the scientific enterprise on solid grounds. I am now going to propose my own account.

II. THREE DIMENSIONS IN EMPIRICAL SCIENCE

I return now to the three dimensions in empirical science I distinguished in chapter 2, for this distinction will provide the framework for my analysis of scientific truth.

First of all, empirical science is a human activity directed toward specific goals concerned with the knowledge of nature and our mastery over it. Second, these goals can be achieved only by using means that are also very specific and constitute the scientific method, whose main characteristic is to formulate theories and submit them to empirical control. Third, as a consequence of the use of that method, we obtain results that constitute the body of scientific knowledge, namely scientific models, statements, and theories.

An adequate account of the rationality of science should include these three levels and their relations. The methods of science and its results will be rational as far as they serve to attain the aim of the scientific enterprise. In turn, the aim of science can be considered rational if it is a worthwhile one and if we can achieve it.

1. The Goals of Science

Natural science is an activity directed toward some specific goals that serve to characterize it, independent of external factors. These goals can be considered a necessary condition and must be present before an endeavor can be regarded as belonging to empirical science. There are two such goals: (1) in natural science we seek knowledge of the natural world, and (2) we require that this knowledge be contrasted with empirical evidence in a controlled way, so that it may serve as the basis for a controlled dominion over nature.

Knowledge of nature can also be achieved using a different approach: through philosophical reflection on the natural world. Also, dominion over nature can be achieved using merely empirical techniques, which have been developed since very ancient times (we usually speak of technology when the techniques are based on scientific grounds). What characterizes empirical science is the combination of the two goals, so that they become like two sides of the same coin. And here the philosophical troubles begin.

Indeed, even if the two sides belong to the same coin, the analogy ends here, because they can develop following different paths and rhythms. Sometimes we have theories that, at a particular time, cannot be submitted to empirical tests. For instance, few consequences of general relativity could be tested for several decades after Einstein formulated the theory, and the testing of theories about the subatomic components of matter, such as superstrings theory, requires experimental devices not available yet. These difficulties only pertain to the availability, at a certain time, of the experiments necessary to test the theories, and so this kind of theory is accepted as belonging to empirical science.

Besides, even if the experiments necessary to test a particular theory are available, this does not mean that we can always establish with certainty the truth of that theory. We sometimes reach a fairly certain kind of knowledge, as when we determine spatial structures such as the double-helical structure of DNA; in other cases we can only claim a conjectural knowledge, as in the study of the microphysical world of subatomic particles.

We can build up theoretical models that work quite well for many purposes, even if we do not know exactly what their truth-value is. The development of quantum physics is an impressive example of such a case, because we faced great difficulties in interpreting its cognitive value since the theory was first formulated in the 1920s; nevertheless, the theory can be applied to many physical problems with great success.

The main difficulties of epistemology, which are neither few nor small, ultimately depend on the combination of the theoretical and the pragmatic features of empirical science. This combination can be considered the crucial step that led to the birth and subsequent progress of natural science and has required the work of many geniuses. Progress in the different branches of the natural sciences has shown the nature and effectiveness of that peculiar combination of theory and praxis, of knowledge and dominion, of modeling and testing.

Sometimes we are told that empirical science is a natural result of our observation and interpretation of the natural world, and that it was not born until the seventeenth century only because ideological prejudices, mainly in the form of religious doctrines, prevented its development. This idea is often associated with a positivist way of thinking that associates religion with primitive stages of humankind and sees modern empirical science as the obvious result of substituting observation and logic for religion. The historical record, however, is more complex and shows that the peculiar combination of the explanatory and predictive features in empirical science was a very difficult outcome that required a great dose of faith in the possibility of science. It also shows that religion, and especially Christianity, played a very important role in providing the kind of faith necessary for the beginning of modern science: a faith in the existence of the ontological presuppositions of science (the existence of a natural order) and of the epistemological presuppositions as well (the human ability to know natural order).

Modern empirical science found its only viable birth as a self-sustained enterprise in the seventeenth century, in a Western European world that, even if tormented by religious disputes, shared in unison the faith in the existence of a personal God who is the creator of the universe and of human beings. The universe, as the work of an infinitely wise, omnipotent, and benevolent God, was seen as an ordered world, and the human being, as a creature who participates in the personal character of God, was seen as capable of knowing that rational world and as having received from God the commandment to know and master it. Although pieces of natural science existed in ancient times, its modern systematic birth was only possible because for a long period many people displayed great ingenuity in their search for explanations about natural phenomena, guided by their faith in the existence of a natural order that could be uncovered by man.

Referring to the work of many scholars who during the Middle Ages prepared the way for the scientific revolution of the seventeenth century, Thomas Kuhn has written:

> During the seventeenth century, just when its full utility was being demonstrated for the first time, scholastic science was bitterly attacked by men trying to weave a radically new fabric of thought. The scholastics proved easy to ridicule, and the image has stuck. Medieval scientists more often found their problems in texts than in nature; many of those problems do not seem problems at all; by modern standards the practice of science during the Middle Ages was incredibly inefficient. But how else could science have been reborn in the West? The centuries of scholasticism are the centuries in which the tradition of ancient science and philosophy was simultaneously reconstituted, assimilated, and tested for adequacy. As weak spots were discovered, they immediately became foci for the first effective research in the modern world. The great new scientific theories of the sixteenth and seventeenth centuries all originate from rents torn by scholastic criticism in the fabric of Aristotelian thought. Most of those theories also embody key concepts created by scholastic science. And more important even than these is the attitude that modern scientists inherited from their medieval predecessors: an unbounded faith in the power of human reason to solve the problems of nature. As the late Professor Whitehead remarked, "Faith in the possibility of science, generated antecedently to the development of modern scientific theory, is an unconscious derivative from medieval theology."[46]

The quote from Alfred North Whitehead is taken from the Lowell Lectures of 1925.[47] There, Whitehead tells us that "there can be no living science unless there is a widespread instinctive conviction in the existence of an *Order of Things,* and, in particular, of an *Order of Nature.*" He adds that, since the time of Hume, fashionable scientific philosophy has denied the rationality of science (I would say that it has denied the ontological and epistemological presuppositions of science—the existence of an objective natural order and of our ability to know it). He searches the origins of the faith in the rationality of nature and of man that made possible the birth of modern empirical science. He argues that "the Middle Ages formed one long training of the intellect of Western Europe in the sense of order," and that "the habit of definite exact thought was implanted in the European mind by the long dominance of scholastic logic and scholastic divinity." Furthermore, he writes that

---

46. Thomas Kuhn, *The Copernican Revolution: Planetary Astronomy in the Development of Western Thought* (Cambridge, Mass.: Harvard University Press, 1957), p. 122.

47. Alfred North Whitehead, *Science and the Modern World* (New York: Macmillan, 1967), pp. 1–18.

"the greatest contribution of medievalism to the formation of the scientific movement" is "the inexpugnable belief that every detailed occurrence can be correlated with its antecedents in a perfectly definite manner, exemplifying general principles. Without this belief the incredible labours of scientists would be without hope," and he concludes that faith in the possibility of science is an unconscious derivative from medieval theology.

Whitehead and Kuhn stress that it was not easy for modern empirical science to find the way that led to its unique viable birth. A strong faith in the rationality of the world and in the ability of man to represent natural order was needed. Doubtless, a great ingenuity was also required to combine the theoretical and pragmatic dimensions of the new approach to nature.

An interesting analysis of the history of this combination is contained in Ernan McMullin's 1984 Presidential Address to the American Philosophical Association at Cincinnati, Ohio, published under the title "The Goals of Natural Science."[48] McMullin distinguishes three kinds of science, which he labels as "P-science," where P stands for prediction; "D-science," where D stands for demonstration; and "T-science," where T stands for theoretical. According to McMullin, the first two kinds of science have existed since ancient times, and the third type emerged in the past few centuries in continuity with them but also as a real innovation that did not exist previously. P-science, which aims "to organize phenomena as economically as possible with a view to exact prediction," is already represented in the great period of Babylonian astronomy from 250 B.C. to 50 B.C. By contrast, the goal of D-science, which represents Aristotle's ideal natural science, is "a knowledge of causes where knowledge is construed as demonstration," and prediction plays no particular role in this kind of science, whose goal is mainly contemplative. Attempts to explain the status of the disciplines that use mathematical methods to discuss physical topics—the sciences that later were called "mixed" or "middle" sciences—introduced an unsolved tension between P-science and D-science, which finally gave rise to the new T-science of the seventeenth century. McMullin tells us about this new T-science:

> What we have in the making here is, of course, a new ideal of science. The goal can still be expressed in Aristotle's phrase as "a knowledge of causes," but there are two crucial modifications, one in the term "knowledge" and one in the term "cause." The *knowledge* that science yields is no longer viewed as demonstrative, as definitive, as necessary. It is probable, fallible, dependent upon continued testing. True, this will continue to be disputed until well into the 19th century, not least because Newton's mechanics seemed to many to provide at least one instance of an old-fashioned D-science. But the notion that testing is needed, and thus that prediction is now a *necessary* part of science, was grasped, I am tempted to say once and for all, already

---

48. Ernan McMullin, "The Goals of Natural Science," in *Scientific Knowledge Socialized,* ed. Imre Hronszky, Márta Fehér, and Balázs Dajka (Dordrecht: Kluwer, 1988), pp. 27–58.

in the 17th century. No longer could prediction and explanation be sundered as they had been for so long. Now the main testimony of an acceptable explanation will be precisely its ability to *predict,* that is, to entail testable consequences. . . . Tracing observed effects back to causes not themselves observed required a *theory,* and in time the notion of a "theory" came to mean primarily the product of this sort of retroduction from effect to postulated cause. The cause in such a case is defined by the theory, and its warrant is no more than, and no less than, the theory itself. . . . The notions of theory and theoretical entity are thus central to this newly emerging model of science, which we can call *T-science.* In T-science, the predictive power characteristic of P-science blends with the explanatory force characteristic of D-science. There can no longer be a science which merely predicts, or one which merely explains.[49]

McMullin emphasizes the combination of explanation and prediction as the most characteristic feature of empirical science. From the historical point of view, the ideal of the new science did not emerge suddenly. Bacon insisted on the relevance of the practical features and astrophysicists of Galileo's generation searched for a purely theoretical knowledge; it was not until the nineteenth century that the knowledge provided by the new sciences would serve as the basis for guiding and accelerating technology. Actually, when McMullin comments that the main testimony of an acceptable explanation in the new empirical science is precisely its ability to predict, that is, to entail testable consequences, he adds:

Note that this was an *empirical* discovery; it had to be shown that a science fully joining the goals of explanation and prediction was *possible.* It could plausibly be argued that this was one of the most revolutionary discoveries in that century of "scientific revolution."[50]

The consolidation of the new science continues to be a consequence of its ability to join the explanatory and the predictive goals. In this, scientific progress exercises a feedback on the goals of empirical science, showing that they can be attained and thus reinforcing the continuity of the scientific enterprise.

McMullin also remarks that, when we speak about the goals of science, we are considering empirical science as an activity that, owing to its internal structure, tends toward the fulfillment of those goals and not to other superimposed goals, however important from the sociological point of view the latter may be:

When I speak of the goals of *science,* I am thinking primarily of science as an activity on the part of a skilled community, not of science in its other, commoner, sense as a body of propositions set down in a

49. Ibid., pp. 41–42.

50. Ibid., p. 41.

textbook or research article. And I am taking the term "goal," in both the main senses of that slippery term. There are the *ideal* goals (also called explicit or acknowledged), the goals that scientists expressly specify as the aims of their work. And then there are the *actual* goals which are embodied in the activity itself. . . . The ideal goals can be discovered from what scientists *say*, though there can be considerable disagreement within the community of scientists in regard to them. To learn the actual goals, one must scrutinize what scientists *do,* and try to determine from the structure of the activity itself what would count as "success" in it. . . . There is room for disagreement regarding the actual goals of a particular instance of scientific activity also, mainly because different interpreters will estimate success differently.[51]

This issue has a special relevance when analyzing the ethical features of empirical science. But it also provides a framework to obtain a general picture of empirical science. Indeed, the methods used and the results obtained in science must be evaluated against the background of the internal aims of the whole enterprise, and can be said to be correct insofar as they enable us to attain the goals of science.

Obviously, it is we who determine the goals of all our activities. In this sense, it may seem meaningless to establish once and for all the goals of the scientific enterprise, making them independent of our will and desires. Nevertheless, this apparent difficulty is easily solved when we distinguish those goals that constitute the scientific enterprise in itself from those superimposed on it that depend on our changing desires. Among the second category we can list, for instance, the desire for reputation, economic profit, political or military power, or the pleasure that one can find working in science. However, no work will be admitted in principle as truly scientific by a community of natural scientists unless it combines the explanatory and the predictive goals inherent to the entire scientific enterprise, defined as the research for a knowledge of nature that can provide a practical dominion over nature, or as a search for explanations (or theories) that can be submitted to empirical control. This characterization of natural science works as a minimum requirement that any piece of science must fulfill to be admitted as scientific by the community of natural scientists.

Philosophers of science disagree about the goals of empirical science, especially when some of them, in light of technology's increasing role in the progress of science, say that instead of distinguishing between pure and applied science we should speak of "technoscience" as a whole; they stress that scientists are no longer autonomous, but depend for their goals and methods on economic, political, and military factors. There is a grain of truth in this position, insofar as scientific experiments very often involve sophisticated technology that requires large amount of money and the weight of social fac-

51. Ibid., p. 43.

tors in the development of science is sometimes very important. Nonetheless, scientists and philosophers usually agree, at least in practice, when deciding whether some piece of knowledge fulfills the minimum requirements to be considered scientific: a combination of explanatory and predictive power.

2. SCIENTIFIC METHODS

The more the sciences progress, the more we can admire not only the complexity of the order of nature, but also the subtleties of our ability to know it. Indeed, the unitary goal that a combination of explanation and prediction entails implies the use of extremely subtle procedures that require a high dose of creativity.

The methods used in empirical science are anything but an automatic application of prefabricated rules. Creativity and interpretation play a central role in scientific progress. In the natural sciences we want to explain the known by the unknown; therefore, we must propose hypothetical explanations that go beyond the available data and we must then test them, creating new experiments and interpreting their results.

In empirical science we use a great variety of particular techniques or methods. What they have in common is a general scheme that consists of two steps: the construction of theories and their empirical testing. Both steps require creativity and interpretation. Even though philosophers of science do not agree on many other particulars, all would agree that creativity is needed to formulate scientific theories and that very sophisticated arguments are needed to test them.

The construction of scientific laws and theories is a task requiring ingenuity and creativity. For instance, Newton's success with his 1687 book *The Mathematical Principles of Natural Philosophy* arose from a bold stroke: he defined an ideal kind of system that consisted of mass points submitted to mutual forces of attraction (the forces of gravity). The Sun, with a diameter of about one and a half million kilometers, can hardly be reduced to a single point in which its entire mass is concentrated. To reduce the Earth to another mass point also supposes a tremendous simplification, as we eliminate from the Earth everything except its mass and consider it as concentrated in a single point. Another supersimplification is made when we reduce all forces to gravity. Nevertheless, this simple idealized model is very effective when we only wish to study the large-scale motion of the stars and of the planets, because the information relevant for that purpose is represented in the model.

If we studied natural objects as they really exist with all their properties, we would not be able to obtain mathematical laws and theories such as those of the modern science of mechanics. In empirical science we use ideal models, which correspond to the features relevant in every case; the development of these models requires a big dose of creativity. For instance, when Gregor Mendel performed the experiments with peas that led him to formulate the laws of genetics, he concentrated on a few traits of those plants and studied them using the combination of mathematics and experiments typical of the developed branches of empirical science. When he presented his results at a meeting of the Scientific Society of Brno, the participants were astonished at the unusual and novel combination of mathematics and biology used. When Mendel sent those results to one of the preeminent scientists of the epoch, he was told that he should try to perform his experiments with other kinds of plants, which he did without obtaining interesting results. Nobody noticed then the first-rate quality of Mendel's results, because they were obtained using concepts and tools that exceeded the usual way of thinking of his time.

This kind of example could easily be multiplied. We do not find scientific objects by simple inspection or observation of nature; rather, we must develop them. We have to build up concepts that may allow us to study some features of nature while leaving others aside, so that the selected features may be subjected to theoretical treatment and related with experiments.

The subject matter of any scientific discipline is constructed through a method that can aptly be called "objectification."[52] The structure of this method can be described in a straightforward way. We cut out certain pieces of the real world or of a hypothetical unobserved reality in such a way that we obtain a mental cross section, and we construct an ideal system as the object of our theories. Further, we relate some of the theoretical entities of this system to the results of real or possible experiments through a set of basic predicates, and we establish rules to interpret that correspondence. Thus each objectification includes both ideal and pragmatic features that are interrelated in a precise way. When we have obtained a well-defined objectification of this kind, we can then proceed with further intersubjective constructions and proofs.

One of the main difficulties in scientific work is to achieve such an objectification for the first time. Of course, objectifications depend on historical circumstances and evolve with them, and they include conventional aspects, components of scientific knowledge that are not obtained from experience or from theoretical proofs. The existence of conventional aspects demonstrates the relevance of creativity and interpretation in the natural sciences.

Let us consider now the second main feature of the method of empirical science: the requirement of empirical control. Empirical control is not achieved through the application of automatic rules but rather requires creativity and interpretation. The possibility of controlling scientific constructs (concepts, statements, and theories) differs according to their proximity to the observational level; obviously, to determine the validity of the constructs that are closer to the possibilities of observation is much easier than the evaluation of the constructs that lie at more theoretical levels.

A methodological difficulty common to all cases of empirical control is due to the use of the hypothetico-deductive method, in which we formulate

---

52. I have already commented on this point in chapter 1, alluding to the "realist objectualism" of Evandro Agazzi and citing some references on this subject.

hypotheses and evaluate them by submitting their logical consequences to empirical control. Powerful as it may be, this method presents a serious drawback, because, as a consequence of the rules of elementary logic, we can never establish with certainty the truth of a hypothesis, however numerous its well-corroborated consequences may be. Indeed, logic permits us to assert the truth of a logical consequence if we know that it is correctly derived from a true premise, but the reverse is not true: we cannot assert the truth of a premise if we know only that its consequences are true. A true premise can produce only true consequences if the latter are correctly derived, but a true consequence can be derived from either a true premise or a false one, or from the conjunction of true and false premises.

This difficulty has been admitted since ancient times. Aquinas wrote in the thirteenth century that the astronomical theories of his time could not be established with complete certainty, because the observed effects could perhaps be explained by different theories.[53] Karl Popper named this situation the "logical asymmetry between verification and falsation" and made it a cornerstone of his epistemology. Popper concluded that, as a consequence of this difficulty, no theory could ever be verified, so that all scientific knowledge is and will always be "conjectural" knowledge. He labeled his conclusion "fallibilism," and it is so widespread among contemporary philosophers of science that it can be said that almost every one of them is a fallibilist (Figure 5.1).

I shall argue that, in spite of that logical difficulty, we can be pretty sure about the truth of many scientific statements. But I also want to stress that, if the hypothetico-deductive method is to have any utility at all, we must use it with a high degree of subtlety. In fact, logical rules alone would lead us to perplexity, as they do not allow us to establish the truth of any hypothesis. If we desire to explain how empirical science works, we must admit that scientists use subtle kinds of reasoning that go beyond pure formal logic.

I do not mean to say that the arguments used by scientists are contrary to any logical rule or are deprived of logical strength, but that they include interpretations that are not the result of pure observation or of purely logical argument alone. These interpretations can sometimes change. I also mean that we know how to deal with problems that from the logical point of view present unsolvable difficulties.

Creativity and interpretation are needed for more than filling logical holes in scientific arguments. Leaving aside these issues, we need to be creative to devise experiments, interpret their results, and use those results in the evaluation of theories. Therefore, the entire field of empirical science is the result of human creativity. We may conclude that, at this level, the rationality of science does not lie in the application of automatic rules or algorithmic procedures, but includes a sophisticated combination of creativity, argument, and interpretation.

53. Thomas Aquinas, *Summa Theologiae* (Torino-Roma: Marietti, 1952), part I, question 32, article 1, ad secundum: p. 169.

(1)	GENERAL EMPIRICAL LAW	All swans are white
(2)	POSITIVE INSTANCES	A, B, C, D..........are white
(3)	NEGATIVE INSTANCES	X is black

> A general empirical law cannot be verified, however
> numerous the positive instances may be.

> A single negative instance shows that a general
> empirical law contains some error.

Fig. 5.1 Logical asymmetry between verification and falsification. (1) "All swans are white" is a general empirical law. (2) We find confirmations of this law, represented by A, B, C, D, and so on. However numerous these instances are, they will never be sufficient to "verify" the general laws because we can never be sure that we will not find new contrary instances. Hence we conclude that we can never verify a general empirical law. (3) A single instance contrary to the law is enough to conclude that that law contains some error. Therefore, a single contrary instance permits us to "falsify" the law. This is a feature of logic; therefore, it holds in every particular case that we can never definitively verify general empirical laws, but we can falsify them.

3. Scientific Constructs

The role of interpretation and creativity at all levels of empirical science becomes even more evident when we realize that even the most elementary concepts used in science cannot be derived from observation and logic alone.

Let us consider, for example, the concepts of mass, time, and temperature, some of the most basic ones in the entire field of science. They are closely related to ordinary experience; nevertheless, to make them useful to science, they must be defined in such a way that they may be submitted to mathematics and may also be measured using adequate empirical instruments. These involve difficulties that can be solved only by the use of subtle methods, including conventional stipulations.

Thus, to measure the value of temperature we must use a law that relates temperature to some observable effects (such as the dilatation of a liquid or a gas). But, how can we establish such a law if we do not know yet how we should measure temperatures? A similar difficulty arises regarding the other concepts. In the case of time, we must know that some periodic motion exists whose duration is always the same, so that it can serve as a basic reference for measuring the duration of other motions; we then find, however, a similar difficulty. Indeed, we may wonder how we can know that a concrete motion is repeated regularly if we do not yet know how we can measure time. If we consider mass, we should add that, according to the theory of relativity, the mass of a body no longer has a fixed value, because it changes according to the speed of the body. These difficulties are real and cannot be overcome by the tools of observation and logic only. Instead, we have been successful in using ingenuity to establish stipulations adequate for our purpose in many cases. Our present scientific standards are the result of the work of very talented, creative people, and creativity continues to be necessary for further progress.

It goes without saying that the role of interpretation and creativity is even more important when we are no longer dealing with basic concepts that are linked to ordinary experience. More sophisticated concepts such as Lagrangian and Hamiltonian functions, hydrogen bonds, or the genetic pool obviously require a great dose of creativity and cannot be reduced to or derived from observations.

The irreducibility of scientific concepts to a combination of observations has a very important consequence: scientific statements, which are composed of such concepts, have a similar status and therefore cannot be verified by using merely observational reports. In fact, we can establish a gradation among scientific statements according to their proximity to the observational level. At one extreme we should place those empirical laws that contain only magnitudes that can be measured directly and, therefore, can be empirically tested in quite a safe way; such is the case, for instance, with Ohm's law: we can easily test the value of this law in a great variety of circumstances, as it establishes a relation between potential difference, electrical intensity, and electrical resistance, three magnitudes that can be directly measured. At the opposite extreme we could place such general principles as the principle of conservation of energy, which is supposed to be true of all natural processes and to include all types of energy; in this case, creativity and interpretation must be employed to define the theoretical concepts and their measurements in an enormous variety of phenomena. The most extreme case of this kind would be the case of principles such as the requirement of special relativity that the laws of physics have the same form when referred to any inertial system of reference. In any case, it can be safely said that testing scientific statements always involves ingenuity, creativity, and interpretation.

Similar remarks can be applied to theoretical systems. Some of them, which are usually called phenomenological, are relatively close to the observational level and therefore their consequences can easily be empirically tested; this is the case, for instance, with classical thermodynamics, which defines thermodynamic systems in terms of temperature, pressure, and volume. But other theories, such as general relativity or quantum mechanics, include very abstract features that are related to observable phenomena only in a very indirect way. This is also the case with statistical mechanics, which explains the laws of classical thermodynamics by using a corpuscular model. In any event, there is a double reason for stressing the role of interpretation and creativity in theoretical systems: on the one hand, because they are composed of statements that transcend the observational level, and on the other hand, because they often include further explanations that belong to an even higher level than usual scientific laws. This is not to say that theories are unimportant; on the contrary, as a consequence of their greater depth, they usually provide a closer grasp of the natural world.

We can now understand better why empiricism does not work. According to the empiricist epistemology of the Vienna Circle, scientific statements and theories should be verifiable in such a way that they can be reduced to observational terms through purely logical derivations. The supporters of this variety of empiricism were moved by a kind of scientism; they desired to show that empirical science is the only kind of valid knowledge and thought that they could establish this view by using a reductionist approach. Ironically, because their reductionist views did not work, they unconsciously undermined the value of the very science they desired to present as a paradigm.

The crisis of the empiricist views of the Vienna Circle, which were widespread in the epistemological field in the 1950s, provoked a crisis in the concept of scientific truth. The new views proposed in the 1960s and 1970s very often represented relativist stances in which the very concept of scientific truth was deprived of meaning or even ignored, as an obsolete and useless idea.

III. THE REACH OF SCIENCE

Empirical science is a human enterprise more complex than previously thought. Usually, theories of scientific rationality try to explain how science works, proposing criteria that could be applied to (future) problems of theory choice and to (past) problems of rationally reconstructing the history of science. However, the difficulties of this task demonstrate the complexity of the enterprise and the highly sophisticated arguments involved; it very often proceeds in a patchwork way and, at the same time, uses rational arguments. Epistemology must take account of the many sides of science, and it is not easy to put them together in a unitary comprehensive interpretation that includes both the descriptive-sociological and normative-logical features.

A century after the discovery of the electron in 1897, nobody has ever seen an electron (or any other subatomic particle), even using the most powerful microscopes. Nevertheless, we know for certain that something like the electrons described in our physical theories exist, and we are able to manipulate and control them. This situation is not an exception in empirical science: it is the rule. The greatness of empirical science lies precisely in the fact that it allows us to know an entire world of entities, properties, and processes that cannot be observed or reduced to observations. The price that science must pay to obtain its results is apparently paradoxical: it must rely on stipulations that cannot be proven. I shall try to show that the existence of conventional factors in science is the usual route used in empirical science to reach an intersubjectivity that ultimately leads to genuinely true knowledge.

1. CONVENTIONAL FACTORS IN SCIENCE

In empirical science, theories must always be submitted to testing. Neverthe-less, experiments are planned and interpreted using concepts that cannot be reduced to mere observation. Nothing like "pure empirical data" exists, and so experimental testing does not consist in merely comparing theories and empirical data.

Today it is generally acknowledged that all kinds of data and experiments are "theory laden," and that theories cannot be proven using only the results of observation. Along these lines, philosophers speak about the "underdeter-mination" of theories by empirical facts as a real feature of the scientific pro-cedure. I have already argued that, when we define magnitudes such as mass, temperature, or time, we cannot rely on mere observation and logical argu-ment; indeed, besides using observation and logic, we must establish some rules that are to be considered as conventions or stipulations. In contrast with the image of an inductive science based on pure data and growing by gener-alizations that can be verified by observation, we must admit that interpreta-tion plays a most important role in empirical science and so a variety of stip-ulations or conventional factors will exist.

This is not to say that we can introduce stipulations in an arbitrary way. We must choose stipulations, because otherwise we could not achieve good results.

Kurt Hübner has forcefully argued in favor of the existence of conven-tional factors in empirical science, labeling them "a priori precepts." He dis-tinguishes five main types of such stipulations, which he calls *instrumental, functional, axiomatic, judicative,* and *normative.* According to Hübner:

> Neither basic statements in science nor natural laws nor axioms per-taining to theories can be founded without "a priori precepts." We need such precepts when we take measurements with instruments, when we formulate natural laws in the form of functions, when we base a theory on axioms, when we stipulate rules for accepting or re-futing theories, and when we define norms to distinguish science from other kinds of world-interpretation. (*Instrumental, functional, axiomatic, judicative* and *normative precepts a priori*).[54]

In other words:

> These five concepts describe those kinds of precepts which are indis-pensable for the formation, examination, and judgement of theories in physics insofar as these theories are related to measurements. . . . This holds because whenever a theory of this sort is sought, we *must* decide on the particular form the theory should have and on particu-lar axioms (thus we must decide in normative and axiomatic pre-cepts); and at the same time we *must* establish a transposition mecha-

54. Kurt Hübner, "Short Abstract of My Philosophical Conceptions and Ideas" (Personal com-munication with author: February 16, 1987), n. 1.

nism linking the theory with the experimental results (hence we *must* devise instrumental, functional, and judicative precepts). However, with regard to particular cases, there is no necessarily valid prescription for *how* we go about all this.[55]

Let us consider in more detail these five kinds of stipulation. First of all, *instrumental stipulations* refer to the instruments used to obtain measurements. Because all measurements mean accepting some laws, establishing units, and interpreting the working of the corresponding instruments, we need this kind of stipulation when dealing with the empirical testing of statements that involve quantitative magnitudes. We need more complex stipulations when we use more sophisticated instruments, and a highly complex set of them when we deal with extremely complex procedures such as those employed in the detectors of subatomic particles.

Functional stipulations refer to the formulation of those scientific laws that have the form of functional relations between magnitudes. We can express some laws by using ordinary language; however, in the more developed stages of empirical science, we must employ mathematical instruments and accept the corresponding stipulations. This kind of tool must be adapted to the specific needs of research; sometimes they are even created for particular purposes, leaving aside those features that should be taken into account in the field of mathematics but are irrelevant when in the field of the empirical sciences. Then new stipulations are needed.

Axiomatic stipulations refer to the choice of the basic axioms of a theory. As we must stop the logical proofs at some point, we must always take as our point of departure some axioms that are accepted as such. One and the same theory can be formalized in different ways, so that we have to choose those statements that we want to consider basic axioms; therefore, there is always an element of convention in this choice. Moreover, scientific theories are always evolving, so that the ideal of a completely perfect formalization is usually very difficult to achieve; as a consequence, the range of options for choosing the axioms of a theory is sometimes quite large.

Judicative stipulations refer to the acceptance or rejection of theories on the basis of experiments. When we submit a theory to empirical tests, we must interpret the empirical observations, judging whether they are consistent with the theory and deciding, in consequence, whether we accept or reject the theory. If we reject it, we must decide whether it is going to be completely rejected or only partially altered, and, in the last case, which part of it must be altered. That we need stipulations becomes crystal clear when we realize that in order to accept or reject theories on the basis of empirical tests we must use instrumental, functional, and axiomatic stipulations, and must decide whether we consider the accepted observational reports as coherent or contrary to the theory being tested, weighing evidence to decide whether we

---

55. Kurt Hübner, *Critique of Scientific Reason* (Chicago and London: The University of Chicago Press, 1983), p. 43.

should introduce new auxiliary hypotheses or new scientific laws, reinterpret some experimental results, or abandon our theory.

Normative stipulations refer to the so-called "problem of demarcation": to distinguishing between empirical science and other cognitive claims. Indeed, as a consequence of the existence of the previous types of stipulations, this fifth type is also necessary when we try to characterize the whole scientific enterprise and to integrate it within the wider area of human experience.

Thus, it seems undeniable that in empirical science we have to introduce conventional factors, conventions, or stipulations. One can explain and classify them as Hübner does or in other ways, but we will always resort to the need for them. This idea was forcefully underscored by Karl Popper in the 1934 first edition of *The Logic of Scientific Discovery,* when he spoke of his criterion of demarcation between science and metaphysics as a proposal for an agreement or a convention,[56] and explained falsification as the logical clash between scientific theories and basic statements, adding that those statements are neither justified by sense data nor can be proven in a definitive way, so that we must decide in every case which statements we are going to consider as basic in our tests.

Popper's remark is important because it has become a commonplace in the contemporary philosophy of science to consider his views as a variation on the positivist account of science provided by the Vienna Circle. This is not the place to vindicate the originality of Popper's epistemology; what really matters here is that, according to the standard account, until Thomas Kuhn, Paul Feyerabend, and others changed the situation in the 1960s, it was generally admitted that science is built up and corroborated using observation statements that were in some way theory-free. Only Kuhn and his followers (adding perhaps some independent authors such as Norwood Russell Hanson) were thought to have introduced the idea that all observational reports are theory-laden and so can be corrected. According to accepted thought, these authors were also the first ones to emphasize the role conventional factors play in the development of empirical science.

Leaving aside issues of historical accuracy, what is wrong with this cliché is that it leads us to see the existence of conventional factors in science under a Kuhnian perspective, that is, as a consequence of the psychosociohistorical features of the scientific enterprise and therefore, as something that, in some way, clashes with logic and reason. If this were the case, to recognize that such conventional factors exist would amount to recognizing that Kuhn is right, so that if we desired to understand empirical science and to determine its value, we would be obliged to adopt a perspective centered on psychosociohistorical factors.

But the existence of conventional factors in empirical sciences was already one of the main ideas of authors such as Henri Poincaré, Pierre Duhem, and Ernst Mach at the end of the nineteenth century. These authors, who were

---

56. Popper, *The Logic of Scientific Discovery,* cit., section 4.

both scientists and philosophers, even exaggerated the role of conventions in science and presented a picture of empirical science that has been labeled "conventionalism." Popper clearly recognized the existence of conventional factors in the development of empirical science; but he denied that science could be considered in the main as a mere collection of conventions or stipulations that are useful for practical purposes, because he considered the scientific enterprise as a search for truth. Popper's insistence on falsifiability referred to the logical features of scientific knowledge but, above all, it referred to the scientific attitude: according to Popper, the hallmark of empirical science is, and should ever be, to search for empirical refutations, because every refutation will provide a clue to better knowledge.

2. SCIENTIFIC OBJECTIVITY

At first sight, the existence of conventional factors in science could seem incompatible with the objectivity that is usually considered characteristic of empirical science. Instead, I hold that it is precisely the use of adequate stipulations that paves the way to scientific objectivity.

To begin with, conventional factors are used in such a way that a specific kind of objectivity emerges as a consequence of their very existence. Indeed, to use conventions means that we act with a certain degree of freedom, but once specific stipulations have been adopted, we are no longer free to interpret measurements, experiments, statements, and theories in an arbitrary way. Hübner aptly expresses this situation in this way:

> Consequently, all empirical statements are dependent on *a priori* precepts with the exception of *metatheoretical statements* of the following type: If we presuppose a certain group of statements *a priori* of the type mentioned above, we will have certain empirical results. (E.g. if we presuppose space to be Euclidean, then we observe gravitational forces; if we presuppose space to be a Riemann space, these forces vanish and everything formerly explained by gravitational forces can now be explained by the curvature of space. Premise and conclusion of these metatheoretical statements are dependent on *a priori* stipulations—but the *if-then-relation* as such does not).[57]

This is an important consequence. Indeed, those metatheoretical statements are the only absolutes in the arguments of empirical science. The value of all scientific statements depends on contexts that include theoretical and pragmatical stipulations; therefore, the objectivity that we reach will also be contextual.

We must immediately add, however, that this does not imply any kind of arbitrariness. On the contrary, once we admit a particular set of stipulations and define an objectification using them, we are no longer free when we determine

---

57. Hübner, "Short Abstract of My Philosophical Conceptions and Ideas," cit., n. 2.

the value of the constructs that we may build within that field. For instance, if we adopt the context that defines classical mechanics, we cannot admit that mass changes with speed or that measures of length and duration depend on the frame of reference, as is the case in relativity theory. Any specific objectification restricts our range of choice when we operate with the basic magnitudes of the theory, measure them, or judge the value of the laws and theories, precisely because we have already chosen to operate in a specific way.

Stipulations and objectifications can change. Hübner proposes a historicist interpretation that echoes Collingwood:

> Since precepts *a priori* can only be deduced from other such precepts they can only be founded, to avoid *regressum ad infinitum*, by the *historical situation* in which they are rooted. The whole of the precepts *a priori* of a special historical situation form a historical *system-ensemble* and we can even define every historical situation by such a system-ensemble. Therefore, every historical situation determines via the corresponding system-ensemble what the facts and fundamental principles will be.[58]

In my opinion, this assertion contains two theses. The first is that the system-ensemble of stipulations has a historical character because it is not unchanging and it can evolve. The second refers to the relationship that exists between every context of objectification and the corresponding historical situation. According to Hübner, if we desire to determine these relationships in a concrete way, we should examine in detail the cultural characteristics of the different historical situations. Actually, Hübner has devoted some attention to historical issues.[59] In any case, this issue cannot be easily settled and should be carefully analyzed to avoid an exaggerated historicism.

Here, I am mainly concerned with the problem of the objectivity of empirical science, and more specifically with the following question: is there some reason why the stipulations of empirical science should not be considered merely arbitrary agreements?

We can, in principle, propose and adopt the stipulations we prefer, provided we are coherent with them. There is no guarantee, however, that any one of them will provide us with new knowledge and new empirical control over the natural world. The range of stipulations that may help us to achieve the aims of the scientific enterprise is very narrow. As a matter of fact, a stock of new proposals are always present in the scientific market that offer themselves as better than currently accepted theories; most do not lead to new interesting predictions and are not taken seriously by the leaders of the scientific community. These leaders can err, and we know that they sometimes have erred; nevertheless, in the natural sciences the number of new proposals that are really interesting is not very high.

---

58. Ibid., n. 4.

59. See, for instance Kurt Hübner, *Die Wahrheit des Mythos* (München: C. H. Beck, 1985).

Should we consider this situation as a mere matter of fact, or can we provide any criteria that may enable us to know when a new proposal is not only internally coherent but also interesting from an objective point of view?

A number of criteria have been proposed to help determine the acceptability of new theories in science. Ian Barbour synthesized those proposals in the following way:

> There are four criteria for assessing theories in normal scientific research:
>
> 1. *Agreement with Data.* This is the most important criterion. . . . Theories are always underdetermined by data. . . . However, agreement with data and predictive success—especially the prediction of novel phenomena not previously anticipated—constitute impressive support for a theory.
>
> 2. *Coherence.* A theory should be consistent with other accepted theories and, if possible, conceptually interconnected with them. Scientists also value the internal coherence and simplicity of a theory. . . .
>
> 3. *Scope.* Theories can be judged by their comprehensiveness or generality. A theory is valued if it unifies previously disparate domains, if it is supported by a variety of kinds of evidence, or if it is applicable to wide ranges of the relevant variables.
>
> 4. *Fertility.* A theory is evaluated not just by its past accomplishments but by its current ability and future promise in providing the framework for an ongoing research program . . .[60]

Some years ago I proposed a list of five criteria that coincide with Barbour's in many respects.[61] The five criteria on my list are actually used by scientists and may be applied not only to hypotheses that are close to the observational level, but also to intermediate- and high-level theoretical systems. The better we can confirm by experiment a higher number of consequences of different kinds, the more we can rely on the hypotheses from which these consequences have been derived, especially if the consequences include accurate predictions that were previously unknown. Moreover, it is not only the quantity of proofs that matters; very often a single proof has more weight than many other proofs together if it is specific enough.

The first criterion is *explanatory power,* the capacity for the hypotheses to explain the problems posed and to account for the available data. For instance, the double-helical structure of DNA was immediately admitted when James Watson and Francis Crick first proposed it in 1953 because it explained the conservation and transmission of genetic material in a very satisfactory way and fitted well with the available data. On a more abstract level, one of the arguments in favor of special relativity and quantum mechanics is that both yield the well-corroborated results of classical mechanics under the appro-

---

60. Ian Barbour, *Religion in an Age of Science* (San Francisco: Harper, 1990), p. 34.

61. Mariano Artigas, *Filosofía de la ciencia experimental. La objetividad y la verdad en las ciencias,* 2d ed. (Pamplona: Eunsa, 1992), pp. 138–142.

priate conditions, namely when we consider systems moving at speeds much lower than the speed of light, in the case of special relativity, or when the systems have a comparatively big mass, in the case of quantum mechanics. Even if it is a matter of debate whether classical mechanics can be considered a particular case of relativity and quantum mechanics, the fact that these theories provide explanations of the already well-tested laws and data supports their adequacy.

The second criterion is *predictive power*. This could be considered as another formulation of the first criterion, insofar as we admit that prediction is only a particular case of explanation. I wish to stress that predictive power plays a first-rate role as a criterion in favor of the acceptance of theories, especially when we deal with previously unknown predictions; indeed, when these kinds of predictions are corroborated, they constitute one of the main arguments in favor of the acceptance of theories in empirical science. For instance, using Newtonian mechanics, the French astronomer Jean Joseph Leverrier predicted in 1846 the existence of a new planet beyond the orbit of Uranus that would explain the anomalies in the motion of Uranus. Its position and size were calculated, so that when the German astronomer Johann Gottfried Galle discovered the planet called Neptune, on September 23, 1846, this was interpreted as the greatest success of Newton's mechanics. Incidentally, Leverrier also calculated an anomaly in the motion of Mercury that he did not succeed in explaining; the success of Einstein's 1915 theory of general relatively in providing a good explanation for this anomaly was one of the main reasons for the acceptance of this theory. The strongest support in favor of general relatively came, nevertheless, when the British expeditions directed by Sir Arthur Eddington corroborated in 1919 the deviation of light due to the effect of gravitational forces such as predicted by Einstein. The big bang model, proposed for the first time by Georges Lemaître in 1927 and refined by George Gamow in 1948, was only a rival to the steady state theory of Thomas Gold and Fred Hoyle until 1964, when Arno Penzias and Robert Wilson discovered the microwave background radiation predicted by the big bang theory, which gained from that very moment the support and interest of the scientific community. Similarly, the 1983 discovery of the W and Z particles by Carlo Rubbia and his team at CERN (Geneva) provided strong support for the electroweak theory proposed by Steven Weinberg and Abdus Salam. It is worth noting that when applying this criterion, what really matters is not only the number of corroborated predictions, but their specific character.

The first and the second criterion are reinforced by the *accuracy of explanations and predictions,* which can be considered as a third criterion because it has a specific relevance by itself. In empirical science, progress is to a great extent the consequence of accuracy in calculation and experiment. Johannes Kepler devoted two years to his initial studies on the orbit of Mars, but he began again when he realized that there was a disagreement of 8 minutes of arch between his theory and Tycho Brahe's data; in his epoch such a difference was not considered relevant, but Kepler's pioneering work was possible because he attributed a greater value to accuracy than other people did. We can also see that to corroborate Einstein's prediction, two scientific expeditions were organized so that they could accurately measure the phenomenon in Brazil and in the Gulf of Guinea on the occasion of a solar eclipse. The detection of the W and Z particles was the result of several years of experimental work in which more than a hundred physicists participated, and it required the development of new techniques and the construction of new equipment.

Convergence of varied and independent proofs is a fourth criterion that reinforces the reliability of scientific constructs. For instance, the big bang model not only was corroborated by the discovery of the microwave background radiation, but is also consistent with data obtained from other predictions, such as the relative abundance of light elements in the universe. The fact that different phenomena that can be tested independently can be explained and predicted by the same theory is a good argument in favor of that theory.

Mutual support is a fifth criterion of the validity of scientific theories. Thus atomic theory steadily increased in reliability during the nineteenth century as it became more and more integrated with the explanations and predictions of other theories and disciplines; today it is successfully used not only in the realm of atomic physics, but also in those of chemistry, molecular biology, astrophysics, and others. Theories become intertwined, forming a kind of net, so that the corroboration of some empirical consequences reinforces the reliability of all the elements of the net.

These five criteria help to overcome the logical difficulties of the hypothetico-deductive method. They enable us to understand that, even if the proofs used in empirical science are not completely conclusive from the point of view of formal logic, we can nevertheless reach a kind of knowledge that can be considered a good candidate for the status of true knowledge.

3. Truth in Science

A further question to consider is the following: can we say that the knowledge of the natural world provided by empirical science is true? I argue that in empirical science we can actually reach a true knowledge of the natural world. Whatever interpretation scientific methods may be given, it cannot be denied that science provides us with extensive knowledge about the composition of matter, the mechanisms of life, and many other features of the real world. My thesis is, on the one hand, that the method employed in empirical science presupposes a basic epistemological realism—that we are able to search for true knowledge of the natural world and to reach it—and on the other hand, that this realism is retrojustified, enlarged, and refined by the progress of science.

This thesis faces an intriguing situation in contemporary epistemology: the strong tendency toward relativist and instrumentalist views. For instance, Bas van Fraassen argues that empirical adequacy is the only requisite for the acceptance of theories,[62] and Larry Laudan, even as he presents himself as an opponent of relativism, concludes:

> given the present state of the art, it can only be wish fulfillment that gives rise to the claim that realism, and realism alone, explains why science works.[63]

I would like to clarify that I do not make this claim. I only consider it to be a necessary condition of science, which is retrojustified by scientific progress. Along these lines, Jarrett Leplin argues that "certain realist assumptions are crucial to the rationality of research."[64] Indeed, unless we admit that our ability to know enables us to grasp real features of the natural world, the entire scientific enterprise, including its results and applications, can hardly be meaningful.

Arguments have raged between supporters and opponents of realism. In addition, supporters of realism disagree about its scope and about the reasons in favor of their position. Some argue in favor of a realism of aspiration rather than a realism of achievement; this position is typical of Popperian epistemology, in which truth is seen as a regulative idea while at the same time, we are told that we can never know whether we have reached it.

Difficulties concerning realism can be summarized by the following chain of reasoning. First, because scientific entities are constructed in the process of theorizing, they do not have a mind-independent ontological status. Second, the process of construction determines the theory-ladenness of any scientific fact, so we could never prove the realistic character of our theories. Third, the logical aspects of the hypothetico-deductive method imply the underdetermination of theories and, as a consequence, the impossibility of assessing the truth of any concrete scientific achievement. Fourth, these features of the scientific method lead to a fallibilist view consistent with the provisional character of any scientific construct and precludes any claim about absolute or definitive truth. And fifth, empirical adequacy may be seen as a sufficient requirement for explaining how science works; accordingly, even if positivism were considered incapable of providing an adequate account of science, it would not be necessary to adopt a realistic view to do justice to actual scientific practice.

These five difficulties are connected to and correspond with real problems.[65] They are grounded in the use of constructions that transcend the

---

62. Bas C. van Fraassen, *The Scientific Image* (Oxford: Oxford University Press, 1980), p. 12 and passim.

63. Larry Laudan, "A Confutation of Convergent Realism," *Philosophy of Science,* 48 (1981): 48.

64. Jarrett Leplin, "Methodological Realism and Scientific Rationality," *Philosophy of Science,* 53 (1986): 31.

65. An interesting analysis of the difficulties that realism must face, accompanied by a moderate realist proposal, can be found in Ernan McMullin, "A Case for Scientific Realism," in *Scientific Realism,* ed. Jarrett Leplin (Berkeley: University of California Press, 1984), pp. 8–40.

realm of experience and include conventions and stipulations. Nevertheless, as we have seen, the very use of these stipulations permits us to formulate intersubjective constructions and proofs that lead to intersubjective results. Empirical science includes a high dose of creativity and interpretation that, at the same time, makes it possible to reach intersubjective proofs that lead to objective results. The apparent opposition between the personal and the objective features of human knowledge is transformed into collaboration. Logical arguments play a central role in empirical science, but scientific progress requires a kind of evaluation that, even when it does not contradict logic, goes far beyond the strict limits of formal logic alone.

Difficulties necessarily arise if we think of truth as a qualification that can only be applied to that which is totally independent of our ability to know and of our active intervention; if this were so, we could never engage in meaningful talk about truth. But this we can do, provided we realize that truth is primarily a qualification of our knowledge, and that this knowledge can be called true if what we assert corresponds with the real situation we intend to reflect. In that case, truth is relative to a particular perspective that includes both theoretical and pragmatical features; this amounts to saying that truth is contextual. However, once we have established a well-defined context, we are no longer free to interpret claims to truth in a subjective way.

Does this mean that we can only achieve a contextual truth? If so, truth would be synonymous with coherence, and there would be no problem with realism. Even those most strongly opposed to the idea of scientific truth would admit that we often reach rigorous proofs; nevertheless, they would argue that proofs are rigorous only within a given presuppositional framework and that, therefore, we can only speak of truth as consisting of relations of coherence. What is at stake then is the possibility of passing from a coherence notion of validity to a correspondence notion of truth.

This passage is not difficult if we realize that the meaning of "truth" as correspondence with reality, even if it is basically the same in all circumstances, has specific features in different cases. Above all, the concept of "truth" is applied to our knowledge; we say that our knowledge is true when it corresponds with reality. But our knowledge includes different kinds of statements, and their correspondence with reality must be evaluated in each particular case, taking into account their specificity.

A few examples may illustrate this point. When we say that an experimental law, which establishes a relationship between the values of several magnitudes, is true, we do not mean that it corresponds like a photograph with some real state of affairs; we only mean that, given the appropriate circumstances, if we measure the values of the magnitudes involved in the law, these values will be related in the way expressed by the law. When we say that a planet, or a galaxy, or a black hole exists that has such and such characteristics, we mean that there is some real entity that possesses these properties. When we say that DNA has a double-helical structure whose components are such and such chemicals, we mean that the spatial structure really exists in the way we describe it and that its chemical components fit well with our description of them. In all these cases, it is not difficult to attribute a truth-value to our statements, but the different meanings of the adjective "true" should be differentiated when applied to different cases. When we try to decide if a theoretical system is true, especially in mathematical physics, the whole issue becomes more difficult. Such systems usually contain mathematical principles and models that, in the best case, can be considered as idealized representations that very often have no factual counterpart, as well as constructs that have a purely instrumental meaning; therefore, we can decide if the experimental laws contained in the theory are true, but it is quite difficult to say that the entire system is true.

I would conclude that prejudices against the use of the concept of truth in empirical science are very often due to a misunderstanding of the meanings this concept acquires in the different cases. Nonetheless those prejudices dissolve when we realize that scientific truth is always contextual and must therefore be interpreted according to the specific features involved in every context.

Thus we can speak of a scientific truth that is contextual and therefore also partial and approximate. And this implies that such truth is perfectible—that it must be conceived as having a somewhat different value according to the different modalities of construction and proof—and that it has a historical dimension, because any context is defined by using constructions that depend on historical conditions.

This explanation of scientific truth combines contextual, semantic, and pragmatical features, which correspond to the theories of truth as coherence, as correspondence, and as praxis. We will meet unsolvable problems if we separate these features.[66] Such problems arise, for example, if we try to establish truth as a correspondence conceived as completely independent of theoretical construction and pragmatic intervention. An interpretation of this kind would amount to illegitimately making scientific truth absolute, because the value of our knowledge would be considered as though independent of our concepts, their references, and the real problems we try to solve with them. My explanation of truth takes into account these dimensions of our knowledge.

The relative aspect of truth, as has been explained, is actually innocuous and does not involve any relativist consequences such as subjectivism or skepticism. It could be compared with the kind of relativity which, in the theory of relativity, implies that well-defined values exist in any framework. Obviously, we must always be aware of the framework we are using in each particular case, but, however difficult this task may be, it can be achieved. We will never reach complete knowledge, but we can obtain a general perspective on the particular perspectives we use.

---

66. This point is stressed in the "internal realism" of Hilary Putnam; see his book *Representation and Reality* (Cambridge, Mass.: The MIT Press, 1988), pp. 113–116.

(A)

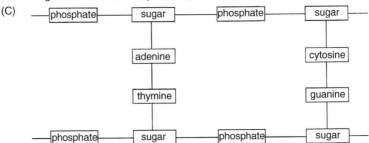

(B) The principle of conservation of energy means that the sum of all kinds of energy (mechanical, eletromagnetic, and so on) is the same at the beginning and at the end of any natural process.

(C)

Fig. 5.2 Scientific truth. Truth means correspondence between our statements and reality. Different kinds of scientific constructs correspond to reality in different ways. (A) Experimental laws, such as Ohm's law, express a relationship between measurable magnitudes. Ohm's law expresses a relationship between three electrical magnitudes: potential (V), resistance (R), and intensity (I). Insofar as we accept the concepts usually used in electricity, this relationship holds in any electrical circuit and can be considered as true. (B) General principles are supposed to hold in a great variety of circumstances. Thus, the principle of conservation of energy should hold for any natural process. Until now, whenever this principle has failed, scientists have introduced new previously unknown factors. This strategy has been useful until now, but if applied to other cases it could lead to undesirable conventionalist positions. In relativity theory, taking into account the equivalence between mass and energy, we should speak about the conservation of mass-energy. (C) The existence of particular spatial or temporal patterns, such as the double-helical structure of DNA, can sometimes be proved beyond any reasonable doubt. We can find, however, that in some particular cases there can exist single-helical DNA.

Construction and test, as they are used in empirical science, presuppose a realist perspective. Theoretical constructs refer to real situations and are used to explain them, and methods of empirical testing serve to prove the explanatory claims of theories. An antirealist perspective would fail to account for the real achievements of the scientific method and even for its fallibilistic aspects.

The realism presupposed by the scientific method does not involve many specific philosophical subtleties. It is centered on the possibility of obtaining true knowledge about reality. Scientific progress shows that this presupposition is basically correct; indeed, instrumentalism and relativism do not fit well with the realist aim of the scientific enterprise or with its results and applications: therefore, we can say that epistemological realism is retrojustified by scientific progress and that it is also refined and enlarged.

The refinements refer to the subtleties involved in scientific practice. The empirical and theoretical aspects of actual scientific practice are intertwined in such a way that both empiricism and rationalism fail to explain how science works. Pragmatism too fails to account for the results that we obtain. Further examination of the scientific method may provide important insights into human knowledge and the philosophical problems related to it.

We can also speak of an enrichment of realism. The progress of science implies that our knowledge has been and continues to be enlarged to an astonishing degree. This refers not only to concrete pieces of information, but also to the exercise of our abilities. The subtleties of the scientific method are not established once and for all; they are expanded and applied in new ways as science progresses. Creativity is an essential part of the scientific method, not only because we construct theories that transcend the available data, but also because the ways of relating ideal constructs with empirical data require the exercise of a creative way of reasoning. Even the work performed to obtain empirical data is creative, because it requires imagination and skill.

All this means that empirical science is highly relevant to understanding how we obtain knowledge and to evaluating our notions of truth and realism, and thereby it is also relevant to examining intelligibility in general. This conclusion is grounded on the existence of scientific truth and on the analysis of the scientific method.

I have argued in favor of a moderate kind of realism that not only leaves room for interpretation and creativity, but requires them. I have stressed that scientific truth is contextual; this implies that there are many different kinds of scientific truth that must be evaluated in every single case, and that this evaluation requires interpretative skills that go far beyond merely automatic procedures. In conclusion I would stress that, even though other perspectives provide a less adequate picture of the reach of scientific knowledge and of the entire scientific enterprise, most of them can also be used to argue for the singularity of the human being as the creative agent of empirical science; actually, although differences among contemporary positions in epistemology are neither few nor small, all these positions would admit that empirical science is a highly creative enterprise that requires a great dose of interpretation that, in its turn, supposes highly developed intellectual skills.

6

*Man
in Nature*

I shall explore in more detail the impact of scientific progress on our image of the human being. First I shall analyze some naturalist perspectives on human knowledge. Naturalism underscores the continuity between human beings and the rest of nature. Insofar as we are natural beings, the naturalist approach may help us uncover interesting features of our human nature. Nevertheless, some versions of naturalism carry the methods of empirical science too far and leave no room for the spiritual dimensions of the human being. When such positions are presented as scientific or as a consequence of scientific progress, they represent a pseudoscientific abuse of science.

I will examine the place of empirical science within the wider field of human rationality, concentrating on reliability and fallibility, because they lie at the root of contemporary problems about the value of human knowledge.

Finally, I shall examine the image of the human being that corresponds to the epistemological consequences of scientific progress. Scientific creativity can be seen as a proof of our singularity and as a capacity that enables us to participate in God's plans, carrying the natural and the human realms to their fulfillment.

I. SCIENCE, EPISTEMOLOGY, AND NATURALISM: FOUR POSITIONS

I will now examine four positions that present themselves as naturalist and are closely associated with epistemology. The first, which is usually called "naturalized epistemology," stresses the idea that epistemology should concentrate on the actual methods and development of empirical science. The second, called "evolutionary epistemology," stresses that evolutionary theory should play a central role in epistemology. Both perspectives can be useful, but in some versions there is a danger of reductionism. The third and the fourth positions, which I call "methodological naturalism" and "anthropological naturalism," deny that human beings possess dimensions other than the material. These perspectives are clearly reductionist; moreover, when presented as if they were a consequence of science, they involve a self-defeating and illegitimate scientism.

1. Epistemology Naturalized

It has been claimed that epistemology should be naturalized, although there is no unanimity about what this means, except on one point: proponents of a naturalized epistemology usually claim that we should study science using the scientific method, considering empirical science to be like any other subject studied by empirical science. Willard Van Orman Quine is usually cited as the original source of this proposal, and Thomas Kuhn is considered a pioneer in this field. Ronald Giere, one of the supporters of naturalized epistemology, has written:

> In arguing a "role for history," Kuhn was proposing a naturalized philosophy of science. That, I argue, is the only viable approach to the philosophy of science.[1]

According to Giere, Kuhn sought to establish "a role for history" when he used history as a source of data for "a theory of scientific inquiry," meaning by "theory" something comparable to theories in the sciences. Because of this, Giere concludes that Kuhn was advocating a naturalized philosophy of science. Geire tries to exploit this line of thought:

> The main thesis is that the study of science must itself be a science. The only viable philosophy of science is a naturalized philosophy of science.[2]

Giere pursued graduate work in philosophy after completing a graduate degree in physics. As an aspiring physicist, he read Kuhn's *Structure* in 1962 with great excitement, but in the end he found Kuhn's account philosophically unacceptable. After some work on probability and induction, which led him to statistics, Giere lost his confidence in the meaningfulness of the philosophical study of the foundations of science. He concluded that

> there are no special philosophical methods for plumbing the theoretical depths of any science. There are only the methods of the sciences themselves.[3]

Dissatisfied with the current approaches to the study of science, Giere continued searching for new perspectives:

---

1. Ronald N. Giere, "Philosophy of Science Naturalized," *Philosophy of Science,* 52 (1985): 331.

2. Ibid., p. 355.

3. Ronald N. Giere, *Explaining Science: A Cognitive Approach* (Chicago: The University of Chicago Press, 1988), p. xvi.

The turning point came about 1982. I began reading some recent works in the sociology of science, particularly several based on the study of scientists in a laboratory setting. I was attracted by the idea of investigating how scientists actually do science, while at the same time I was repelled by the conclusion that science is purely a social construct. But having given up the idea that science embodies some special form of rationality that philosophers might uncover, I was unsure how to formulate my objections. The resolution once again came by a fortuitous encounter with other disciplines, this time the cognitive sciences. . . . I now had the ingredients for a view of science that combined the features I sought. First, the view is thoroughly naturalistic, requiring no special type of rationality beyond the effective use of available means to achieve desired goals. Second, there is room for a modest yet robust scientific realism. . . . Finally, the view makes possible an account of scientific development as a natural evolutionary process.[4]

This view, therefore, can be called a "cognitive approach" to science. This does not mean that the new perspective is simply a study of science under the cognitive perspective. Giere takes cognitive science as a doubtless very important tool, which provides him with a framework suitable for his purpose. He explains this, underscoring once again that there is no rationality besides that involved in the workings of empirical science:

> For me, the only form of rationality that exists is the instrumental use of empirically sanctioned strategies to achieve recognized goals. . . . The problem, then, is to explain how scientists sometimes produce tolerably good representations of the world without appealing to (for me nonexistent) categorical principles of rationality. In short, is it possible to understand science realistically without invoking special forms of rationality? In conceiving *Explaining Science,* my major strategic problem was finding a framework in which to formulate my account of what science is and how it works. . . . Cognitive science provided a framework that suited my purposes, so I used it.[5]

Giere reminds us that "cognitive science" covers a diversity of disciplines and activities, and he analyzes three disciplinary clusters that are especially relevant for his study: artificial intelligence as a branch of computer science, cognitive psychology, and cognitive neuroscience.[6] That he considers cognitive science to be only a tool is clear:

> It has never been my goal that my work should "mingle with" cognitive science or artificial intelligence, good or bad. Rather, in Gly-

---

4. Ibid., pp. xvi–xvii.

5. Ronald N. Giere, "What the Cognitive Study of Science Is Not," in *Cognitive Models of Science,* ed. Ronald N. Giere (Minneapolis, Minn.: University of Minnesota Press, 1992), p. 481.

6. Ronald N. Giere, "Introduction: Cognitive Models of Science," in *Cognitive Models of Science,* cit., pp. xvi–xxv.

mour's terms, my goal has been to produce work that could "mingle with" the best of science studies, that is, work in the history, philosophy, and sociology of science that seeks to develop a comprehensive understanding of the nature of science. What makes my approach "cognitive" is that it employs general frameworks found in the cognitive sciences, and, when applicable, specific results of research in the cognitive sciences.[7]

Clearly, Giere thinks of his approach as a step toward an as-yet nonexistent discipline. The new discipline would substitute specific studies of the actual development of science for current studies on philosophy of science. Giere has devoted a book to analyzing concrete features of scientific work, trying to help readers develop critical skills for understanding and evaluating reports of scientific findings.[8]

Giere underscores an interesting point when he advocates that epistemology should study the actual development of the sciences; indeed, only such a study may provide the necessary basis for philosophical reflection. It is more difficult to evaluate the role that cognitive science can play in epistemology and to conceive that it can solve the problem of scientific truth by its own means. In any case, Giere's position is in danger of reductionism, insofar as he insists that no rationality other than that used in empirical science exists.

Empirical science is grounded on a broader human rationality that makes possible the existence and progress of science itself. On its own level, empirical science does not need an extrascientific foundation; nevertheless, it contains epistemological, ontological, and ethical presuppositions that do not belong to the subjects studied by any branch of empirical science, and can be the subject of philosophical and even theological reflection. Therefore, Giere's claim sounds a bit exaggerated, as if he desired to measure human rationality in general by means of scientific rationality. When human rationality is replaced by some of its particular manifestations, it is difficult to avoid narrowminded images of science that do not represent the richness and variety of the scientific enterprise.

Giere rightly supports a kind of "constructive realism" rather than empiricism; he has argued against the sort of empiricism proposed by Bas van Fraassen. Actually, van Fraassen's empiricism is very different from that proposed by the neopositivists, because he does not attempt to derive scientific constructs from sense data, but only asserts that all we require from scientific theories is that they fit well with the empirical data, not that they be true. This kind of empiricism renews the old tradition that considers "saving the phenomena" as the goal of empirical science. I would agree that, of course, a good theory must save the phenomena, but I would add that we also seek

---

7. Giere, "What the Cognitive Study of Science Is Not," cit., p. 483.

8. Ronald N. Giere, *Understanding Scientific Reasoning* (New York: Holt, Rinehart and Winston, 1984).

for true explanations. That is why I agree with Giere's realist tendency, and I think that he underscores a very important point when he writes:

The question is whether there are any major sciences, or long periods in the life of some major sciences, that fit the empiricist model. It seems hard to deny that there are. Greek astronomy, thermodynamics in the late nineteenth century, and quantum theory in the twentieth century are obvious candidates. It may be more than coincidence that quantum physics is the science van Fraassen knows best. On the other hand, many contemporary sciences, including chemistry, molecular biology, and geology, seem decidedly realistic.[9]

The examples provided by Giere clearly show that we cannot propose a uniform criterion of scientific truth that could be applied to all cases in the same way. Indeed, the first group of theories study natural phenomena that only provide us with some particular data, so that we must build entire abstract theories to account for them; this is why those theories fit well with the empiricist model. The second group of theories refer to very organized, stable natural phenomena that can be represented in a realistic way. Scientific truth is always contextual, and each particular context includes the peculiarities of the phenomena studied and the corresponding possibilities of representing them using our models and concepts.

2. EVOLUTIONARY EPISTEMOLOGY

When a naturalist account of science includes the evolutionary perspective, it produces an "evolutionary epistemology," such as those seen in the work of Karl Popper and of the Nobel Prize ethologist Konrad Lorenz. The main idea behind evolutionary epistemology can be expressed thus: because we are the result of a huge process of evolution, our cognitive abilities should also be considered as the result of a series of trial-and-error approaches by nature to cope with the problems provoked by adaptation to the environment. No wonder, then, that these abilities are quite well adapted to solve the problems of our present situation. This would explain why our knowledge is always tentative and fallible, even though we adopt the kind of realism that corresponds to our biological abilities to know. In this line, it is said that Kant was right when he asserted that our knowledge always depends on categories or ways of knowing that are given prior to any experience. However, Kant was wrong when he thought that our categories were fixed once and for all; those immutable categories should be replaced by changing categories that are the ever-provisioned result of our biological adaptation.

In 1972 Popper published *Objective Knowledge: An Evolutionary Approach,* in which he establishes close links between his epistemology and the evolu-

9. Ronald N. Giere, "Constructive Realism," in *Images of Science. Essays on Realism and Empiricism, with a Reply from Bas C. van Fraassen,* ed. Paul M. Churchland and Clifford A. Hooker (Chicago and London: The University of Chicago Press, 1985), pp. 96–97.

tionary perspective. A 1974 essay by Donald Campbell entitled "Evolutionary Epistemology," on the philosophy of Popper, began:

An evolutionary epistemology would be at minimum an epistemology taking cognizance of and compatible with man's status as a product of biological and social evolution. In the present essay it is also argued that evolution—even in its biological aspects—is a knowledge process, and that the natural-selection paradigm for such knowledge increments can be generalized to other epistemic activities, such as learning, thought, and science. Such an epistemology has been neglected in the dominant philosophic traditions. It is primarily through the works of Karl Popper that a natural-selection epistemology is available today.[10]

Campbell stressed the parallel between the growth of knowledge seen as the result of the trial-and-error method and biological evolution seen as the result of the combination of chance mutations and natural selection, noting that Popper elucidated this parallel in his first book, *The Logic of Scientific Discovery*, in 1934. Campbell concluded:

This essay has identified Popper as the modern founder and leading advocate of a natural-selection epistemology. The characteristic focus is on the growth of knowledge. The problem of knowledge is so defined that the knowledge of other animals than man is included . . . It is argued that, whereas the evolutionary perspective has often led to a pragmatic, utilitarian conventionalism, it is fully compatible with an advocacy of the goals of realism and objectivity in science.[11]

In his reply in *The Philosophy of Karl Popper*, the collection of essays that included Campbell's essay, Popper appeared to like Campbell's best, as he wrote:

Professor Campbell's remarkable contribution is perhaps the one which shows the greatest agreement with my epistemology . . . there is scarcely anything in the whole of modern epistemology to compare with it; certainly not in my own work. . . . For me the most striking thing about Campbell's essay is the almost complete agreement, down even to minute details, between Campbell's views and my own. I shall try to develop one or two of these points a little further still, and shall then turn to the very rare and comparatively minor points where there may be some difference of opinion.[12]

Then, in his specific comments on Campbell's essay, Popper referred to human knowledge as compared with animal knowledge:

10. Donald T. Campbell, "Evolutionary Epistemology" in *The Philosophy of Karl Popper*, ed. Paul A. Schilpp (La Salle, Ill.: Open Court, 1974), p. 413.

11. Ibid., pp. 450–451.

12. Karl R. Popper, "Campbell on the Evolutionary Theory of Knowledge," in *The Philosophy of Karl Popper*, cit., p. 1059.

The main task of the theory of human knowledge is to understand it as continuous with animal knowledge; and to understand also its discontinuity—if any—from animal knowledge.[13]

If we read this passage in isolation, we could think that Popper asserts that there is practically no difference between human and animal knowledge (and, therefore, between human and animal beings). However, this conclusion would be erroneous. Popper underscores the continuity between humans and animals regarding a particular aspect that he describes as "knowledge situation"; namely, that both are active explorers that use the trial-and-error method, rather than passive recipients of information impressed on us from outside. This passage is preceded by the following words:

What is so notable about human knowledge is that it has grown so very far beyond all animal knowledge, and that it is still growing.[14]

The last part of Popper's comment on Campbell is extremely interesting, because it shows that Popper, the agnostic evolutionist, strongly feels that the discontinuity between animals and humans is enormous and that this discontinuity can be best appreciated when we consider the argumentative capacity that is needed to build up empirical science. He speaks of this point as important and is not ready to compromise on it; in his comments, he gently complains that Campbell does not mention this point, and he feels necessary to excuse him by saying that "Campbell's beautiful essay covers a great many things; he may have been reluctant to say more."[15] In Popper's own words:

I come now to my last comment. It is, I think, an important one, and it is related to the difference between man and animal, and especially between human rationality and human science and animal knowledge . . . (Campbell) nowhere seems to allude to my view that human descriptive language differs from all animal languages in being also argumentative, and that it is human argumentative language which makes criticism possible, and with it science.[16]

As an agnostic, Popper sees the appearance of the descriptive and argumentative functions of language, which are necessary for the existence and progress of empirical science, as a mere result of evolution. But in another place he tells us that it is a most mysterious result and adds that evolution cannot be considered an ultimate explanation:

Now I want to emphasize how little is said by saying that the mind is an emergent product of the brain. It has practically no explanatory value, and it hardly amounts to more than putting a question mark at

13. Ibid., p. 1061.
14. Ibid.
15. Ibid., p. 1065.
16. Ibid., p. 1064.

a certain place in human evolution. Nevertheless, I think that this is all which, from a Darwinian point of view, we can say about it . . . evolution certainly cannot be taken in any sense as an ultimate explanation. We must come to terms with the fact that we live in a world in which almost everything which is very important is left essentially unexplained . . . ultimately everything is left unexplained.[17]

Indeed, if someone takes evolution as an ultimate explanation, everything remains essentially unexplained. This is not to deny the relevance of the evolutionary approach. But evolution does not fully explain the problems connected with the singularity of human beings. In some way, these problems become even more acute, because evolution includes the quite mysterious development of cognitive abilities and of their biological grounding.

In the end, evolutionary epistemology should not be considered an obstacle to the singularity of human beings. On the one hand, evolutionary origins do not explain everything and may even pose more and deeper problems than they solve. On the other hand, the argumentative abilities that make science possible provide impressive evidence about the singularity of human beings, whatever their origins may be.

3. Methodological Naturalism

I shall now examine the reductionist naturalism that interprets scientific progress as a proof that no dimensions other than those studied by the sciences can be considered on objective grounds. Attempts at reducing human beings to their material dimensions are anything but new; we find them in very ancient times. In modern times, however, they often present themselves as a consequence of scientific progress.

If we take into account the methodological gap existing between empirical science and metaphysics, we can easily realize that such attempts are doomed to failure. That is why their supporters must use deceptive arguments. The argument I will examine consists in arbitrarily turning the "methodological agnosticism" of empirical science, which by its very nature limits its scope to the study of spatiotemporal natural patterns, into an "ontological materialism." In this case, the tricky move is a methodological leap, which consists of an extrapolation which is illegitimate from the logical point of view.

Jacques Monod, who received the Nobel Prize for his work in molecular biology, proposed this kind of argument in his book *Chance and Necessity*. The argument is interesting as a paradigm that is repeatedly used whenever scientific method is taken as opposed to spirituality. Monod defines "the postulate of objectivity," which he maintains is an essential part of the scientific method:

The cornerstone of the scientific method is the postulate that nature is objective. In other words, the *systematic* denial that "true" knowl-

17. Karl R. Popper, *The Self and Its Brain* (New York-London-Heidelberg-Berlin: Springer, 1977), pp. 554–555.

edge can be got by interpreting phenomena in terms of final causes—that is to say, of "purpose" . . . To be sure, neither reason, nor logic, nor observation, nor even the idea of their systematic confrontation had been ignored by Descartes' predecessors. But science as we understand it today could not have been developed upon those foundations alone. It required the unbending stricture implicit in the postulate of objectivity—ironclad, pure, forever undemonstrable. For it is obviously impossible to imagine an experiment which could prove the *nonexistence* anywhere in nature of a purpose, of a pursued end. But the postulate of objectivity is consubstantial with science; it has guided the whole of its prodigious development for three centuries. There is no way to be rid of it, even tentatively or in a limited area, without departing from the domain of science itself.[18]

This message can be translated into plain words as: "If you want to work in empirical science, you must follow the rules of the game, which are very successful." For example, you must seek for natural laws and, if you admit the existence of a creator and provident God, you should not introduce divine action as an explanation in physics or biology. Of course, this is a triviality. But Monod transforms this triviality into an apparently deep methodological issue when he speaks of a "postulate of objectivity." He labels this a postulate because it will be undemonstrable forever, but it is undemonstrable precisely because there is nothing to be proved. It only means that in empirical science we only admit explanations that can be submitted to experimental control. Of course, human spirituality and divine action do not belong to that realm: if we desire to study them we should employ a different approach.

Monod's postulate of objectivity would remain a mere methodological error were it not for the fact that he attempted to obtain an entire antimetaphysical and antireligious doctrine from it. Indeed, Monod tells us that objective knowledge (the kind obtained in the empirical sciences by applying the postulate of objectivity) is the only authentic source of truth, and so we must depart from the "animist" tradition (which would include metaphysics and religion as well). "Objective knowledge is the *only* authentic source of truth,"[19] writes Monod, and once we have realized this, "ethics, in essence *nonobjective,* is forever barred from the sphere of knowledge."[20] Finally he tells us that the decision in favor of objectivity is an ethical one and that it constitutes the base of the scientific enterprise:

> But—and here is the crucial point, the logical link which at their core weds knowledge and values together—this prohibition, this "first commandment" which ensures the foundation of objective knowledge, is not itself objective. It cannot be objective: it is an ethi-

18. Jacques Monod, *Chance and Necessity: An Essay on the Natural Philosophy of Modern Biology* (New York: Alfred A. Knopf, 1971), p. 21.

19. Ibid., p. 169.

20. Ibid., p. 174.

cal guideline, a rule for conduct. . . . It is obvious that the positing of the principle of objectivity as the condition of true knowledge constitutes an ethical choice and not a judgement arrived at from knowledge, since, according to the postulate's own terms, there cannot have been any "true" knowledge prior to this arbitral choice. . . . Hence it is from the ethical choice of a primary value that knowledge starts.[21]

Monod's position is pure and hard scientism, presented as the consequence of an ethical choice that makes the progress of empirical science possible. Monod concludes:

The ancient covenant is in pieces; man knows at last that he is alone in the universe's unfeeling immensity, out of which he emerged only by chance. His destiny is nowhere spelled out, nor is his duty. The kingdom above or the darkness below: it is for him to choose.[22]

Monod's naturalism presents the human being as a merely chance product of blind natural forces. But this conclusion is the consequence of a defective argument that takes for granted that empirical science is the only source of truth, and, at the same time, presents this as the result of an ethical choice. Monod interprets empirical science as a lifestyle that excludes the acceptance of metaphysical or religious doctrines and that is superior to all other lifestyles, because it is useful and progressive. But the argument is completely defective, because it gratuitously turns the difference that exists between empirical science and metaphysics and religion into an opposition.

In fact, Monod probably perceived that something was wrong with his argument, because in 1972, facing some criticisms, he said that his "postulate of objectivity" was in need of clarification; that many readers and critics of his book were confused by his use of the word "objectivity"; that, if he were to rewrite his book, he would use some other word.[23]

4. ANTHROPOLOGICAL NATURALISM

Another kind of reductionism relies directly on the achievements of science, which would allegedly prove that human beings can be completely explained in terms of physical stuff. Its most fashionable version uses neuroscience as the basis of the attempted reduction. I shall examine it only insofar as it is related to my argument, concentrating on those features more closely related to the methodology of empirical science.

Paul Churchland and his wife Patricia are especially active in this area, providing arguments for a position that is usually considered strongly material-

21. Ibid., p. 176.

22. Ibid., p. 180.

23. Jacques Monod, "On Chance and Necessity," in *Studies in the Philosophy of Biology. Reduction and Related Problems,* ed. Francisco J. Ayala and Theodosius Dobzhansky (Berkeley and Los Angeles: University of California Press, 1974), p. 357.

ist. In a book that analyzes the consequences of the philosophy of science on his philosophy of mind and vice versa, he writes:

it is no longer possible to do major work in the philosophy of mind without drawing on themes from the philosophy of science and the several sciences of the mind-brain. I wish now to suggest that the instruction and information has begun to flow vigorously in the opposite direction. Very shortly it will no longer be possible to do major work in the philosophy of science without drawing on themes from the philosophy of mind and from the related disciplines of computational neuroscience, cognitive psychology, and connectionist artificial intelligence.[24]

Clearly, this position lines up with a naturalized epistemology that, in this case, presents itself as openly materialist. What kind of results does it obtain?

The author presents arguments for a new neurophysiology-based epistemology, but we only find suggestions that cannot account for the subtleties involved even in elementary epistemology. For example, in a discussion of the nature of theories, the author proposes a very general "picture of learning and cognitive activity" that "encompasses the entire animal kingdom" and relates cognitive theory with neurobiology. He says:

We are all of us processing activation vectors through artfully weighted networks. This broad conception of cognition puts cognitive theory firmly in contact with neurobiology.

Then, he offers some new insights on elementary problems that he alleges can be solved by the new approach. However, when we arrive at problems that involve the use of arguments, the author writes:

It remains for this approach to comprehend the highly discursive and linguistic dimensions of human cognition, those that motivated the classical view of cognition. We need not pretend that this will be easy, but we can see how to start.

Finally, the author faces the objection that normative epistemology cannot be completely naturalized: notions such as "justified belief" and "rationality" cannot be explained in terms of a descriptive theory. He answers:

While it may be true that normative discourse cannot be replaced without remainder by descriptive discourse, it would be a distortion to represent this as the aim of those who would naturalize epistemology. . . . It is only the *autonomy* of epistemology that must be denied. . . . We speak of *rationality,* but we think of it as a feature of *thinkers,* and it is a substantive factual matter what thinkers are and what cognitive kinematics they harbor.[25]

24. Paul M. Churchland, *A Neurocomputational Perspective: The Nature of Mind and the Structure of Science* (Cambridge, Mass.: The MIT Press, 1992), pp. xv–xvi.

25. Ibid., pp. 195–196.

The point is precisely: how can we know what thinkers are? It goes without saying that, as far as we are natural beings, our material dimensions can be studied using the approach used in the natural sciences. But Paul Churchland seems to claim something more. If he claims that advances in neurobiology show that human beings should be considered purely material, he cannot use empirical science to support his claim. Actually, the cognitive abilities that make empirical science possible are a necessary condition for the existence of all branches of science, neurobiology included; therefore, these abilities cannot be explained using only the methods of empirical science. The success of the scientific approach shows that, even though we are natural beings, we also transcend the physical level.

When he discusses the nature of explanation, Churchland notes in conclusion, that as he looks back over the chapter, he is distressed "at how fragile is the account proposed, and how sketchy are the few details provided."[26] Indeed, this makes the entire approach very problematic.

Again and again the same difficulties appear. Thus, Patricia and Paul Churchland conclude an essay on the possibility of reducing psychology to neuroscience by saying that:

> producing such a reduction will surely be a long and difficult business. We have here been concerned only to rebut the counsel of impossibility, and to locate the reductive aspirations of neuroscience in a proper historical context. Second, it should not be assumed that the science of psychology will somehow disappear in the process. . . . At this level of complexity, intertheoretic reduction does not appear as the sudden takeover of one discipline by another; it more closely resembles a long and slowly maturing marriage.[27]

This clarification was necessary, because they previously spoke of their position as "eliminative materialism." In a later paper Patricia Churchland insists that they do not deny the existence of specific psychological phenomena that must be explained. She says that they sought a label better than "eliminative materialism" for their position, because they felt this expression was misleading, so that now they call their view "good-guy materialism," arguing that this expression has a pleasant ring, prejudices the reader in its favor, and leaves open how much revision our current ideas will undergo as psychology and neuroscience proceed.[28]

I would suggest, in this line, that the best solution would be to stop talking about "materialism" and such things. We know that our cognitive abilities are closely related to physical dimensions that we are beginning to ex-

---

26. Ibid., p. 229.

27. Paul M. Churchland and Patricia S. Churchland, "Intertheoretic Reduction: A Neuroscientist's Field Guide," in *The Mind-Body Problem: A Guide to the Current Debate,* ed. Richard Warner and Tadeusz Szubka (Oxford: Blackwell, 1994), p. 53.

28. Patricia S. Churchland, "Do We Propose to Eliminate Consciousness?" in *The Churchlands and their Critics,* ed. Robert N. McCauley (Oxford: Blackwell, 1996), p. 298.

plore by means of empirical science, and we can guess that this knowledge will continue its steady progress. But progress in cognitive science and neurobiology, like progress in any other field of empirical science, presupposes self-awareness, creativity, descriptive and argumentative abilities, capacity of evidence, and other related skills that belong to a kind of "commonsense psychology" that exists previous to the scientific study of the human being.

The Churchlands dismiss what they call "folk psychology" as primitive and self-defeating, and they try to replace it with hard scientific theories. Nevertheless, hard science is based on epistemological presuppositions that include what they call "folk psychology," and these presuppositions are retrojustified, enlarged, and refined by scientific progress. Feedback is especially relevant in this case, because here, thanks to the progress of science, we learn things that are directly related to our cognitive abilities.

W. Mark Richardson has analyzed how these issues are related to Christian ideas about human beings. He aptly remarks that:

> Christian theism today, even of a rather generic, noncontroversial sort, has a recognizable core understanding of human agency, and this core is inalienably wedded to what is frequently called commonsense psychology. Commonsense psychology (CSP) is the view that our ordinary understanding of human capacities of perception, rationality, intentionality, free will, and so forth, is essentially accurate and not basically deceptive about the reality of mind itself; that these capacities are necessary conditions of personal identity; and that they determine within limits the nature and course of human action. CSP fully recognizes the status of first person experience reports that arise from these phenomena. Since this experiential level cannot be exhaustively rendered in third person reports (for instance, the neuroscientific explanation of perception does not fully capture the "experience of seeing"), to rely strictly on the external level would compromise essential aspects of our self-understanding.[29]

Richardson analyzes the relationship that exists between Christian theism's core tenets and commonsense psychology in more detail, remarking that commonsense psychology is not a theory of mind, because it is based on first-person accounts of experience. He says that this commonsense psychology has received a rather rough treatment in many quarters of present-day philosophy of mind and adds:

> The broad class of theories of mind named eliminative materialism best exemplifies the antagonistic relation between CSP and current work in the field. Daniel Dennett and Patricia Churchland are prominent representatives of this position. The eliminativists treat the whole network of mental concepts in ordinary language (CSP) as

---

29. W. Mark Richardson, "The Theology of Human Agency and the Neurobiology of Learning," in *Religion and Science. History, Method, Dialogue*, ed. W. Mark Richardson and Wesley J. Wildman (New York and London: Routledge, 1996), p. 351.

naïve and unsophisticated theory. . . . The eliminative materialist view adds that "folk psychology theory" (as they call CSP) is basically an antiquated picture of the mind held only by those who do not know enough neuroscience to get rid of it. They conjecture that a richer, more comprehensive theory of mind-brain based in neuroscientific categories will replace it. . . . In this symbiotic relation a gradual shift is predicted toward a more "scientific" conceptuality in psychology, causing our picture of human beings to be so altered that our present self-understanding will be unrecognizable.[30]

Richardson formulates two major criticism against the claims of eliminative materialism. On the one hand, he underscores that this theory rests on a promissory note, which he terms a usual characteristic of this kind of claim; it relies on promises of future achievements. On the other hand, he remarks that this materialism is incompatible with the most basic tenets of a Christian theology:

> it would seem puzzling if a theologian were to accept the premises of this research program: that our ordinary view of ourselves (as rational, intentional beings who make valuations, discriminations, and choices, and form purposes) will someday be recast in forms that may render some of our most immediate and intuitive assumptions about conscious experience illusory.[31]

Eliminative materialism is untenable for another reason: it is incompatible with the basic epistemological assumptions of empirical science, which include the first-person experiences listed by Richardson as components of commonsense psychology.

The kind of neurophilosophy proposed by the Churchlands presents itself as associated with scientific progress, not only because it claims to be the natural consequence of progress in neurobiology, but also because it allegedly provides us with new, previously unsuspected tools for promoting scientific progress. In a review of the history of epistemology, Patricia Churchland says:

> If, by means of psychology, history of science, and neuroscience, we can determine how the brain conducts its epistemic/cognitive business, then we can proceed to get a theory concerning how to maximize efficiency in that business and hence how to maximize rationality in scientific inquiry. That is, I think, the heart of Quine's view. It is thoroughly naturalistic, and it is a view I find irresistible.[32]

That perspective would be fascinating, if only it were true. However, I seriously doubt that better understanding of how our brain works will enable us

---

30. Ibid., pp. 356–357.

31. Ibid., p. 357.

32. Patricia S. Churchland, *Neurophilosophy: Toward a Unified Science of the Mind/Brain* (Cambridge, Mass.: The MIT Press, 1993), p. 264.

to predict which theory of unification we should formulate in microphysics or which new accelerator we should build to test it.

Perhaps the main lesson we can extract from all of this is that we should learn to look at empirical science, and even more at the human being who does it, with more respect. Specifically, instead of using the methods and results of science as a tool for making pictures of science and science-makers at our own caprice, we should admire the great results that we have achieved and the subtleties of the methods we employ. We should recognize that we understand hardly anything about the real nature of the subtleties implied by scientific methods. We can learn from this analysis that an enormous disproportion between our achievements in empirical science and our understanding of them exists. Theories of scientific rationality are very far away from the quality of our achievements in science itself. Perhaps we should learn to admire more what we are, and to dismiss as nonsense theories that attempt to measure human beings by comparing us with some of our particular achievements, and even replacing us with them.

II. THE VALUE OF HUMAN KNOWLEDGE

The problem of the reliability of science plays a central role in human life. Jürgen Habermas began his best-known book:

> If we imagine the philosophical discussion of the modern period reconstructed as a judicial hearing, it would be deciding a single question: how is reliable knowledge possible.[33]

Indeed, one of the main novelties the development of empirical science has brought about is that, for the first time in human history, we have at our disposal a body of scientific empirical knowledge that is highly reliable in both theory and practice. In fact, the achievements of empirical science are usually the framework in which philosophical discussions are posed and solved in modern times; these discussions must take into consideration the threats of scientism, which sees empirical science as the only way to true knowledge, or at least as the paradigm that should be imitated by any serious claim to knowledge.

Paradoxically, the enormous success of empirical science is usually accompanied in our days by a fallibilist epistemology that stresses that scientific knowledge is always conjectural and provisional. At first sight, fallibilism seems incompatible with scientism, but it is easy to combine the two; for example, when someone says that, because empirical science is the best example of reliable knowledge and reaches only conjectural explanations, we should not attempt to reach true and certain knowledge in other areas. Therefore, fallibilism adds new and important problems.

---

33. Jürgen Habermas, *Knowledge and Human Interest* (London: Heinemann, 1972), p. 3.

1. SCIENCE AND FALLIBILISM

Fallibilism is closely linked to Karl Popper. Even though its origins can be traced back to authors like Peirce, and Popper himself presents Xenophanes as his predecessor in ancient Greece, Popper's ideas on the epistemology he has labeled fallibilism have exercised an enormous influence on contemporary thinking. We should differentiate, however, between a weak kind of healthy fallibilism and a strong kind of fallibilism that may lead to seriously misleading consequences.

1.1. TWO KINDS OF FALLIBILISM

Popperian fallibilism is closely linked to his "falsificationism." In this perspective, scientific progress takes place when we identify concrete errors in our theories; therefore, to consider a theory true would be to take a dogmatic position that would stop further progress. This view is widespread in contemporary epistemology and can be exemplified by the words of an "interested bystander" introduced by John Worrall in a fictitious epistemological dialogue: "Everyone nowadays is, I take it, a fallibilist." However, fallibilism is a difficult concept, as can be grasped if we examine the problems involved in the full quotation of Worrall's interested bystander:

> Everyone nowadays is, I take it, a fallibilist about scientific *theories:* by this I mean not a fallibilist *in principle* (this position seems to be dictated by logic alone) but a fallibilist *in practice*—the history of science clearly shows that even the most successful high level theories may eventually be rejected (even if they do standardly "live on" as "limiting cases").[34]

These statements require nontrivial qualifications about what the rejection of a theory means, as Worrall himself remarks, and they involve not only logical arguments, but also some difficult epistemological and historical issues. If we want to clarify the problems related to fallibilism, we should first clarify what fallibilism means.

When applied to knowledge, the term "fallibilism" expresses the fact that our knowledge is not perfect. The *Collins Cobuild Dictionary* defines the term "fallible" in this way: "if you say that someone is fallible, you mean that their judgement or knowledge is not perfect and they may make mistakes. If you say that something is fallible, you mean that it is not perfect and may be wrong."[35] Therefore, the adjective "fallible" may be applied to the subjects who know, or to the methods they use, or to their statements. In all cases, when we assert that they are fallible we accept that they may be wrong.

If we ask what the problem is that Popper wants to solve, the answer is not difficult: doubtless, the central problem of Popper's epistemology is the *growth*

---

34. John Worrall, "Why Both Popper and Watkins Fail to Solve the Problem of Induction," in *Freedom and Rationality,* ed. Fred d'Agostino and Ian C. Jarvie (Dordrecht: Kluwer, 1989), p. 268.

35. See "Fallible," in John Sinclair, editor in chief, *Collins Cobuild English Language Dictionary* (London and Glasgow: Collins, 1987), p. 513.

of knowledge. Popper's approach to this problem is also quite clear; he says that, to evaluate any cognitive claim, what really matters is our *attitude* toward it. The basic Popperian rule is that we should not try to protect our conjectural explanations against contrary evidence; rather, we should seek counterexamples that may help us to see where we are mistaken so that we may improve our conjectures.

Fallibilism is most healthy if we interpret it as a methodological attitude in science and other circumstances of our life. It is linked to the recognition that scientific knowledge is always contextual and therefore partial, and also that we can err in our evaluations. It can be identified with a healthy attitude of "reasonableness." This is what I call a "weak" fallibilism. A "strong" fallibilism would declare that we can never know whether our knowledge is correct, and that we cannot know anything with certainty.

This strong fallibilism is usually based on the implicit assumption that we can attain certainty only if we can provide a purely logical proof of our ideas; thus, as every proof must be based on some suppositions, we will easily become prisoners of an infinite regress in our attempted proofs. Nevertheless, the idea of certainty as an automatic consequence of purely logical proofs is a part of modern Cartesian rationalism that would prevent us from considering true and certain the very existence of an external world, of other minds, and so on. The problem changes completely if we adopt a more realistic idea about certitude, recognizing, for instance, that we can possess a knowledge that is partial, limited, and perfectible, but is at the same time certain for most purposes.

Fallibilism is so widespread that even authors who criticize antirealist views proclaim their allegiance to it. This is so, for example, with Harvey Siegel[36] and Nicholas Rescher. Siegel's adherence to fallibilism is most significant, because he asserts it as a point of agreement with Harold Brown, in spite of Brown's commitment to a pragmatic notion of truth that was later abandoned under Siegel's critique.[37] Rescher's adherence to fallibilism is also remarkable because it is expressed in a context in which a realistic position is being argued for. Rescher proclaims that "the quintessentially cognitive aspiration of getting at the truth about the world's ways is the very essence of the scientific enterprise" and that "abandoning the pursuit of truth as a regulative ideal would hamstring from the very outset the scientific project of rational inquiry into nature." These declarations notwithstanding, his arguments for a realistic view mainly refer to merely subjective aims, because, as he says, "we must accept a fallibilistic view of science."[38] Whereas a weak interpretation of fallibilism would mean

36. Harvey Siegel, *Relativism Refuted: A Critique of Contemporary Epistemological Relativism* (Dordrecht: Reidel, 1987), p. 113.

37. See Harold I. Brown, *Perception, Theory and Commitment: The New Philosophy of Science* (Chicago: Precendent Publishing, 1977), pp. 151–153; Harvey Siegel, "Brown on Epistemology and the New Philosophy of Science," *Synthese,* 56 (1983): 61–89; Harold I. Brown, "Response to Siegel," *Synthese,* 56 (1983): 91–105.

38. Nicholas Rescher, *Scientific Realism* (Dordrecht: Reidel, 1987), p. 33.

only that scientific truth is partial and therefore perfectible, the stronger version asserts that we can never obtain true knowledge; in the latter case the task of seriously defending realism becomes very difficult. A strong version of fallibilism provides an image of science very different from the one that results when we admit the possibility of achieving true, concrete knowledge.

1.2. FALLIBILISM AND RATIONALISM

The strong version of fallibilism, that we cannot reach any kind of certainty in scientific knowledge (and in human knowledge in general), depends too much on the classical rationalist view. It reacts against it, but accepts the equation between legitimate certitude and a *perfect and absolute* certitude obtained as a mere consequence of *logically linear* arguments. The idea of perfect and absolute knowledge is the target against which the attacks of fallibilism are directed. Explaining the main lines of his evolutionary epistemology, Gerhard Vollmer has written:

> An *absolute* justification of human knowledge is not possible. Every such attempt to pull ourselves out of the swamp of uncertainty leads to a threefold impasse, namely: either in a circle—which is logically faulty; or in an infinite regress—which is practically impossible; or to an arbitrary suspension of the postulate of justification—which leads to dogmatism. This treble alternative of dead ends was aptly called the "Münchhausen trilemma" by Hans Albert.[39]

This trilemma is a commonplace in Popperian literature. It was formulated by Popper in his first book under a slightly different form and name (as Fries' trilemma), when he examined the limits of scientific proofs and concluded that proofs can never be definitive:

> The problem of the basis of experience has troubled few thinkers so deeply as Fries. He taught that, if the statements of science are not to be accepted *dogmatically,* we must be able to *justify* them. If we demand justification by reasoned argument, in the logical sense, then we are committed to the view that *statements can be justified only by statements.* The demand that *all* statements are to be logically justified (described by Fries as a "predilection for proofs") is therefore bound to lead to an *infinite regress.* Now, if we wish to avoid the danger of dogmatism as well as an infinite regress, then it seems as we could only have recourse to *psychologism,* i.e. the doctrine that statements can be justified not only by statements but also by perceptual experience. Faced with this *trilemma*—dogmatism *vs.* infinite regress *vs.* psychologism—Fries, and with him almost all epistemologists who wished to account for our empirical knowledge, opted for psychologism.[40]

39. Gerhard Vollmer, "On Supposed Circularities in an Empirically Oriented Epistemology," in *Evolutionary Epistemology, Rationality, and the Sociology of Knowledge,* ed. Gerard Radnitzky and William W. Bartley, III (La Salle, Ill.: Open Court, 1987), p. 174.

40. Karl R. Popper, *The Logic of Scientific Discovery* (Boston: Unwin Hyman, 1990), pp. 93–94.

In a Popperian line, Hans Albert summarized the trilemma in few words, changing its name and a part of the argument:

The adoption of a general principle of justification which implies a guarantee of truth involves a trilemma of infinite regress, vicious circle or recourse to dogma.[41]

William Warren Bartley III adopted a different view in his examination of the trilemma. He said that it is not a true trilemma and that there are many other possibilities besides the three mentioned.[42]

In my opinion, the problem only arises, as Popper aptly notes it, "if we demand justification by reasoned argument, in the logical sense" and require complete proofs that cannot be provided even in mathematics (Figure 6.1).

Vollmer argues that "it is not the goal of epistemology to give *absolute* justifications for claims to knowledge and truth" and adds that:

If we had such knowledge, true, reliable, universal, objective knowledge, epistemologists might feel the obligation to explain how such is possible. But so far, nobody has exhibited a single piece of *perfect* knowledge. Thus, there is nothing to explain; the problem simply does not exist.[43]

Following this argument, Vollmer uses the classical example of Newton's theory and insists in opposing *perfect* and *absolute* knowledge to fallible knowledge:

But is Newton's theory *absolutely* true? No! . . . we even know that it *is* actually false. . . . Concerning objectivity, we are much better off, now. Our knowledge—uncertain, imperfect, conjectural, preliminary, fallible as it may be—finally has a *chance,* at least, to be objective, to be true for the real world as it is. *Perfect* knowledge about nothing, or imperfect knowledge about the real world—what do we prefer? Of course, there is no choice (Newton's theory *is,* in fact, false); but if there were a choice, would we not choose the second alternative?[44]

Insofar as fallibilism is formulated against "absolute knowledge," strong fallibilism could also be labeled "absolute fallibilism," which excludes any form of certitude and concludes that all empirical knowledge is conjectural. This kind of fallibilism emphasizes that *absolute and perfect* knowledge is beyond our reach. I agree with this. But we cannot conclude that *any* kind of certitude is beyond our reach. There are different kinds and degrees of knowledge, truth,

41. Hans Albert, "Science and the Search for Truth," in *Rationality: The Critical View,* ed. Joseph Agassi and Ian C. Jarvie (Dordrecht: Nijhoff, 1987), p. 69.

42. William W. Bartley III, *The Retreat to Commitment* (La Salle, Ill.: Open Court, 1984), pp. 211–216.

43. Vollmer, "On Supposed Circularities in an Empirically Oriented Epistemology," cit., p. 175 (italics mine).

44. Ibid., p. 176 (italics mine in the case of "absolutely" and "perfect").

Fig. 6.1 Certainty in empirical science. Sir Karl Popper insisted that we can never reach certainty in empirical science. This is true if we identify certainty with absolutely sure knowledge resulting from full logical proofs (which, in fact, cannot be obtained). Nevertheless, sometimes we have very good reasons to be quite sure about the truth of a scientific statement. On June 6, 1980, I wrote to Karl Popper saying that, in my opinion, many scientific statements are true and we can be sure of their truth, although they are partial and can be improved. He kindly answered me in a handwritten letter saying: "I also think that many scientific statements are true. I also think that we can be pretty sure of the truth of some of them. But no theory was better tested than Newton's—and we certainly cannot be sure of it; Einstein has shown that it is possible that Newton's theory may be false."

I also think that many scientific statements are true. I also think that we can be pretty sure of the truth of some of them. But no theory

This is the only occasion I know of in which Popper explicitly said that we can be "pretty sure" of the truth of some scientific statements. Obviously, it is more difficult to assess the truth of abstract theoretical systems such as Newton's mechanics and Einstein's relativity.

certitude, and theoretical constructs. If we introduce necessary qualifications, we may realize that, in many cases, we can obtain a knowledge that is quite certain.

As a matter of fact, fallibilists usually admit some kind of realism, and they also admit that scientific results, even though not established with certainty, possess a value that transcends the merely instrumental level. Popper, usually considered the main supporter of fallibilism, admits a high dose of realism and argues that science is a strong reason in favor of realism in a way that practically coincides with my argument:

> We can then assert that almost all, if not all, physical, chemical, or biological theories imply realism, in the sense that if they are true, realism must also be true. This is one of the reasons why some people speak of "scientific realism." It is quite a good reason. . . . However one may look at this, there are excellent reasons for saying that *what we attempt in science is to describe and (so far as possible) explain reality*. We do so with the help of conjectural theories; that is, theories which we hope are true (or near the truth) . . . our conjectural theories tend progressively to come nearer to the truth; that is, to true descriptions of certain facts, or aspects of reality.[45]

Because strong fallibilism can easily lead to confusion, when we speak of fallibilism we should make clear whether we refer to its weak or its strong ver-

45. Karl R. Popper, *Objective Knowledge*, cit., p. 40.

sion. Albert tells us that fallibilism, in its original context, "arises from a critique of the solutions of epistemological problems offered by the rationalist tradition" and results "from the impossibility of maintaining the fusion of truth and certainty implied by classical rationalism."[46] But what should be done then is simply to abandon classical rationalism, to renounce a kind of absolute, definitive, and perfect kind of knowledge that would be the consequence of completely perfect logical proofs. Such a knowledge is outside the reach of human beings. We should accept, instead, a more realistic picture of human knowledge that leaves room for different kinds of evidence and legitimate certainty.

1.3. SCIENTIFIC CREATIVITY AND FALLIBILISM

Further reflections on Popper's fallibilism can underscore the relevance of creativity and interpretation in empirical science.

Popper's fallibilism is closely related to his falsificationism, another doctrine often misrepresented. Sometimes we are told that Popper claimed that the falsification of scientific theories implies their definitive rejection as a consequence of their disagreement with empirical data that would be, in their turn, the result of pure observation and would therefore be pieces of definitive empirical knowledge. For instance, Ian Barbour writes:

> This hypothetico-deductive view dominated philosophy of science in the 1950s and early 1960s. It assumed that data are describable in a theory-free observation language and that alternative theories are tested against these fixed, objective data. Even though *agreement* with data does not *verify* a theory (since there may be other theories that would also agree), it was claimed by Karl Popper and others that *disagreement* with data will conclusively *falsify* a theory. But studies in the history of science cast doubt on this claim.[47]

Instead, Popper stressed explicitly that it is we who *decide to accept* statements as basic statements and to use them as potential falsifiers of theories:

> Every test of a theory, whether resulting in its corroboration or falsification, must stop at some basic statement or other which we *decide to accept*. If we do not come to any decision, and do not accept some basic statement or other, then the test will lead nowhere. But considered from a logical point of view, the situation is never such that it compels us to stop at this particular basic statement rather than at that, or else give up the test altogether. For any basic statement can again in its turn be subjected to tests, using as a touchstone any of the basic statements which can be deduced from it with the help of some theory, either the one under test, or another. This procedure has no natural end . . . we arrive in this way at a procedure according to

---

46. Albert, "Science and the Search for Truth," cit., pp. 69–70.

47. Ian Barbour, *Religion in an Age of Science* (San Francisco: Harper, 1990), p. 32.

which we stop only at a kind of statement about whose acceptance or rejection the various investigators are likely to reach agreement. . . . If some day it should no longer be possible for scientific observers to reach agreement about basic statements this would amount to a failure of language as a means of universal communication. It would amount to a new "Babel of Tongues": scientific discovery would be reduced to absurdity.[48]

Popper forcefully stressed the role of conventions or stipulations in empirical science in this first book. Nancey Murphy acknowledges this; speaking of Wolfhart Pannenberg's position on Popper, she notes:

In Popper's view, the basic statements upon which science relies are not incorrigible—they are accepted on convention by the scientific community but can always be called into question by later discoveries and subjected to testing and perhaps revision.[49]

Murphy rightly attributes to Popper the idea that basic statements are *accepted on convention,* but later she adds some nuances that may be misleading, not least because she quotes Popper in a way that apparently supports her position. She writes:

Popper's basic statements were reports of repeatable experiments or observations rather than the philosophers' sense data. Such reports are not incorrigible; if called into question they can always be tested by attempts to falsify further observable consequences drawn from them. Here we see the beginning of the end of the logical positivists' foundationalism in that science is no longer seen to rest upon an *indubitable* foundation. Popper still saw the structure of science to be that of an edifice built upon observation statements, but he used the metaphor of pilings driven into a swamp.[50]

The last comment could be misleading, because it can be taken to mean that even if there are differences between Popper and the positivists, this difference is not important, because Popper himself sees science as an edifice built on observation statements. It could seem to suggest that Popper's view only modifies the account of empirical science provided by the positivists, who presented the edifice of science as built upon observation statements. This, however, is not the case, for three reasons.

The first is contained in the text quoted by Nancey Murphy, wherein Popper writes:

The empirical basis of objective science has thus nothing "absolute" about it. Science does not rest upon solid bedrock. The bold structure

48. Popper, *The Logic of Scientific Discovery,* cit., p. 104.

49. Nancey Murphy, *Theology in the Age of Scientific Reasoning* (Ithaca and London: Cornell University Press, 1990), p. 27.

50. Ibid., p. 54.

of its theories rises, as it were, above a swamp. It is like a building erected on piles. The piles are driven down from above into the swamp, but not down to any natural or "given" base; and if we stop driving the piles deeper, it is not because we have reached firm ground. We simply stop when we are satisfied that the piles are firm enough to carry the structure, at least for the time being.[51]

Here, Popper explicitly says that we should formulate "bold" theories that go far beyond observational data. Then, when he says that the edifice of science is "like a building erected on piles" which "are driven down from above into the swamp," the piles in his metaphor do not refer to observation statements, but to bold theories that "are driven down from above into the swamp" on a basis that cannot be considered firm ground. This picture of science has nothing to do with the positivist account, which considered science to be built up on observation statements through an inductive method whose value Popper strongly denied.

Actually, and this is the second reason in favor of my argument, in a footnote, Popper referred to a report of his theory published in 1932 by Rudolph Carnap and said that he agreed with Carnap's report except in a few details, including:

the suggestion that basic statements (called by Carnap "protocol statements") are the starting points from which science is built up.[52]

Rudolph Carnap tried to show that scientific theories could be reduced to observation statements, so that pure logic alone would suffice to build up the edifice of science. Popper explicitly denied this in his first book, even though it was published in a series directed by the Vienna Circle, at a time when Carnap was not only one of the most preeminent members of the Circle, but also an author who, unlike others connected with the Circle, seemed to look with sympathy at the ideas of the young Popper.

Last, Popper himself distinguished his "basic statements," where "basic" means that they are used to test theories (they are "test statements"), from "observational statements," where "observational" means that they are derived from our immediate experiences. The paragraph quoted by Murphy belongs to section 30 of Popper's *Logic of Scientific Discovery*. Shortly before, in section 28, Popper argues at some length that his "basic statements" are completely different from the "observational statements" of the positivists. According to Popper's own account, one of the traits his basic statements should possess is that they should refer to observable events, but he immediately adds that this has nothing to do with the psychological certainty ascribed by the positivists to our immediate experiences. Instead, this requirement means that the basic statements should be intersubjectively testable, a point that is clearly underscored by Murphy.

51. Popper, *The Logic of Scientific Discovery*, cit., p. 111.

52. Ibid., p. 104.

My point is that Popper represents empirical science as an adventure in which creativity plays a major role in the formulation of new theories, and interpretation also plays a major role when we decide to accept or to reject a theory on the basis of the results of experiments. Therefore, we should always be ready to modify our theories and our decisions in the light of better evidence. This is a healthy kind of fallibilism that corresponds to the limits of our knowledge and favors the advance of science. Unnecessary problems arise if we follow rationalist arguments and conclude that, as our knowledge is never "perfect" and "absolute," we can never reach any kind of certainty.

2. FOUR FEATURES OF THE RELIABILITY OF SCIENCE

Fallibilism apparently provides an easy way to reconcile science with metaphysics and religion. Nevertheless, it is a wrong way: on the one hand because, as already noted, it is easy to combine scientism and fallibilism, and on the other hand because in empirical science we often reach highly reliable pieces of knowledge. Ian Barbour begins one of his books with this point:

> The first major challenge to religion in an age of science is the success of the methods of science. Science seems to provide the only reliable path to knowledge. Many people view science as objective, universal, rational, and based on solid observational evidence. Religion, by contrast, seems to be subjective, parochial, emotional, and based on traditions or authorities that disagree with each other.[53]

Therefore, an explanation of the reliability of science is needed if we want to foster dialogue between science and religion.

My account of the reliability of science is based on the account of objectivity and truth that I have developed. It avoids skeptical and relativist interpretations incompatible with the real progress of the sciences, as well as the excesses of scientism, showing that empirical science leaves room for metascientific considerations and even requires them.

In technical matters, the term "reliability" is used to refer to the guarantees that a device offers for its correct performance. In epistemology, we can speak about the reliability of scientific constructs in the following sense: they will be reliable insofar as they serve to reach the objectives of the scientific enterprise.

These objectives are two: knowledge of nature and its controlled domination. They are mutually related so that, in some respects, they are two aspects of a single goal. In fact, theoretical knowledge without practical applications may be relevant and legitimate as a philosophical insight, and the domination of nature on purely empirical grounds may be important in practical life; empirical science, however, combines both aspects. Theories must lead to consequences that can be submitted to empirical testing, and this testing must have a theoretical basis.

---

53. Barbour, *Religion in an Age of Science,* cit., p. 3.

To reach this goal, theories must fulfill two requirements: they must be expressed and proved in an intersubjective way (*intersubjectivity*), and the proofs of their validity must be related to empirical tests (*empirical testability*). Furthermore, we seek theories that not only can explain (and therefore predict) known facts, but may also allow us to anticipate the unknown. In this sense, *predictability* plays an important role in science. And we require that new achievements do not contradict the body of well-corroborated knowledge, but add new knowledge, so that we can recognize *progress* in the development of science.

Thus, reliability includes these four features: *intersubjectivity, empirical testability, predictability,* and *progress,* which correspond to the standard picture of empirical science. The question now is: how can we explain them?

2.1. INTERSUBJECTIVITY

In empirical science we reach a peculiar kind of intersubjectivity because we focus on natural patterns, which are repeatable spatiotemporal structures. No wonder, then, that we are able to formulate laws that allow us to make predictions. I have considered natural order as a presupposition of empirical science that is justified, enlarged, and enriched by scientific progress. If our world were much more disordered than it really is, our own existence would not be possible and empirical science, such as we know it, could not exist at all.

Also, the arguments that we use in empirical science are expressed in intersubjective languages and must include well-established references to empirical facts, so that anyone can examine whether the arguments and the empirical proofs are valid. I have already shown that, to achieve this kind of intersubjectivity, we must introduce conventional stipulations. These stipulations refer to intersubjective rules for the use of instruments, the expression of scientific laws, the systematization of theoretical systems, and the acceptance of theories.

Therefore, scientific intersubjectivity results from the combination of two factors: an objective fact—the existence of ordered natural patterns—and a subjective fact—the introduction of stipulations that make it possible to establish an intersubjective language. This is not an impersonal property of empirical science; rather, we play a most active role in it. We can achieve it because the natural world is full of spatiotemporal patterns, but our representation of them is not "given" by nature itself, nor is it the result of applying some automatic method. We represent the natural world by using intersubjective languages and prove the truth of our claims by using intersubjective proofs.

Can we prove our theories in a completely logical way? No, we cannot do so. We could reach full demonstrability only if the basic statements we use were grounded on ultimate evidence. We have such forms of evidence and use them in science, but if we desire to construct ideal systems and to measure magnitudes, we have to use conventional stipulations. We arrive at the same conclusion if we consider the logical character of hypothetico-deductive systems, which do not permit us to reach complete certainty about their consequences. Therefore, scientific intersubjectivity implies using some conventional elements.

Are we obliged to admit, then, a conventionalist epistemology? Is reliability reduced to the usefulness of conceptual tools? In a way, theories are indeed symbolic tools. But the success of an objectification when it is applied to solve concrete problems, providing explanations and making possible empirical control, shows that it contains some kind of truth. We must bear in mind that this truth is contextual, in the sense that the meaning of our statements is relative to the corresponding objectification, and partial, because every objectification refers only to some aspects of the natural world.

The peculiar objectivity of empirical science is related to the existence of spatiotemporal patterns. The very idea of empirical control, based on repeatable observations and experiments, presupposes that those patterns exist, and the success of empirical science retrojustifies, enlarges, and refines that assumption. Thus, the peculiar intersubjectivity of empirical science is possible because we focus on the study of spatiotemporal patterns of the natural world and because, to study those patterns, we adopt stipulations that enable us to construct commonly accepted areas of theorizing and proving.

We should not be surprised that other cognitive approaches do not possess the specific kind of intersubjectivity empirical science possesses. The peculiar reliability of empirical science is obviously an advantage for many purposes, but it is limited only to those dimensions of reality that can be submitted to empirical control. This kind of approach is insufficient and inadequate when we study the spiritual dimensions of human beings and other metascientific issues.

In the end, the intersubjective character of the explanations and proofs used in empirical science arises from two factors: our focusing on natural repeatable patterns and the use of stipulations that are accepted upon agreement. Once more, we may marvel at our capacity of creativity and interpretation that enables us to use intersubjective proofs to reach results that are valid from an objective point of view.

2.2. EMPIRICAL CONTROL

As long as we remain in the context of an accepted objectification, there is no problem in testing hypotheses if they are formulated in a rigorous way within the context of that objectification. Problems may arise if we do not yet know how to perform the experiments necessary to test the theory or if we are not able to build the necessary equipment, but these problems do not challenge the testability of our theories in principle.

Every time we create a new objectification, we must specify the operational criteria that make empirical tests possible. Thus, from a descriptive point of view, empirical testability can be explained using the concept of objectification, which can also be considered a sufficient condition for the existence of intersubjective proofs and empirical testability. Indeed, once we have defined a theoretical model and have established criteria that relate the model with the results of repeatable experiments, we can formulate intersubjective proofs and can submit our formulations to empirical tests.

There is a close relationship between reliability and empirical testing. When we are able to perform repeatable experiments, we can use them to test hypotheses. This presupposes that we have at hand the concepts and criteria that define an objectification. For instance, if we did not possess criteria for measuring lengths, times, and masses, we could not submit the laws of mechanics to empirical tests.

The problem again turns out to be that, to define an objectification, we need to introduce conventional elements. Does this mean that the acceptance of theories is also regulated by convention?

We have already seen that, on the one hand, we can always evaluate the correspondence between hypotheses and facts as a relation of the type "if . . . then . . .," which is valid from the intersubjective point of view. We have also examined the criteria that enable us to determine if a theory can serve to attain the goals of the scientific enterprise: *explanatory power, predictive power*, the *accuracy* of explanations and predictions, *convergence of independent proofs*, and *mutual support* of different theories. Therefore, we can easily understand that, when we work within well-defined objectifications, it is possible to establish a rigorous correspondence between theoretical explanations and observed facts. Admittedly, it is possible to build arbitrary theories that can fit well with the observed facts; however, if we apply these criteria consistently, such theories will surely fail. It is most unlikely that an arbitrary theory would succeed in providing accurate explanations and predictions, supported by independent proofs, and that it would cohere with the well-corroborated theories.

There is no reason, however, why we should extend this kind of requirement to areas outside empirical science. Such criteria are meaningful when we search for a knowledge of the natural world that may be submitted to empirical control. But if we search for some other kind of understanding, we should use criteria adequate for that purpose.

2.3. PREDICTIVE POWER

Predictive power is often the most desired characteristic of empirical theories. Empirical proofs, especially when they consist of predictions of previously unexpected facts that are accurately corroborated, are usually the strongest proofs. Any new theory is seriously considered if it provides one prediction of that kind.

There is undoubtedly a kind of mystery surrounding predictive power. We could explain it away saying that, after all, we try and try again, never knowing in advance when our trials will be right, and hoping that sometimes our predictions will be correct. Nevertheless, this does not explain how abstract and very sophisticated theories may serve to predict the existence of entities, properties, or processes.

To explain the existence of successful predictions it seems necessary to admit that an interconnectedness exists between the different components of the natural world and that our theories grasp this objective natural order in some way. Admittedly, abstract theories that occupy a privileged place, especially in mathematical physics, are not a mere copy of natural order but are our own constructions; nevertheless, they describe objective features of the natural world. Otherwise, it is hardly conceivable that we could derive from them enormously specific new predictions that afterward receive empirical support.

On the other hand, predictive power is a component of the reliability of science in quite a different sense, which is, however, most important and much less mysterious. Insofar as we are able to establish well-corroborated scientific laws, we can use them to predict the occurrence of some of the factors involved in them when we know the behavior of other factors. This is the usual method followed to reach mastery over nature. Thus, to say that empirical science is reliable simply means that it can be used for practical purposes or that it provides the tools necessary to manage natural phenomena in a controlled way. This was the original promise announced very loudly by Francis Bacon, and scientific progress has been such that even Bacon himself could not have dreamt the extraordinary power science has provided us with.

We should not expect this kind of success from enterprises other than empirical science. Specifically, metaphysics and religion do not aim to provide a controlled mastery over nature. When scientific progress is interpreted as if it rendered unnecessary the recourse to religion, we can conclude that religion is being considered in a superficial way. Today we also know that the predictive power of empirical science can be used to achieve both good and bad goals; mastery over nature is not enough, for to be properly used it needs a moral orientation.

2.4. PROGRESS

As a component of the reliability of science, progress means that it is possible to recognize a kind of cumulative progress in empirical science, so that new achievements do not replace preceding ones, but add to them. One of the main advantages of empirical science is that it presents an impressive record of uninterrupted progress.

Nevertheless, this very progress is the most controversial feature of empirical science. In recent times, it has been argued that science progresses through revolutions that imply changing entire conceptual frameworks, so that, in the end, the very notion of cumulative progress becomes useless. This line of thought has been emphasized by Thomas Kuhn and others who stress the relevance of social factors in understanding the actual course of empirical science.

The sociological approach can easily tackle other aspects of the reliability of science. Intersubjectivity presents no mystery when scientists are seen as sharers of the same theory or paradigm: theories are accepted on agreement.

Obviously, it is more difficult to explain empirical control and predictive power; however, because the sociologist–philosopher of science does not intend to explain the success of science, these difficulties can be dismissed. In the sociological perspective there is no room for an objective record of scientific progress, which would be completely unintelligible. It is not surprising, then, that the debate originated by Kuhn and his followers has centered mainly on the impossibility of recognizing objective progress, and that is why their adversaries have criticized them as irrationalists or as being unable to explain the existence of a rational record of objective progress in the development of empirical science.

The charge of irrationalism refers to particular cases of theory choice, which are considered in the Kuhnian perspective as a kind of "gestalt-switch" or quasi-religious conversion, and to the overall progress of science. The sociologist approach often insists too much on the "irrational" features of those processes, but sometimes their opponents seem to search for an account of scientific activity that would be too "rational." In fact, scientific progress very often operates in a patchwork way, and there is no guarantee that progress in one direction may not provoke stagnation in others.

These difficulties are anything but new. Nobody would claim that empirical science always progresses along a perfectly linear road. Even the neopositivists, who claimed scientific rationality as the paradigm of any valid knowledge, spoke about a "rational reconstruction" of science that would provide a systematization of scientific knowledge according to rational rules. Systematizing is an essential part of the scientific enterprise. Precisely because a major part of scientific progress consists of conquering small new domains in our knowledge of nature, general theories that unify many of those small domains are most welcome. Nevertheless, systematizing is always a means to reach the goals of science; it is never an end.

The desire to provide criteria to evaluate progress in science may be due to the ever-increasing necessity of choosing between difficult and expensive research programs. However, scientism also sometimes lies behind an exag-

$$P_1 \longrightarrow TT_1 \longrightarrow EE_1 \longrightarrow P_2 \longrightarrow$$

Fig. 6.2 A scheme of scientific progress. Karl Popper used to represent the progress of science by using this tetradic scheme: we begin with a problem P_1, propose a tentative theory TT_1 to solve it, criticize the theory and proceed to error elimination EE_1, arrive at a new problem P_2, and so on. Theories should always be evaluated by considering how well they solve the problems they are intended to solve. No scientific theory is absolutely complete or definitive, even though we may progress in our attempt to reach theories closer to the truth.

This insight leads to an attitude which is always open to new findings. Nevertheless, one-sided insistence on the "negative" side of the procedure (error elimination) would leave unexplained the positive value of our findings.

gerated interest in these problems and in rational reconstructions of science. Because scientism presents empirical science as the model of any meaningful claim to knowledge, it needs to elaborate an image of science rational enough to serve as such a model. If we leave aside scientistic prejudices, we will easily recognize that we need not force the actual historical record, which contains not only a great number of steps in the right direction, but also others that are not so progressive. It also contains steps that undoubtedly can be considered progressive; even though we cannot determine how they are related to other progressive steps.

In short: not a few problems about cumulative progress, incommensurability between theories, and other related topics arise when there is an excessive interest in showing that the actual record of empirical science, or its reconstructions, corresponds to perfectly rational criteria of progress. If we leave aside this kind of interest, we will easily realize that empirical science presents an impressive record of progress and will be able to understand why. Indeed, insofar as we are successful in the three former aspects of the reliability of science (intersubjective proofs, empirical control, and predictive power), we can automatically say that we have achieved progress. Then we will also easily understand why there is no such record of progress in other cognitive enterprises that do not include references to natural spatiotemporal patterns and to the corresponding empirical control of our representations of them.

2.5. RELIABLE KNOWLEDGE

John Ziman, in his book *Reliable Knowledge*,[54] provides explanations of the reliability of science different from those I have provided. To better clarify my own position, I shall comment on some of his ideas.

In a section entitled *Extra-logicality,* Ziman offers some comments that are closely related to my argument:

> Science depends fundamentally on human powers of perception, recognition, discrimination and interpretation . . . there is no computer program, no formal algorithm, no string of logical operations, to which these processes are equivalent, or to which they can, in any practical sense, be reduced. *Therefore*—and this is one of the most important characteristics of the "consensibility" model of science—*scientific knowledge cannot be justified or validated by logic alone.*[55]

This conclusion is a necessary corollary of the existence of conventional factors in science. Ziman explains it another way saying that logicality is a property of the type of communications that carry scientific knowledge or, in other words, that it is a part of the formal requirements that make a mes-

---

54. John Ziman, *Reliable Knowledge: An Exploration of the Grounds for Belief in Science* (Cambridge: Cambridge University Press, 1991).

55. Ibid., p. 99.

sage unambiguous. I do not deny that this is also a part of the story; however, I think Ziman stresses the role of sociological factors in science too strongly.

In a discussion of the "consensibility model of science," Ziman refers to an earlier book,[56] where he tried to show that:

> Scientific knowledge is the product of a collective human enterprise to which scientists make individual contributions which are purified and extended by mutual criticism and intellectual cooperation. According to this theory *the goal of science is a consensus of rational opinion over the widest possible field.*[57]

Ziman tells us that in his new book he deliberately turns away from the sociological aspects of science. Nevertheless, when shortly afterward he presents his "consensibility model of science," he tells us:

> We shall assume that scientific knowledge is distinguished from other intellectual artifacts of human society by the fact that its contents are *consensible.* By this I mean that each message should not be so obscure or ambiguous that the recipient is unable either to give a whole-hearted assent or to offer well-founded objections. The goal of science, moreover, is to achieve the maximum degree of *consensuality.*[58]

Therefore, even though he tells the reader that sociological aspects will be left aside, Ziman characterizes scientific knowledge and the goals of science in sociological terms.

Ziman recognizes that "this model imposes constraints upon the *contents* of science."[59] Indeed, the requirement that scientific knowledge must be "consensible" implies intersubjectivity and all the conditions necessary to reach an intersubjective consensus. Nevertheless, I feel that Ziman's perspective includes too many sociological components. Thus, when he refers to truth, he says that scientific knowledge contains many fallacies or mistaken beliefs that are held and maintained collectively; that the use of mathematical language does not make the messages any truer; that the logic of statements about the real world is three-valued, because they cannot all be given the status of "true" or "false" but can be "undecided"; that our scientific system does not necessarily tell us the truth.[60] Even if we admit that these remarks contain a grain of truth, it seems that Ziman always stresses the uncertainty of our knowledge.

I agree with Ziman in many respects but I think that one does not do jus-

56. John Ziman, *Public Knowledge: The Social Dimension of Science* (Cambridge: Cambridge University Press, 1967).

57. Ziman, *Reliable Knowledge,* cit., pp. 2–3.

58. Ibid., p. 6.

59. Ibid.

60. Ibid., pp. 8, 14, 26, 100, 105.

tice to the aims and results of empirical science when truth is relegated to a secondary place and sociological factors play the leading role. In any case, it can be easily noticed that a more realistic account of science and reliability, such as the one proposed here, corresponds much better to the aims and results of the scientific enterprise and provides a framework that can be integrated with other perspectives. Ziman's ideas can be easily provided with a more satisfactory ground within this framework; that is why I am going to call it "an open epistemology."

3. An Open Epistemology

This explication of the reliability of science makes it possible to avoid misinterpretations related to scientism, which tend to spoil the dialogue between science and religion. Scientism regards empirical science as the pattern to be imitated by every approach to reality. Sometimes those who oppose scientism wrongly think that they must deny the value of scientific knowledge, or at least limit its scope to some surface features of the natural world. Actually, the only rigorous way to overcome scientism is to recognize the real value of empirical science, precluding extrapolations or underevaluations. Only in this way will we be able to integrate scientific rationality within its true broader context, revealing its multiple connections with the different features of human rationality.

If the natural sciences give us a knowledge that possesses a special kind of reliability, this is because in those sciences we focus on spatiotemporal, repeatable patterns and use an intersubjective language that includes theoretical and pragmatic stipulations. We can also use this approach in some aspects of the human and the social sciences. Nevertheless, insofar as we deal with dimensions that transcend the realm of those patterns, we will be unable to attain the empirically reliable knowledge that we can reach in the natural sciences. The human factor introduces deeper dimensions that cannot be captured with the instruments used to know the material world (Figure 6.3).

In fact, to obtain reliable knowledge in the natural sciences we need to isolate phenomena that can be submitted to theoretical and practical control. Thus, we often uncover and control deep levels of the natural world, while we are unable to explain others that are more superficial but too complex for us.

My perspective excludes any form of scientism and underscores the notion that every objectification supposes that we limit our attention to a definite realm of properties. Therefore, we would act in an irrational way if we were to establish that only some privileged kind of objectifications are legitimate, or that we could reach valid knowledge only through the objectification used in empirical science.

As already noted, we do not need to accept a realistic picture of science to show how scientific progress enriches our knowledge of our cognitive abilities. Indeed, a mere description of the arguments used in empirical science may suffice for that purpose. I argue for a stronger interpretation of scientif-

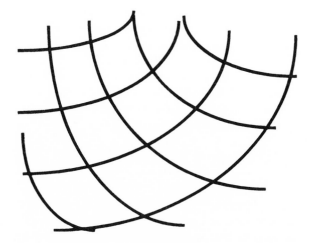

Fig. 6.3 Science and scientism. Sir Arthur S. Eddington, the British astronomer who directed the teams that observed in 1919 the binding of light rays under the effect of gravity (the first important test of Einstein's general relativity), compared the reach of scientific theories with the size of the holes of a net. An ichthyologist using a net whose holes are one square foot in size can say nothing about the existence and properties of fish that measure less than a foot. In a similar vein, the study of spatiotemporal patterns by means of magnitudes and repeatable experiments cannot by itself affirm or deny the existence and value of metaphysics, spirituality, and religion. Thus scientism, which claims that we cannot find meaningful knowledge outside empirical science, is not itself a consequence of empirical science. It is rather the result of illegitimate extrapolations and, insofar as it presents itself as a consequence of science, it is a deceptive and contradictory kind of pseudoscience.

ic knowledge because I think that this is the only picture that represents the real value of empirical science, so that we should take it as the most suitable partner in the science–religion dialogue.

The very use of the method of empirical science presupposes, at least implicitly, a minimal dose of realism, namely that we possess the ability to attain a cognitive grasp on the natural world. In this line, Jarrett Leplin has written:

> At least a minimal epistemic realism, holding that science can achieve theoretical knowledge, is crucial to rationality at the level of method. Specifically, I claim that unless the researcher presumes there to be some truth of the matter as to whether the entities and processes he theorizes about or experiments on exist and as to what their properties are, unless he treats such questions as epistemic objectives in the organization and direction of his work, much of that work is pointless and arbitrary. At best it is guesswork that cannot be construed to instantiate rationally grounded, generalizable principles.[61]

61. Jarrett Leplin, "Methodological Realism and Scientific Rationality," *Philosophy of Science*, 53 (1986): 32.

I would add that the presumption must not be explicit. One can be a realist in practice, working under the guide of implicit realistic assumptions, while being an opponent of realism in theory.

It is important to remember that the kind of scientific realism I support admits truth in science, but stresses that scientific truth is always contextual and therefore partial, gradual, and perfectible. Truth is above all a property of our statements, and as there are many different kinds of scientific statements, there are also many different kinds of scientific truth. Obviously it is not the same thing to assert the truth of an experimental law such as Ohm's law, of the model of a spatial structure such as that of DNA, of a general principle such as the principle of the conservation of energy, of a structural principle such as the requirement of the invariance of the physical laws under a certain change of frame of reference in the theory of relativity, of an entire theoretical system such as nonequilibrium thermodynamics, of the description of a collection of historical facts such as biological evolution, and so on.

Last but not least, I agree with Leplin's reference to

> my argument, which seeks not to explain the success of scientific methods but to establish the necessity of realist assumptions to the rationality of scientific methods.[62]

I do not think every piece of empirical science must have explicit realist assumptions or a realist meaning; I think the opposite is true. But only a realistic position can do justice to the overall aims of the scientific enterprise and to its actual achievements.

I have argued that, because empirical science concentrates on the study of spatiotemporal natural patterns and uses intersubjective theories that are submitted to intersubjective tests, it possesses a kind of reliability that we cannot find in other human cognitive enterprises. However, this does not mean that it possesses a monopoly on true knowledge. The progress of science is based on presuppositions whose analysis constitutes a metascientific task and leads to metascientific results. Moreover, other approaches, such as metaphysics and religion, have a different character, but they are not an alternative lifestyle, as if one were obliged to choose between science and the rest; rather, they must take seriously the knowledge provided by the sciences, and they represent perspectives that are complementary with scientific ones. Last but not least, scientism leads to contradiction, because its main thesis, that science is the only source of valuable knowledge or is the paradigm that should be imitated by any other knowledge, is neither scientific nor can it be derived from science; rather, it is opposed to the rigor characteristic of the natural sciences.

Scientism is based on a mistaken interpretation of the reliability of science and has as a consequence a very narrow view of human knowledge. I have proposed an explanation of the reliability of science that acknowledges the

62. Ibid., p. 43.

reach of empirical science and also its peculiar reliability, and, at the same time, stresses the complementarity that exists between empirical science and other kinds of human knowledge. It avoids the excesses of scientism and of sociologism and is able to combine the valuable features that other interpretations contain. That is why I call it "an open epistemology."

III. HUMAN SINGULARITY

Scientific progress is one of the most outstanding achievements of human beings. It is paradoxical, therefore, that it is sometimes used to argue that we are nothing but an accident in cosmic history. The image of the human being that creativity, argument, and interpretation suppose is most coherent with the metaphysical and religious views that represent the human person as a unitary being possessing material and spiritual dimensions who is able to collaborate with God in the fulfillment of God's plans.

1. Scientific Arguments for Human Singularity

Creativity, argument, and interpretation play a most important role in empirical science. We speak of creativity when a real innovation is produced, especially when it is relevant. Until the 1960s, philosophers of science usually accepted the distinction between the "context of discovery" and "context of justification." They also accepted that the context of discovery, which refers to the invention of new theories, was not properly the subject of epistemology; rather, it is the subject of psychology, and a very special subject indeed, because no fixed rules or roads exist that automatically lead to interesting discoveries. Logical analysis of science should concentrate completely on the context of justification, on the study of the methods used to examine the acceptability of scientific theories once they have been created. Scientific creativity would only be an interesting subject for historical case studies that could provide some moral for future action but no rules. In the preface to a collection of such case studies, we read:

> There have been many analyses of creativity from all points of view. Arthur Koestler has built on the analogy with humor where two habitually incompatible aspects of life meet in the explosive moment; while Hanson saw a model of creative insight in the way an observed pattern can suddenly change its significance. . . . One could go on and on, but the only conclusion that seems to emerge is that there cannot be any prescribed method of creativity however much may be learned of the conditions that promote it.[63]

63. Rutherford Aris, H. Ted Davis, and Roger H. Stuewer, eds., *Springs of Scientific Creativity: Essays on Founders of Modern Science* (Minneapolis: University of Minnesota Press, 1983), p. vi.

Of course, great advances in empirical science suppose an equally great dose of creativity. We admire Newton, Maxwell, Einstein, Heisenberg, Schrödinger, and other first-rate physicists because they have been able to formulate entirely new systems in mathematical physics that explain many kinds of phenomena and provide accurate predictions of others that were unknown. This kind of creativity includes, at least implicitly, "faith" in the existence of an objective natural order that can be known by combining theory and experiment in a way that shows the intimate unity of materiality and spirituality in our being and in our knowledge. Above all, independent of this subjective faith, the unity of materiality and spirituality in our knowledge is the very basis of all kinds of scientific progress.

Scientific progress supposes the existence of a unity between theoretical explanations and empirical tests. It supposes that we are able to represent the world as an object, so that we substitute the real world with idealized models that we can manage more easily. Therefore, it supposes that we are self-aware beings conscious of our position in the physical world, who know that the natural world is a part of our being and provides us with the necessary conditions for our activity, but who also know that we transcend the physical world. We can represent it; we can investigate its structures by combining our intellectual and empirical skills; we can pose all sorts of questions about its composition, its structure, the laws that govern its behavior; and we can meaningfully pose questions referring to its remote origin and evolution. This clearly shows that we possess an argumentative capacity that allows us to transcend our immediate experience. However, our argumentative capacity is tightly related to the material conditions of our existence, so the scientific quest must combine and balance both elements.

Creativity is an essential ingredient to any achievement in empirical science, be it big or small. To pose problems, which is the first step in any kind of scientific activity, implies that one goes beyond the "given" facts, data, or situations; therefore, creativity is present from the very beginning of scientific work. For the same reason, creativity will also be present in any successive step. It is needed to propose a new hypothesis, plan experiments to test that hypothesis, interpret the results of experiments, and evaluate the congruence between the hypothesis and the evidence.

Creativity refers to the introduction of new ideas; interpretation, to our decisions and evaluations; argument, to establishing a logical connection between known data and unknown explanations. These three concepts are closely related, even though not identical. Thus, in empirical science, argument involves creativity and interpretation, because we can never establish a completely necessary logical link between a set of empirical data and a theoretical explanation. Interpretation always includes a kind of creativity, because it is we who decide and establish a new interpretation.

The role that creativity and interpretation play in empirical science is related to the existence of conventional factors. If theories are always empirically underdetermined, creativity is needed to formulate them and interpretations must be used to evaluate them. Argument is also an essential feature of empirical science, because science is above all a search for as yet unknown explanations for existing problems, and we must use arguments if we want to obtain such explanations and evaluate them.

Recognizing these essential ingredients of empirical science should not involve any risk, because everyone admits a nonreductionist approach to epistemology and, as a consequence, accepts that every step in the natural science implies some dose of interpretation. Logical positivism, operationalism, and different forms of empiricism have failed in their attempts to provide reductionist accounts of empirical science, and no one today would claim that merely automatic methods are sufficient to promote and explain scientific progress.

Popper emphasized the central role that our argumentative capacity plays in empirical science and stressed that this capacity is a clear hallmark of human singularity. His critique of the materialistic explanations of the human being is clear enough in this respect. In his contribution to the book *The Self and Its Brain,* Popper goes so far as to propose a kind of interactionism as a solution to the mind–body problem, and he strongly criticizes materialist theories. His ideas may seem insufficient when considered in the light of a spiritualistic metaphysics and are problematic insofar as interactionism is too dependent on a Cartesian dualism. Nevertheless, they also show that a person like him, not committed to any specific metaphysical or religious position, can reach a nonmaterialistic view of the human person that is also compatible with an evolutionary perspective.

Popper considers human language as one of the main factors that explain the existence and progress of empirical science and distinguishes four functions of human language. Thus, when he criticizes physicalism, one of the main theses of the neopositivists, he writes:

> This criticism of physicalism relates to the analysis of the functions of language that was introduced by my teacher, Karl Bühler. He distinguished three functions of language: (1) the expressive function; (2) the signal or release function; and (3) the descriptive function. I have discussed Bühler's theory in various places, and I have added to his three functions a fourth—(4) the argumentative function. Now I have argued elsewhere that the physicalist is only able to cope with the first and the second of these functions. As a result, if faced with the descriptive and the argumentative functions of language, the physicalist will always see only the first two functions (which are also always present), with disastrous results.[64]

Popper holds that expressive function, which consists of an outward expression of inner states, can be found not only in animals, but also in plants and even in such instruments as a thermometer. The signaling function pre-

---

64. Karl R. Popper (with John C. Eccles), *The Self and Its Brain* (New York-London-Heidelberg-Berlin: Springer, 1977), p. 57.

supposes the expressive function and is also present in animals, plants, and instruments. The descriptive function presupposes the two lower ones and enables us to make statements that can be *true* or *false;* Popper notes that false descriptions are beyond animal powers. The argumentative function adds argument, with its values of *validity* and *invalidity,* to the three lower functions.[65] The descriptive and argumentative functions are necessary for the existence and progress of empirical science and are closely related to the singularity of human beings.

We can analyze what descriptive and argumentative functions imply: self-awareness, the sense of evidence, the capacity to combine experience and conceptualization, and the ability to build up theoretical models and to test them.

2. IMMANENCE AND TRANSCENDENCE

Only a narrow range of philosophical positions are compatible with the characteristics of the human being that we must admit to explain how science works. Stanley Jaki has shown that rationalism and empiricism are incompetent to explain the actual working of empirical science, whereas a Christian anthropology that sees the human being as a unity of body and soul is a much better candidate. He has written:

> The notion of man as a unity of body and soul may appear almost trouble-free when—and this is the chief concern in these lectures—a close look is taken at the ravages of inner logic which is at work when either man's body or man's soul is ignored in modern philosophical and scientific discourse. Pascal already noted that logic and spelled out in his inimitable way the results in store. In the abstract perspective of Descartes' mathematical physics man readily transformed into a mere mind—an angel of sorts. In the markedly empirical biological perspective, as articulated by Darwin, man inevitably turned into an ape. It tells something of the intrinsic nature of science that such one-sided presentations of man were to meet their rebuttal in further major scientific conquests.[66]

Concluding this work, Jaki makes a most interesting remark:

> Unlike an angel who needs no conquests, and unlike an ape uninterested in them, man thrives on conquests which are the fruit of a mysterious union in him of matter and mind.[67]

Jaki's reference to "mystery" is all-important and we should bear it in mind when we reflect on the peculiar character of the human being. If we adopt a

---

65. Ibid., pp. 58–59.

66. Stanley L. Jaki, *Angels, Apes, and Men* (La Salle, Ill.: Sherwood Sugden, 1983), pp. 7–8.

67. Ibid., p. 99.

kind of monistic explanation of the human being, be it spiritualist or materialist, instead of a mystery we will find an entire set of contradictions.

What the various methods used in empirical science have in common is a peculiar combination of theory and empirical control, which requires a subject capable of combining them. Moreover, this combination cannot be considered a merely external aggregation; both aspects, the rational and the empirical, are closely intertwined in every step of the workings of science. Even in the most elementary steps, defining and measuring the basic magnitudes of physics requires that kind of intertwining of theory and experiment. Theoretical definitions include implicit or explicit references to the procedures of measure, and measurement requires as a necessary element theoretical interpretations. Advanced steps such as the construction of new theoretical systems require the same combination at a more advanced level. This holds true throughout the entire range of scientific procedures, because we propose and evaluate theories and experiments all the time.

In fact, the development of epistemology clearly shows the complete failure of strong versions of empiricism or conventionalism, to say nothing of idealism, as these positions cannot account for even the more elementary achievements of empirical science.

It is evident that we are natural beings, and this fact accounts for the empirical and pragmatic features of the scientific enterprise. But scientific progress shows that we transcend the natural world. Indeed, we are able to represent it as an object and to build up idealized models that serve not only to represent specific features of the world, but also to conjecture the existence of unobserved features. We can use arguments to test the adequacy of our models. And, as a consequence of our use of those abilities, we make enormous progress in our scientific work. All this clearly shows that, even though we are natural beings, we also transcend the natural level.

Scientific rationality is a part of the wider field of human rationality, related to our ability to use inferences and argument to evaluate our claims to knowledge. By definition, "reason" means giving to each thing the appropriate weight; therefore, reasoning is necessary whenever we want to advance in our quest for explanations. Indeed, we do not have the kind of intuitive and immediate knowledge that theologians attribute to angels; we cannot deduce the nature of reality from some *a priori* principles as if we were the ultimate cause of being; we cannot discover the correct explanations by ascending from pure facts by merely logical steps. Progress in science requires following a sequence of steps in which creativity and interpretation are combined and an attitude of reasonableness that is closely connected with values.

In scientific rationality we use scientific arguments to transcend our ordinary experience and to know the natural order that underlies appearances. It includes the capacities of objectification and conceptualization and the capacity for argument that includes experiment. It combines the empirical and the rational dimensions in a single argument. It is exercised through creativity and interpretation. And it requires, as its only viable basis, a capacity of self-reflection that exists in a being that, at the same time, is a natural being and transcends nature.

Thus, the feedback of scientific progress on the epistemological presuppositions of science demonstrates that we transcend nature even though we are a part of it. Scientific creativity is a proof of our singularity. It shows that we possess dimensions that transcend the natural level and can be labeled as spiritual. The very existence and progress of the natural sciences are two of the best arguments for our spiritual character. But, at the same time, the success of the scientific method shows that our spiritual dimensions related to creativity and argument are intertwined with our material dimensions, so that we are a single being constituted by both aspects. The existence of human spiritual dimensions that are intertwined with material conditions may be considered a plain fact that is corroborated by the explanation of the existence and progress of empirical science.

Further problems arise when we try to explain in more detail what "spiritual" means in this context. A fashionable answer can be provided using the concept of "emergence." This is the position sustained by W. Mark Richardson. We have already seen that he remarks that Christian theism today has a recognizable core understanding of human agency that is closely related to commonsense psychology. He also refers to materialistic positions, such as those of Daniel Dennett and Patricia Churchland, concluding that "it seems obvious that the theologian will find a more compatible relation with research programs other than eliminativism and its fully materialistic cousins." He describes an emergent theory of mind as a good candidate for an explanation that can be combined with theology.[68]

Obviously, if by "emergence" we mean that in the course of evolution new features have begun to exist, then whoever accepts evolution should be an emergentist. Emergentism is usually proposed as something else, such as a "theory of mind" or an explanation of the new features embodied by the human being.[69] In any case, it is not difficult to agree with Popper, the agnostic, who says that speaking of the emergence of the human mind amounts to nothing more than putting a question mark at a certain place in human evolution. Sir John Eccles, who won the Nobel Prize for his work in neurophysiology and collaborated with Popper on a study of the human being, repeatedly analyzed the arguments in favor of materialism, found them faulty, and concluded:

> I am constrained to attribute the uniqueness of the Self or Soul to a supernatural spiritual creation. To give the explanation in theological terms: each Soul is a new Divine creation. . . . This conclusion is of

68. Richardson, "The Theology of Human Agency and the Neurobiology of Learning," cit. pp. 351–371.

69. For a brief history of the modern use of that concept, see Manfred Stöckler, "A Short History of Emergence and Reductionism," in *The Problem of Reductionism in Science,* ed. Evandro Agazzi (Dordrecht: Kluwer, 1991), pp. 71–90.

inestimable theological significance. It strongly reinforces our belief in the human Soul and in its miraculous origin in a Divine creation. There is recognition not only of the Transcendent God, the Creator of the Cosmos . . . but also of the loving God to whom we owe our being.[70]

Although I do not like the interactionism proposed by Popper and Eccles, this conclusion seems inescapable. A personal being requires a personal cause. It is also understandable that, because God's action extends to every entity, property, and process in the real world, in our case the effect of this divine action reaches a completely special level as it creates beings who possess the unique characteristics of the person: mainly, our peculiar kind of self-awareness, the capacity of finding and giving meaning to our life, the capacity of loving and behaving in an ethical way, and the capacity of loving God and having personal contacts with him. This perspective is most coherent with the image of the human being as the maker of science who must be capable of representing the physical world as an object and who possesses the descriptive and argumentative capacities that make empirical science possible.

To accept the special divine creation of every human soul does not mean that God's action contradicts the course of nature. That the existence of human beings is linked to a certain degree of biological organization is evident in the living world, so that there is room for both the continuity of nature and the discontinuity implied by a specific divine action that produces a new level of being. Of course, there are further problems in connection with this issue, especially those related with immortality, but these lie outside the limits of my present argument.

3. THE MEANING OF SCIENCE

We may conclude that scientific progress retrojustifies, enriches, and refines the epistemological presuppositions of science. Indeed, it shows that we possess an ever-increasing ability to build models and theories, to obtain and interpret data far from our ordinary experience, and to evaluate our theoretical constructs. Thanks to this progress, we know our own capacities better and are able to develop them in a line of increasing creativity that corresponds to God's plans.

All this is most coherent with the view that man is a cocreator who participates in God's plans and can carry the natural and human realities to ever more evolved states. Of course, we are not creators in the same sense in which God is the Creator that provides the radical principle of being for everything. Our causality is limited to the created powers that can only transform what already exists; we always need some preexisting basis for our action. Moreover, the very possibility of our acting depends in every concrete case on

70. John C. Eccles, *Evolution of the Brain: Creation of the Self* (London and New York: Routledge, 1991), p. 237.

God's will. Nevertheless, analysis of the scientific enterprise clearly shows that we are really creative. Therefore, we can say that God has endowed us with a creative power that is a limited participation in God's omnipotence.

Philip Hefner has proposed a theology of the human being as "the created co-creator."[71] I find that expression particularly meaningful and illuminating, provided it is understood within the above limits, as Hefner himself writes:

> I recommend that we think of the human being as the *created co-creator*. This term does a number of things. Because we are *created,* we are reminded that we are dependent creatures. We depend for our very existence on our cosmic and biological prehistory; we depend on the creative grace of God. Yet, we are also *creators,* using our cultural freedom and power to alter the course of historical events and perhaps even evolutionary events. We participate with God in the ongoing creative process. In addition, the term "created co-creator" connotes the fact that we have a destiny. We have a future toward which we are being drawn by God's will. Only when we understand what this destiny is will we be able to measure and evaluate the direction we take in our creative activity.[72]

The scientific enterprise acquires a completely new and fascinating meaning when we see it as a task that God has entrusted to us so that we may increasingly participate in his knowledge and mastery over the natural world. Then, cultivating science becomes a human task with divine meaning, and it should be carried out with a deep gratefulness and respect toward the plans of the Creator.

Mastery over nature was one of the main ideas that stimulated the birth of empirical science in the Christian Western world. It implies a real though not absolute creativity. Our possibilities are limited by our own capacities and by the constraints imposed by the external natural world. Our attitude to this magnificent view of the human being as a created co-creator should be one of humility on account of our great limitations, and, at the same time, one of gratitude and daring. Our mastery over nature should not be tyrannical; rather, scientific progress opens ever-greater possibilities for promoting a civilization where, respecting nature as a part of our own being, all human beings might be able to develop the capabilities God has endowed us with.

71. Philip Hefner, *The Human Factor, Evolution, Culture, and Religion* (Minneapolis, Minn.: Fortress Press, 1993).

72. Philip Hefner, "The Evolution of the Created Co-Creator," in *Cosmos as Creation: Theology and Science in Consonance,* ed. Ted Peters (Nashville, Tenn.: Abingdon Press, 1989), pp. 225–226.

PART IV

Science
and Values

The meaning of science is twofold: pursuit of truth and service to humankind. The new worldview presents a creative universe that has made possible the existence of creative intelligent beings who are, at the same time, carriers of insignificance and grandeur.

7

Scientific
Values

M y argument culminates in the consideration of the ethical presuppositions of science and the feedback of scientific progress on them. My
analysis of the ontological presuppositions of science and the impact of scientific progress on them concluded that natural order appears now as the result
of a huge and most sophisticated process of self-organization that manifests nature's creativity and is most consonant with the action of a personal God who
endows his creatures with marvelous potentialities so that they may cooperate
with God's plans. Then I analyzed the epistemological presuppositions of science, showing that scientific progress strongly underscores the singularity of
the human being, who is able to combine in an extremely creative way intellectual and empirical abilities, in a manner highly consonant with the personal character of a being who both belongs to the natural world and transcends
it. Now I turn my attention to the ethical presuppositions of science, which
refer to empirical science considered as a goal-directed human activity.

Science works because we consider its goals to be values; otherwise we
would not pursue them. Therefore, we can translate our question into a question about values: how are scientific values related to the human values that
give meaning to our life?

As a preliminary step to examining the deepest implications of that question, I will analyze why we should admit the existence of scientific values,
which values are essentially linked to the scientific enterprise, and what the
impact of scientific progress is upon them.

I. WHY VALUES?

Empirical science is usually considered to be a value-free enterprise independent of the personal and subjective factors associated with values. How-

ever, as a goal-directed human activity, it must include some kind of values, those that refer to its goals and to the means necessary to achieve them.

1. A Value-Free Science?

To talk about values in connection with empirical science is not easy. The hallmark of empirical science is objectivity, which, by its very nature, means independence from subjective and personal factors, whereas values are closely related to personal interests and commitments. That explains why, for a long time, it has been said that empirical science has nothing to do with values; only applied science or technology, which deals with the practical problems of human life, is said to be involved in problems about values. In addition, scientists generally have had a vested interest in considering science to be value-free, because they were afraid that, if they permitted discussions about values within their science, they would get involved in tiresome discussions and would lose their autonomy.

It appears easy to open the doors of science to values when we realize that objectivity itself can be considered a value. Nevertheless, objectivity seems incompatible with any kind of value that involves evaluation. If one accepts the classical distinction between facts and values, it seems inescapable that one should also accept the distinction between the field in which objectivity is the rule and another, legitimate but completely different, field of subjective feelings, emotions, interpretations, and preferences. This second subjective area includes all those values other than objectivity that would be excluded from the scientific approach.

We may even ask why we should consider objectivity at all. It seems to be closely linked to the analytic perspective that tries to rationalize everything, leaving aside the most cherished features of human life and creating a kind of rational void where there is no place for feelings or personal evaluations. Someone could argue that perhaps we should control objective science and not let it invade the realm of human values.

This issue holds a central place in some important problems facing our civilization. For example, Monod's naturalism represents the human being as a merely chance product of blind natural forces, as if this were the logical result of the "postulate of objectivity" essential to the natural sciences. He asserts that empirical science is the only source of truth and presents this assertion as the result of an "ethical" choice. However, the very fact that Monod acknowledges scientific objectivity as a value shows that there is something more in empirical science than meets the eye. I would be ready to identify Monod's "postulate of objectivity" with an "ethical presupposition" of empirical science—that it is possible, convenient, and effective to adopt the scientific perspective to obtain reliable knowledge about the natural world. But this has nothing in common with Monod's scientism. On the contrary, the ethical character of this presupposition clearly shows that there are other areas in which knowledge-claims and evaluations are possible, and we can even add that these areas should include knowledge-claims more fundamental than those of empirical science, because they provide the basis for the evaluation of the entire scientific enterprise.

Misunderstandings of scientific objectivity and of its ethical meaning are common in contemporary culture. Herbert Marcuse, in the context of the neo-Marxist Frankfurt School, has many points in common with Monod. The coincidences are all the more striking in light of the fact that Monod overvalues empirical science while Marcuse undervalues it.

According to Marcuse, scientific rationality is "uni-dimensional," because it reduces human problems to those features that can be treated using analytical reason, leaving aside the issues most relevant for our existence. In this perspective, scientific rationality is conceived as essentially instrumentalist, because it is centered around the study of means and instruments and separated from the social reality that could determine their use. When instrumentalist thinking projects itself onto social reality, the necessary consequence is lack of freedom, because everything is controlled by technical means that provide more productivity and comfort.[1]

This unidimensional rationality would be assumed, according to Marcuse, by analytical philosophy. This philosophy therefore has an intrinsic ideological character, because it tends to leave social reality as it is. That is why analytic philosophy is qualified by Marcuse as academic pseudomasochism, autohumiliation, and autodenunciation of the ineffectiveness of philosophy.[2]

I would not deny that some of these criticisms may be right. However, my point here is that both Monod and Marcuse, in spite of profound differences in their evaluation of science and scientific objectivity, agree in their evaluation of scientific rationality as completely disconnected from any broader context. Both take it as a purely instrumental reason completely divorced from any metaphysical context. Both see it as leading to ethical perplexities. It is completely neutral regarding ethics, which means that, if we take it as a way of life, objective values cease to exist. Actually, this is the conclusion reached by Monod, who, paradoxically, strongly asserts the value of scientific objectivity on the basis of an alleged ethical decision that, according to his own doctrine, should be considered groundless. If we recognize scientific objectivity as an important value in itself, and not only because it leads us to obtain results important for technical purposes, then we are dealing with the *search for truth* as an *ethical value,* and this is hardly compatible with the scientistic perspective that considers empirical science to be "the *only* authentic source of truth." We cannot prove that the pursuit of truth is an ethical value using science alone; if we admit that empirical science is the only source of truth, we cannot even justify the notion that the scientific search for truth is

1. Herbert Marcuse, *One-Dimensional Man* (London: Routledge, 1964), pp. 157–158.

2. Ibid., pp. 172–173.

an ethical value. Therefore, empirical science is undervalued if we disconnect it from its metaphysical and ethical foundations.

Marcuse tells us that values, when separated from objective knowledge, become merely subjective. He points out that the only way to attribute some real validity to them would be to admit a kind of metaphysical sanction, such as the natural and divine law. But he states that the scientific outlook rules this out as unverifiable and not objective, because it cannot be treated using the scientific method. Marcuse adds that these difficulties cannot be solved using Aristotelian or Thomisic philosophies, which he considers to have been refuted by scientific reason. The result would be that everything is ruled by scientific reason, which considers its objects to be mere instruments. To overcome this antihumanitarian situation, Marcuse proposes that the structure of science itself should change. Changes in social structure would produce a different, pacified world, in which science would find different empirical conditions, so that it would obtain facts and concepts essentially different from our present facts and concepts.[3]

It is difficult to imagine what kind of society is being advocated by Marcuse and more difficult to imagine what kind of new science would result from it. Would the laws of physics, chemistry, and biology change? If we follow the indications provided by Marcuse, the answer should be affirmative, but Marcuse does not provide the slightest hint about this issue.

Monod and Marcuse represent two paradigmatic cases. Both reduce scientific objectivity to the analytic level; Monod extrapolates this, considering scientific objectivity to be the only kind of objective knowledge, and Marcuse criticizes this position as disconnected from the real human situation. My question is directed to the common basis they share: can scientific objectivity be reduced to the analytic level? Can it be considered a merely instrumental tool?

As Monod himself acknowledges, scientific objectivity is closely linked to ethics. It is we who decide to adopt an objective perspective, create the means that make its existence possible, work within that perspective, obtain specific results thanks to the use of that method, and should integrate that method and its results within the wider framework of human experience. If we forget this wider framework, scientific objectivity becomes an ethically blind choice that would lead us, as Monod puts it, nowhere. More exactly, using his words, that choice would lead us to know that we are alone in the universe's unfeeling immensity, out of which we emerged only by chance.

We may wonder how an ethical choice could lead us to a conclusion such as that. We may also wonder how is it possible to assert that empirical science is the only source of truth on the basis of an ethical choice. It seems far more reasonable to admit that scientific objectivity is an ethical value because it represents a concrete way of searching for truth, and searching for truth is an ethical value in human life.

---

3. Ibid., pp. 166–167.

Empirical science can be considered value-free if we limit our explanation only to its more "technical" or pragmatic features. Indeed, one can learn how to work well in science and can do good work, irrespective of philosophical and religious ideas. However, even the least philosophically minded scientist follows a path characterized by the search for a knowledge of nature that can be submitted to empirical control, so that it may provide the basis for a controlled dominion over nature. Otherwise, that work won't be considered to belong to empirical science. Of course, our scientist can completely forget all this or even deny it. But it is a matter of fact that the presuppositions of scientific activity will always be implicitly present in scientific work and can be the subject of philosophical reflection. At the level presently being considered, these presuppositions include an ethical component: that the twofold objectives of empirical science are worth pursuing.

Empirical science can also be considered value-free insofar as we take it not as a goal-directed human activity, but as a collection of results: surely, many of these results will have no ethical significance. However, even in this case we should not forget that sometimes even a single result or group of findings may have implications for our worldview and, in this way, can have an impact on some of our values or, at least, on the means of evaluating them or putting them into practice.

2. THE AUTONOMY OF SCIENCE

One of the main reasons in favor of thinking of empirical science as value-free is that this seems the only viable way to protect the autonomy of the scientific enterprise. In this, the distinction between pure and applied science serves to reinforce the noncommitment of pure science to any kind of metascientific values; indeed, pure science seems completely committed to its own goals and procedures, and only applied science or technology can be related to extrascientific values.

This perspective is represented, for example, by Imre Lakatos when he says:

> *In my view, science, as such, has no social responsibility.* In my view it is society that has a responsibility—that of maintaining the apolitical, detached scientific tradition and allowing science to search for truth in the way determined purely by its inner life.[4]

Nevertheless, we should notice that Lakatos refers to the "search for truth" as an essential characteristic of science that must be respected and even favored by society. In so doing, he acknowledges the search for truth as an ethical value; otherwise, it would be difficult to explain why society has the responsibility of respecting it. The search for truth is not a supreme value; we

---

4. Imre Lakatos, "The Social Responsibility of Science," in *Mathematics, Science and Epistemology*, Philosophical Papers, vol. 2, ed. John Worrall and Gregory Currie (Cambridge: Cambridge University Press, 1978), p. 258.

cannot justify, for example, any kind of experiment on human beings by arguing that it could lead to progress in the medical sciences. Scientific values exist and must be harmonized with other ethical values.

Even if we admit the distinction between pure and applied science, scientists must not forget how their results can be used. Thus, Lakatos continues his reflections:

> Of course scientists, as citizens, have responsibility, like all other citizens, to see that science is *applied* to the right social and political ends. This is a different, independent question.[5]

As a matter of fact, pure and applied sciences are closely intertwined in our days. On the one hand, the costs of research in pure science are often very high, requiring the intervention of organizations capable of affording them; in consequence, states and other public or private enterprises exercise an increasing control on scientific research and orient it toward their political, military, and economic interests. On the other hand, progress in many scientific areas requires the use of highly sophisticated technology, so that the frontiers between the theoretical and the pragmatic dimensions of empirical science cannot be easily established. It is sometimes said that, instead of insisting on the distinction between pure and applied science, we should rather speak of a single reality called "technoscience."

I am ready to admit the increasing dependence of pure science on external goals and technology. Nevertheless, I think the distinction between pure and applied science continues to be valid and important, primarily because empirical science is, above all, a human activity guided by the search for a knowledge of the natural world, a search for true knowledge. Whatever the particular purposes of a specific piece of research, it will consist, from an objective point of view, of an effort to obtain new information about the natural world, and the reasons used to support the validity of that information must be logically valid.

Therefore, scientific research is basically autonomous, because it is guided by the search for truth and uses objective arguments to achieve that goal. Problems related to the involvement of science in political, military, or economical enterprises must be tackled by adopting an ethical perspective that should define the rightness of the goals and means involved in every particular case. This does not mean, however, that empirical science is not related to values. Rather, the search for truth is a very important value, as is commitment to objectivity in the use of argument, as required by the search for truth. This kind of value is not imposed from without; it is a part of science itself. Indeed, empirical science would simply be meaningless without it. They are implicit values that act as ethical presuppositions of the entire scientific enterprise.

Before analyzing the ethical values related to science and the feedback of

5. Ibid.

scientific progress on them, I shall first analyze several positions on this issue, in an attempt to show that a wide range of values can be related to empirical science and to evaluate the role that those values can play in my argument about the general presuppositions of science.

II. EVALUATING SCIENTIFIC VALUES

The first approach to scientific values I will analyze provides a map of the relationships between science and values and can be useful as the basis for further inquiries. The rest refers to particular values: to the search for truth; to the values inherent in empirical science as an institutionalized enterprise; and to the epistemic values used to evaluate scientific theories. Finally, I shall examine an approach that, from the point of view of a moral philosopher, attributes a strong moral value to empirical science.

1. RECONNECTING SCIENCE AND ETHICS

The positivist account of science tends to minimize the contacts between science and ethics, underscoring the point that empirical science deals with facts and is therefore value-free. The main aim of positivism is precisely to "purify" science from any external "contamination." Stephen Toulmin, considered one of the main representatives of the transition from the positivist to the postpositivist philosophy of science in the 1960s and 1970s, refers to the "puristic" view that presents science as most intellectual and least ethically implicated, and says that this view continues to have great attractions:

> No doubt this "puristic" view of science . . . had, and continues to have, great attractions for many professional scientists. Since "rational objectivity" is an indispensable part of the scientific mission, and the intrusion of "values" into science had come to be regarded as incompatible with such objectivity, all concern with values (or other arbitrary, personal preferences) had to be forsworn in the highest interest of rationality. Certainly, the professional institution of science tended to be organized on this basis.[6]

Toulmin argues that this is a consequence of the professionalization of science through the establishment of distinct scientific disciplines in the nineteenth century:

> As a result of this change, scientific workers divided themselves up into new and self-organized collectivities, and acquired a collective consciousness of their specialized intellectual tasks, as contrasted with

6. Stephen Toulmin, "How Can We Reconnect the Sciences with the Foundations of Ethics?" in *The Roots of Ethics, Science, Religion, and Values,* ed. Daniel Callahan and H. Tristram Engelhardt, Jr. (New York and London: Plenum Press, 1981), p. 406.

the broader concerns of philosophical, literary, and theological discussion more generally. . . . In short, if we are to understand how science came to part company from the foundations of ethics, we need to focus attention on the history of scientific specialization. It was the development of specialization and professionalization that was responsible for excluding ethical issues from the foundations of science, and so, though inadvertently, destroyed most of the links between science and the foundations of ethics.[7]

Searching to reconnect science and ethics, Toulmin points out that during the twentieth century, physiology and psychology have succeeded in securing their own positions as sciences, so that human beings themselves have become legitimate issues for scientific investigation. As a consequence, the concepts of "normal" functioning and "good" health can be discussed as problems belonging to both science and ethics. This would mean that a crucial incursion by science into the foundations of ethics has taken place. Given the increasing involvement of basic science in human welfare, mainly in the medical area, it is becoming clear that the professional organization and priorities of scientific work are related to ethical acceptability and social value; the very existence of bioethics is an indication of this change. Therefore, changes in the social context of science could help to end the divorce between science and ethics.

On this basis, Toulmin tries to indicate the points at which issues originating in the natural sciences can give rise to evaluative issues. He distinguishes three levels in science: science considered as a collective activity, the personal commitments of scientists, and the actual contents of the sciences. Regarding the first level he says:

> As a collective activity, any science is of significance for ethics on account of the ways in which it serves as an embodiment or exemplar of applied rationality.[8]

The objectivity that characterizes the sciences could thus be useful for a counterattack against relativism and subjectivism in ethics. In reference to the second level, Toulmin states that the respect for rationality that is a part of the moral character of the scientist's motivation could teach us something about our attitudes in other areas of life. Finally, the actual content of the sciences can contribute to a better understanding of our place within the natural world. Toulmin says that the phase of scientific development into which we are now moving requires that we become participants in many of the natural phenomena and processes that are the subject of scientific investigation, and invokes Heisenberg's uncertainty principle to show that the new situation includes the whole spectrum of late twentieth-century science. He alludes to the use in science of the concepts of "function" or "adaptation." He offers all

7. Ibid., pp. 408, 411.

8. Ibid., p. 418.

of this as a sign of the interconnectedness of human conduct and natural phenomena. In his conclusion, Toulmin refers to the concept of responsibility as a major field in which we should renegotiate the relations between the sciences and the foundations of ethics.

Loren Graham agrees with many of Toulmin's contentions. But Graham sees more connections between science and ethics than Toulmin does. Graham introduces two categories that represent different approaches to this issue, which are labeled "expansionism" and "restrictionism":

> By Expansionism I mean that type of argument which cites evidence within the body of scientific theories and findings which can supposedly be used, either directly or indirectly, to support conclusions about ethical, sociopolitical, or religious values. I call this approach Expansionism because its result is to expand the boundaries of science in such a way that they include, at least by implication, value questions. . . . The logical alternative to Expansionism is Restrictionism, an approach that confines science to a particular realm or a particular methodology and leaves values outside its boundaries.[9]

Graham proposes a kind of middle way that would avoid the excesses of expansionism and restrictionism, speaking about an entire set of connections between science and values, and exploring the spectrum of science–values interactions described by Toulmin. Graham analyzes seven kinds of linkages between various fields of science and various types of values,[10] of which I shall now briefly consider.

The first kind of linkage is based on "value terms within science," including terms belonging to the social and biological sciences, such as "normal," "abnormal," "deviant," or "adaptation." Graham holds that these terms are value-laden, and in spite of efforts made to eliminate them, they are unavoidable.

The second linkage is based on "scientific theories or hypotheses alleged to impinge on values." More common and more significant than the previous one, this category, according to Graham, consists of "value attributions given by individuals to theories or hypotheses found in the sciences"; the source of the value is "the person who is trying to find significance for human values in science." Among these are the ideas of the social Darwinists in the nineteenth century; the links sometimes established by Niels Bohr when he used nuclear physics to explain human attributes; the connection between Lamarckism and social and political questions made by many writers in Germany and Russia in the 1920s; and controversies in ethology and sociobiology. Graham argues that "areas of scientific investigation such as sociobiology are inextricably linked to values."

9. Loren R. Graham, "Commentary. The Multiple Connections between Science and Ethics: Response to Stephen Toulmin," in *The Roots of Ethics*, cit., pp. 427, 429.

10. Loren R. Graham, *Between Science and Values* (New York: Columbia University Press, 1981), pp. 355–382.

A third kind of linkage is based on "the empirical findings of science," which can impinge on existing social values. Graham focuses on the Copernican hypothesis and adds that "the possibility of new scientific data having an impact on social values continues today."

The fourth kind of linkage is based on "the methods and sources of science." According to Graham, people who emphasize this type of link believe that "the source of scientific creativity and the methods by which science proceeds have value meanings." Einstein and Heisenberg are quoted as supporters of this view, which refers to values such as harmony, perfection, truth-seeking, and elegance.

A fifth kind of linkage is based on "technological capabilities." According to Graham, technology can influence our values by making it possible to perform actions that in the past were either impossible or extremely difficult, and by altering the speed and scale of these actions.

These five kinds of linkage refer to the influence of science and technology on values. The sixth linkage, however, refers to the reverse influence of values on science and technology. Graham refers to the influence of external factors on the development of science and to the more obvious case of social factors impinging on the procedures, limits, and applicability of science and technology; biomedical issues are an important example of the latter case.

Finally, Graham tells us that, even though it is likely that a factual statement cannot logically entail a normative one, there are innumerable examples of science and technology interacting with social values. Graham also adds that this kind of interaction is most interesting, because "it is in this relationship between science and society where the historically interesting value conflicts arise." Graham concludes:

> Seen in its social context, science is far from value-free. The value transformations in which it plays a crucial role are of immense intellectual and social importance. . . . We are now in a new era in our understanding of science–value relationships, and this new period brings with it both novel opportunities and novel dangers. . . . We also have left behind the view that science is value-free, not because all of science is value-laden (it is not), but because the value-free approach to science is simply inadequate to describe what is currently happening in the relationship between science and values.[11]

Clearly, both Toulmin and Graham perceive multiple connections between science and values. I agree with them globally, but it is important to note that their approach is mainly sociological and historical; in consequence, it depends on contingent circumstances, and it cannot be applied to the general presuppositions of science.

The first two types of linkage described by Graham rely on subjective perspectives that, even if legitimate, do not correspond to intrinsic features of

---

11. Ibid., pp. 373 and 377.

the sciences. The third, which refers to the empirical findings of science, also has a contingent and quite accidental character. The fourth kind of linkage refers to an essential character of empirical science—its method—but the examples given again refer not to central characteristics but to accidental attitudes. Although the fifth and sixth kinds of linkage are enormously important, they refer to technology rather than science. Finally, when Graham says, in the seventh point of the list, that it is in the relationship between science and society that historically interesting value conflicts arise, I cannot help thinking that some of those conflicts—or perhaps all of them—could have been avoided if both sides had adopted a more rigorous approach. In conclusion, even though Graham's list seems to provide a wide map of the relationship between science and values, the seven items contained in that list do not correspond to general characteristics of empirical science.

The sociological approach adopted by Graham is completely correct if we wish to analyze the relationship between science and values from a perspective centered on the sociological and historical features of the issue, but it is not useful if we seek for more essential connections.

It is easier to connect some of Toulmin's comments with my perspective, especially the three levels in science he enumerates. Toulmin sees empirical science, considered as a collective activity, as an exemplar of applied rationality; he says that respect for rationality in the sciences could teach us something about our attitudes in other areas of life; and he adds that the actual content of the sciences could contribute to a better understanding of our place within the natural world. These three characteristics of the sciences can be related to the ethical presuppositions of empirical science and to the feedback of scientific progress on them.

2. THE ETHICAL BASIS OF SCIENCE

If we admit that the search for truth is an essential feature of the aim of science, we can easily connect science and values. It is easy to perceive that the search for truth is an ethical value, and a very central one indeed.

I have already made note of Karl Popper's stress on the statement that in empirical science we search for a true knowledge of the natural world. Popper adds, in this context, that the search for truth presupposes ethics. In his own words:

> I am on the side of science and of rationality, but I am against those exaggerated claims for science that have sometimes been, rightly, denounced as "scientism." I am on the side of the *search for truth,* and on intellectual daring in the search for truth; but I am against intellectual arrogance, and especially against the misconceived claim that we have the truth in our pockets, or that we can approach certainty. It is important to realize that science does not make assertions about ultimate questions—about the riddles of existence, or about man's task in this world. This has often been well understood. But some

great scientists, and many lesser ones, have misunderstood the situation. The fact that science cannot make any pronouncement about ethical principles has been misinterpreted as indicating that there are no such principles; while in fact the search for truth presupposes ethics.[12]

Here, as elsewhere in his work, Popper speaks in the same breath of the search for truth and of our inability to know whether we have reached it. I have already explained that an interpretation of Popper's fallibilism in a strong sense, as implying that our knowledge is always conjectural, will meet big difficulties; indeed, in many cases we know for certain that our knowledge is at least partially true, and Popper himself claims that in science we make progress toward theories increasingly closer to truth, which implies that we know something about the positive value of our knowledge. These difficulties can be overcome if we interpret fallibilism in a weaker sense, as an expression of the limits of our knowledge.

Popper asserts that truth is a regulative idea for the entire scientific enterprise. He also perceived that science alone cannot be considered as an ultimate arbiter, because it is built on some presuppositions that lie outside its range. We can, however, ask what he means when he says that the search for truth presupposes ethics.

Popper's answer to this question is clear, and he explains his views in a way that deserves an extensive quotation:

The principles that form the basis of every rational discussion, that is, of every discussion undertaken in the search for truth, are in the main *ethical* principles. I should like to state three such principles.

1. The principle of fallibility: perhaps I am wrong and perhaps you are right. But we could easily both be wrong.

2. The principle of rational discussion: we want to try, as impersonally as possible, to weigh up our reasons for and against a theory: a theory that is definite and criticizable.

3. The principle of approximation to the truth: we can nearly always come closer to the truth in a discussion which avoids personal attacks. It can help us to achieve a better understanding; even in those cases where we do not reach an agreement.

It is worth noting that these three principles are both epistemological and ethical principles. . . . Thus ethical principles form the basis of science. The idea of truth as the fundamental regulative principle—the principle that guides our search—can be regarded as an ethical principle. The search for truth and the idea of approximation to the truth are also ethical principles.[13]

12. Karl R. Popper, "Natural Selection and the Emergence of Mind," in *Evolutionary Epistemology, Rationality, and the Sociology of Knowledge,* ed. Gerard Radnitzky and William W. Bartley, III (La Salle, Ill.: Open Court, 1987), p. 141.

13. Karl R. Popper, *In Search of a Better World. Lectures and Essays from Thirty Years* (London and New York: Routledge, 1992), p. 199.

Popper's text clearly shows that he considers the search for truth to be based on ethical dispositions such as open-mindedness, detachment of personal interests, and respect for argument and that he sees these dispositions as closely linked to recognizing the potential unity and equality of all men, admitting the limits of our knowledge, and being intellectually honest.

This can be applied not only to empirical science, but also to any kind of rational discussion. The peculiarity of empirical science is that, as a collective enterprise, it includes institutionalized requirements that are closely related to the ethical dispositions just quoted. Obviously, insofar as ethics is mainly a matter of personal dispositions, no one can force us to adopt them. Scientists may act in a nonethical way, even in their scientific work. Nevertheless, the overall outcome of empirical science tends to favor respect for argument. This leads us to consider the institutional values of empirical science.

3. Science as a Social Institution

Robert Merton is generally recognized as a pioneer in the field of the sociology of science. His 1942 paper "The Normative Structure of Science" contains an analysis of the values of empirical science considered as a social institution.[14] In the introduction to this paper, Norman W. Storer synthesizes its content:

> The paper is essentially a definition of the four major norms, or institutional imperatives, that comprise the ethos of science and a statement of their interdependence as well as their functional relationships to the formal goals of scientific work: "the extension of certified knowledge."[15]

Merton presents the four norms as derived from the goal and the methods of science; however, he also stresses that they have a moral value on their own:

> The institutional goal of science is the extension of certified knowledge. The technical methods employed toward this end provide the relevant definition of knowledge: empirically confirmed and logically consistent statements of regularities (which are, in effect, predictions). The institutional imperatives (mores) derive from the goal and the methods. . . . The mores of science possess a methodologic rationale but they are binding, not only because they are procedurally efficient, but because they are believed right and good. They are moral as well as technical prescriptions.[16]

Leaving aside the controversial expression "certified knowledge," we can appreciate that Merton attributes to his four norms two kinds of value. First,

14. Robert K. Merton, *The Sociology of Science: Theoretical and Empirical Investigations* (Chicago and London: The University of Chicago Press, 1973), pp. 266–278.

15. Norman W. Storer, "Prefatory Note," in *The Sociology of Science,* cit., p. 226.

16. Merton, *The Sociology of Science,* cit., p. 270.

they are "procedurally efficient" as the appropriate means to achieve the goals of empirical science using the corresponding specific methods; thus, if we desire to evaluate Merton's norms, we should examine their efficiency in the context of the goals and methods of empirical science. Therefore, the ethical character of the norms will depend on the ethical character of the goals and methods of science, so that, if these goals and methods are good and the norms are efficient, the norms will also be ethically good. Second, Merton says that the norms "are binding because they are believed right and good"; thus, the norms possess their own ethical character, and this is why they are binding.

Merton's four norms are *universalism, communism, disinterestedness,* and *organized skepticism.*

Universalism means that truth-claims must be independent from the race, nationality, religion, class, and personal qualities of their protagonist, so that they are to be subjected to "preestablished impersonal data." Merton relates universalism to the impersonal character of science and to democracy, because he sees the open democratic society as being characterized by "impersonal criteria of accomplishment and not fixation of status."

Communism refers to the "sense of common ownership of goods," so that "the substantive findings of science are a product of social collaboration and are assigned to the community." Recognition and esteem must be the sole property right of the scientist, and "recognition is contingent upon publication." Close to this communism is the "imperative for communication of findings," opposite to any kind of secrecy. The sense of "dependence upon a cultural heritage" is linked to "the essentially cooperative and selectively cumulative quality of scientific achievement." "The humility of scientific genius" results from the awareness of the dependence on the collaboration of others. It should be noted that Merton presents the term "communism" in inverted commas, as though he realizes that we should find a more appropriate term.

Disinterestedness does not mean altruism. Instead, like the other norms, it refers to patterns of institutional control. Scientific research involves the verifiability of results by fellow experts. Merton asserts that "the activities of scientists are subject to rigorous policing, to a degree perhaps unparalleled in any other field of activity." Disinterestedness is based on the public and testable character of science. It is related to "absence of fraud"; in empirical science, "spurious claims appear to be negligible and ineffective." Scientists usually are not involved in a direct relationship with a lay clientele; rather, they are subject to a control exercised by qualified compeers.

Organized skepticism "is both a methodological and an institutional mandate" that includes "the temporary suspension of judgement" and "the detached scrutiny of beliefs in terms of empirical and logical criteria." Merton notes that this characteristic "appears to be the source of revolts against the so-called intrusion of science into other spheres," that it has "periodically involved science in conflict with other institutions," and that "resistance on the part of organized religion has become less significant as compared with that of economic and political groups," as "skepticism threatens the current distribution of power."

Merton's four norms have been reformulated by André Cournand and Michael Meyer with explicit reference to the conduct of individual scientists, considering them as moral attitudes necessary for the effective working of the scientific community. They translated Merton's four norms into five obligations: *objectivity* or *intellectual integrity, honesty, tolerance* or respect for the good faith of other scientists, *doubt of certitude* or readiness to question what is accepted as certain, and *selflessness* on behalf of the growth of scientific knowledge. They added further considerations that refer to failures in the observance of this code and to the growing concern within society about science.[17]

In a brief survey, Ian Barbour refers to proposals advanced by Robert Merton, Jacob Bronowski, H. Richard Niebuhr, and Michael Polanyi.[18] According to this survey, a list of values intrinsic to science could also include rationality, freedom of thought, right of dissent, cooperation, loyalty to truth, truth seeking, truth telling, trust and common loyalties, and personal responsibility for one's claims.

That list could easily be expanded. For example, in a study presented to a 1975 meeting of the American Association for the Advancement of Science, the authors distinguished two main types of values: *terminal values,* which refer to desirable end-states, and *instrumental values,* which refer to desirable modes of behavior instrumental to the attainment of those desirable end-states. They established a list of 18 terminal values and 18 instrumental values that were used as the basis of a study that comprised a survey on the perceived values of science and an analysis based on editorials published by *Science* magazine. The 18 terminal values, ordered according to the result of the survey, were a sense of accomplishment, wisdom, a world of peace, freedom, social recognition, self-respect, national security, equality, a world of beauty, a comfortable life, inner harmony, family security, happiness, an exciting life, pleasure, true friendship, love for nature, and salvation. The 18 instrumental values, ordered by the same criterion, were intellectual, ambitious, logical, broadminded, capable, responsible, imaginative, useful, independent, self-controlled, honest, courageous, clean, obedient, polite, understanding, cheerful, and loving.[19]

A list of values like the ones just quoted obviously depends on our interests. This study is centered on the relationship between scientific values and those of other institutions; this is why it includes among them salvation, friendship, pleasure, loving, cheerful, and polite, which, although low on this

17. André Cournand and Michael Meyer, "The Scientist's Code," *Minerva,* 14 (1976): 79–96.

18. Ian Barbour, *Ethics in an Age of Technology* (San Francisco: Harper, 1993), pp. 28–29.

19. William A. Blanpied and Wendy Weisman-Dermer, "Value Images of Science and the Values of Science," *Proceedings of the AAAS Interdisciplinary Workshop on the Interrelationships between Science and Technology, and Ethics and Values,* Reston, Va., 10–12 April 1975 (Washington, D.C.: American Association for the Advancement of Science, 1975).

list, occupy higher places in other institutions. Similarly, referring to a list of scientific values, Barbour stresses that "the actual motives of scientists are more mixed than this idealized picture acknowledges"; and that "it seems dubious that an adequate social ethic could be derived from them." I agree with Barbour's conclusion about honesty, considered as a scientific value:

> I would maintain, however, that such honesty is not primarily the result of the personal virtue of the individual scientist but rather of the institutional structure of science and the requirement that results be reproducible by other scientists. In short, important ethical values are intrinsic to science, but we should not expect them to give us an adequate social ethic or to provide motivation for ethical choices outside the institutions of science.[20]

Merton includes his scientific values as a part of "the ethos of science," which he defines this way:

> The ethos of science is that affectively toned complex of values and norms which is held to be binding on the man of science. The norms are expressed in the form of prescriptions, proscriptions, preferences, and permissions. They are legitimatized in terms of institutional values. These imperatives, transmitted by precept and example and reinforced by sanctions are in varying degrees internalized by the scientist, thus fashioning his scientific conscience.[21]

Scientific values correspond to the rules of the scientific profession and they are the result of the requirements of working in empirical science. Let us recall that in empirical science we seek a knowledge of nature that may be submitted to empirical control and, therefore, may serve as the basis to obtain a controlled dominion over nature. These objectives impose severe limits on the acceptability of methods and theories. Indeed, the requirement of empirical control implies intersubjective testing and, therefore, the use of intersubjective language that may be related to the results of repeatable experiments, so universalism is a necessary consequence. And institutionalized universalism implies the other values.

We should not forget that the institutionalized values that reflect the normative structure of science are derived from the goals of the scientific enterprise. Above all, they are instrumental with respect to these goals and reflect the compromise of working in pursuit of them; a scientist who does not respect them will, sooner or later, be rejected by his or her peers. Barbour is right, therefore, when he stresses that these values are independent from the personal virtues of the scientists. For example, when Merton speaks about "organized skepticism" as "the detached scrutiny of beliefs in terms of empirical and logical criteria" and adds that this characteristic has "periodically involved

---

20. Barbour, *Ethics in an Age of Technology,* cit., p. 29.

21. Merton, *The Sociology of Science,* cit., pp. 268–269.

science in conflict with other institutions," alluding to "resistance on the part of organized religion," we should recall that these conflicts have often been due to scientists overstepping the limits of their science. In fact, a correct religious attitude usually is the best antidote to the excesses of scientism.

Of course, insofar as the institutionalized values of science imply a kind of rightness and goodness in themselves, they can help to promote the virtues of the scientists and can help to spread the corresponding proper attitudes in other fields of human life. Sometimes, the spreading of scientific values is seen as a most important factor for human progress. In this line, Mario Bunge has written:

> Important changes in outlook and behavior, both individual and collective, can be expected from a widespread diffusion of the scientific attitude. . . . The universal adoption of a scientific attitude might render us wiser: it would make us more cautious in receiving information, in keeping beliefs and in making forecasts; it would render us more stringent in testing our opinions and more tolerant to other people's opinions; it would make us more eager to freely inquire into new possibilities and readier to get rid of consecrated myths; it would enhance our trust in experience guided by reason and our confidence in reason checked by experience; it would stimulate us to plan and control action better, to select aims and to search for norms of conduct consistent with such ends and with available knowledge rather than with habit and authority; it would foster the love of truth, the willingness to acknowledge error, the thrust to perfection and the understanding of the inevitable imperfection; it would give us an ever young world-view founded in tested theories instead of a die hard untested tradition; and it would encourage us to hold a realistic view of human life: a well-poised rather than either an optimistic or a pessimistic view.[22]

This appreciation is too optimistic. Actually, it has a kind of scientistic flavor and should be completed with ideas set out by the same author in other places, in which materialism is presented as the ontology of science. Here, we may wonder whether this is compatible with a true scientific attitude. Scientists are human beings who do not become morally better than others by working in science. Ethical values are something more than the rules of science. It would be a bad tactic to oppose the goods involved in the scientific attitude to the evils involved in other attitudes, because the roots of ethical values lie outside science. The progress of science has helped to develop a mature attitude in many fields of human experience; nevertheless, if not complemented by other sources of inspiration, it can also easily lead to a functionalist attitude that does not leave room for values other than pragmatical and instrumental ones.

---

22. Mario Bunge, *Scientific Research. I. The Search for System* (New York, Heidelberg, and Berlin: Springer, 1967), pp. 33–34.

4. EPISTEMIC VALUES

Studies about science and values very often center on a particular set of values, which are usually called "epistemic values." These are the values used as criteria to decide the acceptability of scientific theories. I shall analyze them following the studies devoted to this topic by Thomas Kuhn, Ernan McMullin, and Larry Laudan.

4.1. VALUE JUDGMENT AND THEORY CHOICE

In 1973, Thomas Kuhn answered critics of his view that theory choice is dependent on the collective judgment of scientists,[23] by saying that he does not deny the existence of objective criteria that help to choose between competing theories; in fact, he takes for granted that everyone knows which these criteria are. To avoid misunderstandings, Kuhn formulates and explains the criteria which characterize a good scientific theory and selects five of them: *accuracy, consistency, scope, simplicity,* and *fruitfulness.*

Kuhn explains that a theory is *accurate* if its consequences agree with the results of existing experiments and observations. That it is *consistent* refers to its internal absence of contradiction and to its consistency with other accepted theories. *Broadness of scope* means that its consequences should extend beyond the particular data it was initially designed to explain. *Simplicity* refers to bringing order to otherwise isolated phenomena. And *fruitfulness* refers to the capacity to promote new findings in scientific research.

These criteria, as Kuhn himself tells us, represent a synthesis of a larger number of criteria that scientists use to decide the acceptance of theories. But Kuhn explains that they "are not by themselves sufficient to determine the decisions of individual scientists":

> My point is, then, that every individual choice between competing theories depends on a mixture of objective and subjective factors, or of shared and individual criteria.[24]

Examining the philosophical implications of this position, Kuhn asks why philosophers of science have for so long neglected the subjective elements that regularly enter into the theory choices scientists make; he believes that they usually suppose that, if scientists behave in a rational way, they will arrive at the same decision, a view he does not share. He argues that

> the choices scientists make between competing theories depend not only on shared criteria—those my critics call objective—but also on idiosyncratic factors dependent on individual biography and personality. . . . What the tradition sees as eliminable imperfections in its rules of choice I take to be in part responses to the essential nature of science.[25]

---

23. Thomas S. Kuhn, "Objectivity, Value Judgment, and Theory Choice," in *The Essential Tension* (Chicago and London: The University of Chicago Press, 1977), pp. 320–339.

24. Ibid., p. 325.

25. Ibid., pp. 329–330.

Kuhn speaks of "values" in this context because values belong to the class of "criteria that influence decisions without specifying what those decisions must be," and he adds:

I am suggesting, of course, that the criteria of choice with which I began function not as rules, which determine choice, but as values, which influence it.[26]

Scientists committed to the same values may make different choices, because there is some ambiguity in the application of values. Accuracy would be the least ambiguous of the five values. Following Kuhn's comments, we can rank them in the following order: accuracy, fruitfulness, scope, consistency, and simplicity.

Kuhn adds that different disciplines possess different sets of shared values. Values are in part learned from the experience of scientists and evolve with it. But Kuhn claims that his position should not be interpreted as if theory choice were a matter of taste.

Kuhn intends to defend himself from the charge of subjectivism by showing that he admits the existence of objective criteria that are used by scientists when they choose between rival theories. His five criteria are well selected and approximately coincide with the five criteria I proposed when I considered a similar problem—how scientists solve the uncertainties implied by the underdetermination of scientific theories. He rightly stresses that, even though the five criteria are useful, they must be supplemented by the appreciation of the scientists; therefore, theory choice is not a matter of taste but includes evaluations that cannot be eliminated. Theory choice cannot be decided by the automatic impersonal application of a kind of algorithm. I agree with all this. I have repeatedly stressed that interpretation plays an important role in every step of empirical science. Nevertheless, one may wonder why Kuhn speaks of "values" in the context of theory choice. We will see how Ernan McMullin clarifies this issue.

4.2. THE VALIDATION OF SCIENTIFIC VALUES

Ernan McMullin has discussed Kuhn's ideas and added three important points. The first refers to the nature of the values employed in the appraisal of theories. McMullin writes:

The values involved in theory appraisal and the rationality of which they form a part are in the end *instrumental* values, means to the ends science in general is expected to realize. They are not ends in themselves. They can be justified only by the extent to which they further the goals that science is taken to aim at.[27]

---

26. Ibid., p. 331.

27. Ernan McMullin, "The Goals of Natural Science," in *Scientific Knowledge Socialized,* ed. Imre Hronszky, Márta Fehér, and Balázs Dajka (Dordrecht: Kluwer, 1988), p. 51.

Elementary as it may seem, this comment expresses an important feature of the epistemic values we are dealing with. Values connected with the institutional dimension of science have an instrumental character, but they also possess a kind of goodness that belongs specifically to them. The values we are examining now have only an instrumental character, which depends on their being instruments to pursue the cognitive and pragmatic goals of empirical science.

Referring to the validation of epistemic values, McMullin notes, following a suggestion by Kuhn, that:

> This rationality (of empirical science) is learned by the experience of scientists, as Kuhn says, and as I have tried to illustrate here in detail.[28]

This means that we have learned, and continue to learn, to appreciate these values through the practice of empirical science. For example, one of the steps that led to the birth of modern empirical science as a self-sustained enterprise was the relevance Kepler attributed to a small difference between observed data and theoretical prediction in the motion of the planet Mars, at a moment when the degree of accuracy of such concordance was not considered that important (in fact, the consequence of Kepler's decision was that he would begin his work again, abandoning the results obtained over a long time). Since that time, we have learned that accuracy plays a most important role in empirical science. The ideas of explanatory and predictive power are ancient, but we have learned how to combine them in the evaluation of scientific theories since the seventeenth century.

McMullin sees in this a convergence between the historical and the logical perspectives. This point is most important for my argument, because it clearly shows the feedback of scientific progress on scientific values: in this case, on the instrumental values that are employed to help us in theory choice. The experience acquired in the development of science teaches us which values are relevant for the evaluation of theories and how they can be applied.

McMullin's third remark refers to a further aspect of the evaluation of epistemic values that is also closely related to my argument. McMullin argues for a moderate realism and states that, if we admit that empirical science not only aims at truth, but also in some way attains it, we can conclude that the epistemic values we use to appraise our theories are correct. Thus, the progress of science teaches us what kinds of values we should use to appraise our theories, and the cognitive success of empirical science shows that those values were the right ones. McMullin writes:

> the characteristic values scientists have come to expect a theory to embody are a testimony to the *objectivity* of the theory, as well as of the involvement of the subjectivity of the scientist in the effort to at-

28. Ibid., p. 50.

tain that objectivity. . . . There is a further argument I would use in support of this conclusion, but it is based on a premise that is not shared by all. That is the thesis of scientific realism. I think that there are good reasons to accept a cautious and carefully-restricted form of scientific realism . . . The version of realism I have in mind would suggest that in many parts of science, like geology and cell-biology, we have good reasons to believe that the models postulated by our current theories give us a reliable, though still incomplete, insight into the structures of the physical world. . . . Obviously, the realist thesis will not hold, or will hold only in attenuated form, where theory is still extremely underdetermined (as in current elementary-particle theory) or where the ontological implications of the theory are themselves by no means clear (as in classical mechanics).[29]

I agree with this view. I have already explained my adherence to a kind of moderate realism like that proposed by McMullin; if we admit this, the feedback of scientific progress on the presuppositions of science becomes crystal clear. A realist sees empirical science as a quest for truth that leads us to obtain a knowledge of the natural world that is often true; the truth of this knowledge is contextual and therefore partial, but also "true" truth. As science progresses, we progress in achieving the goals of the scientific enterprise; therefore, we progress in reaching an objective knowledge that requires, in McMullin's words, "the involvement of the subjectivity of the scientist in the effort to attain that objectivity."

Speaking about values in science, McMullin includes several interesting clarifications. He distinguishes *emotive* values, which lie in the feelings of the subject rather than in a characteristic of the object, and *characteristic* values, objective properties that count as values in a particular kind of entity because they are desirable for an entity of that kind. He also comments on the distinction made by the logical positivists between subjective *valuing,* which would be foreign to science, and *evaluation* as an estimate of the degree to which some action, object, or institution is embodied in a given instance. He argues that value judgment, which includes both value and evaluation, plays a central role in science.[30] McMullin asserts that "theory-appraisal is a sophisticated form of value judgement," so that theory-decision is always value-laden.[31] The reasons provided by McMullin to support his thesis are similar to those I have used to show that stipulations are needed in every major step in empirical science.

Nevertheless, McMullin carefully notes that the values used in the evaluation of theories are not ethical values such as those required in scientific work

---

29. Ernan McMullin, "Values in Science," in *Introductory Readings in the Philosophy of Science,* ed. E. D. Klemke, Robert Hollings, and A. David Kline (Buffalo, N.Y.: Prometheus Books, 1988), pp. 367–368.

30. Ibid., pp. 350–352.

31. Ibid., pp. 362–363.

as a communal enterprise. This is consistent with his assertion that those epistemic values are instrumental. The search for truth, as a goal of science, can
be considered an ethical value by itself, and McMullin, from his realistic perspective, argues that truth is a sort of horizon-concept or ideal of the scientific enterprise.[32]

Both Kuhn and McMullin strongly stress that theory appraisal is value-
laden. This is consistent with my emphasis on the role of interpretation in
empirical science. This should not be considered as a novelty in the realm of
philosophy of science. McMullin notes that ideas of this kind were already
present in Karl Popper's work in 1934; one can regret once more, however,
that Popper's ideas are presented jointly with Carnap's and are introduced in
a paragraph that refers to "the logical positivists."[33]

4.3. PLURAL AIMS IN SCIENCE?

In his book *Science and Values,* Larry Laudan proposes to overcome the difficulties contained in the ideas of Kuhn and others. Laudan proposes to replace
"the classical hierarchical model" of scientific decision-making with what he
calls a "reticulated model of justification." He uses a three-level approach to
science, distinguishing aims, methods, and theories (which contain factual
claims). According to the hierarchical model, the aims determine the methods, and the methods determine the results or factual claims. His reticulated
model is the result of considerations like the following:

> we must change the hierarchical model by insisting that our factual
> beliefs drastically shape our views about which sorts of methods are
> viable, and about which sorts of methods do in fact promote which
> sort of aims. . . . The reticulational approach shows that we can use
> our knowledge of the available methods of inquiry as a tool for as-
> sessing the viability of proposed cognitive aims. . . . Equally, the retic-
> ulated picture insists that our judgements about which theories are
> sound can be played off against our explicit axiologies in order to re-
> veal tensions between our implicit and our explicit value structures.[34]

The aims of science determine the methods, because these are nothing but
the means used to achieve the aims. And theories are the result of the application of specific methods. Laudan proposes a "triadic network of justification" in which each of the three components acts on the other two, so that
there are mutual interactions in all directions. Thus, he writes:

> Where the reticulational picture differs more fundamentally from the
> hierarchical one is in the insistence that there is a complex process of
> mutual adjustment and mutual justification going on among all three

32. Ibid., p. 353.

33. Ibid., pp. 355–358.

34. Larry Laudan, *Science and Values: The Aims of Science and their Role in Scientific Debate* (Berkeley: University of California Press, 1984), p. 62.

levels of scientific commitment. Justification flows upward as well as downward in the hierarchy, linking aims, methods, and factual claims. No longer should we regard any one of these levels as privileged or primary or more fundamental than the others. Axiology, methodology, and factual claims are inevitably intertwined in relations of mutual dependency. The pecking order implicit in the hierarchical approach must give way to a kind of leveling principle that emphasizes the patterns of mutual dependence between these various levels.[35]

I agree that mutual interactions exist among the three levels. Nevertheless, I wonder whether Laudan's position can be reconciled with the existence of general aims common to the entire scientific enterprise, aims that determine a general method common to every kind of scientific work. Laudan writes:

> There is no single "right" goal for inquiry because it is evidently legitimate to engage in inquiry for a wide variety of reasons and with a wide variety of purposes. Those who imagine that there is a single axiology that can or should guide investigation into nature have failed to come to terms with the palpable diversity of the potential ends and uses of inquiry.[36]

This reasoning begins with the obvious and immediately goes too far. Indeed, nobody would deny that particular purposes exist in the different domains of scientific research. Nevertheless, if research is to be accepted as empirical, it must satisfy the requirements implied in the general aims of the scientific enterprise: to provide a knowledge of the natural world that can be submitted to empirical control and that may be used to obtain controlled dominion over nature. In empirical science, the plurality of particular ends, and even more the plurality of subjective purposes, must be combined with coincidence in the common basic goals; otherwise, we are no longer within the realm of empirical science.

Laudan seems to forget the obvious common goals of empirical science when he says that "central cognitive values shift," and that the only legitimate demands of a theory of scientific rationality would be

> that our cognitive goals must reflect our best beliefs about what is and what is not possible, that our methods must stand in an appropriate relation to our goals, and that our implicit and explicit values must be synchronized.[37]

If we admit this, then we should conclude, with Laudan, that progress in science is always relative to changing goals, "to our own view about the aims and goals of science," "to some set of aims."[38] Laudan concludes:

35. Ibid., pp. 62–63.

36. Ibid., pp. 63–64.

37. Ibid., p. 64.

38. Ibid., pp. 65–66.

There is simply no escape from the fact that determinations of progress must be relativized to a certain set of ends, and that there is no uniquely appropriate set of those ends.[39]

This would mean, however, that our ideal of empirical science changes. We can wonder whether this is the case. Surely, Newton's ideal of empirical science did not coincide with Descartes'. Perhaps this is the kind of shift Laudan has in mind. Laudan does compare Newton's theory of light and Descartes' optics to illustrate his ideas. If we adopt a broad historical perspective and apply the idea of empirical science to contemporary physics as well as Cartesian physics, we may find as many changes of aims, methods, and values as we desire. If we limit ourselves to an examination of empirical science in the usual contemporary sense, its general aims and methods are no longer changing; at the very least, they do not change in their essential traits.

Laudan's texts clearly show that his scientific values only refer to particular changing aims. It is unclear whether we can use them to characterize the entire scientific enterprise and to distinguish it from other cognitive claims. Laudan's values can enter into my argument only as instrumental values to evaluate the acceptability of our theories.

5. EMPIRICAL SCIENCE AS A MORAL TASK

In an essay devoted to exploring the relationship between objectivity in morality and objectivity in science, Alasdair MacIntyre expounded his views about the ethical meaning of empirical science[40] and concluded that natural science is a moral task.

MacIntyre proposes a framework that serves as the base to formulate his argument. He differentiates between human activities he calls *practices,* which include empirical science, and *institutions,* which are bearers of practices: in the present case, scientific institutions would be the scientific communities organized in different ways. He further distinguishes two kinds of goods associated with practices, namely *internal* goods, which correspond to the nature of the practices, and *external* goods, rewards contingently associated with participation in the practices. Then, he introduces the concepts of *rules of practice,* which are necessary to achieve the internal goods of the corresponding practices, and *institutional rules,* which embody or support rules of practice.

This framework can be used to represent empirical science as goal-directed human activity with an institutional character. It is interesting to note, however, that MacIntyre thinks it can also be applied to human activities very different from natural science, as he writes:

---

39. Ibid., p. 66.

40. Alasdair MacIntyre, "Objectivity in Morality and Objectivity in Science," in *Morals, Science and Sociality,* ed. H. Tristram Engelhardt, Jr., and Daniel Callahan (Hastings-on-Hudson, N.Y.: The Hastings Center, 1978), pp. 21–39.

By a *rule of practice* I shall mean a rule whose point and purpose is de-rived from its role within a form of activity which has goods internal to it. Examples of such forms of activity or practices are *chess, natural science, and painting.* Internal goods are defined by contrast with goods external to a practice. . . . *External goods,* then, are those contingently related rewards—candy, money, reputation, status, power—which may derive from successful participation in a practice; *internal goods* are those achievements of excellence which exhibit human aesthetic, imaginative, intellectual, and physical powers at their highest . . . *insti-tutions* are the bearers of practices. *Chess, scientific inquiry, and painting* are examples of practices; chess club and federations, universities and laboratories, galleries, museums, and art dealers are examples of cor-responding institutions.[41]

MacIntyre uses his framework to analyze the authority of the rules of prac-tice and of the institutional rules. On this basis, he refers to impersonality and objectivity as a consequence of the subordination of individual experience to the authority of the rules:

It is they alone (internal goods) which confer authority on the rules defining the practice, the rules without which the goods internal to the practice cannot be achieved. . . . Institutional rules may be justi-fied in a number of ways, but they possess authority insofar as they embody or support rules of practice. . . . In the context of a practice, however, the individual is not generally or usually a judge or an ar-biter; he or she is a participant in acknowledging an authority whose character has emerged in the history of the practice in question. . . . It is this subordination of individual experience and thought that supplies the crucial element of impersonality and objectivity to prac-tices. Examples of practices in which such authority and such objec-tivity have been crucial are law, painting, and natural science. Within each of these practices there have been sustained tasks and projects, which have gradually emerged over long stretches of time.[42]

So far, MacIntyre's analysis has had chiefly a sociological character, which probably explains why objectivity is seen as an effect of the subordination of the individual to the communal practice. Now MacIntyre introduces three factors that have great relevance in our argument: moral considerations, sci-entific realism, and the role played by history:

like art and law, natural science is a set of projects which embodies a moral task. That moral task is partially but importantly defined by the commitment of science to realism. . . . Where we stand on the issue of realism and how we write the history of science are questions which have to be answered together or not at all.[43]

41. Ibid., pp. 28–29 (italics mine).

42. Ibid.

43. Ibid., p. 30.

We may be surprised to find empirical science again accompanied by two activities of a very different status. In this case, art and law replace painting and chess. This change is justified, for MacIntyre is speaking now about morality. In any case, in his focus on science, MacIntyre now introduces the statement that natural science embodies a moral task. This is an extremely important assertion, which is justified by the appeal to realism, or, more exactly, to the commitment of science to realism. It is the search for truth, considered as an internal good of science, that is at stake here, and the search for truth has obvious moral connotations.

The reference to history as a justification of realism is also important. We can perceive here an echo, from a different point of view, of Kuhn and McMullin saying that we learn to appreciate scientific values through the actual development of science, which agrees with my emphasis on the feedback of scientific progress on the ethical presuppositions of science.

MacIntyre adopts a strong historical perspective rather than a semantic one, as he himself discusses how realism is considered in his paper:

> It will be conceived only secondarily as a semantic thesis and not at all as an hypothesis. Rather, it will be regarded as what Kant called a regulative ideal. What did and does it regulate? The scientists' interpretation of their own task . . . since Galileo, realism has been the ideal which at once sets constraints upon what is to count as the solution of a scientific problem and provides an interpretation of scientific results . . . the practice of science through time presupposes a continuous adherence to realist goals.[44]

Thus, realism is seen as a presupposition of empirical science that confers meaning on the scientific enterprise. Empirical science makes sense insofar as it consists in the search for truth, and commitment to this task explains why science is a moral task. Scientific progress implies the historical fulfillment of this task; it shows that the task can be achieved and also that we progress in our morally laden effort to reach a true knowledge of the natural world.

Historical considerations play a central role in MacIntyre's interpretation. Finding unity in the historical development of science would be an important key in our attempt to understand empirical science as a meaningful activity; MacIntyre sees realism as the clue that leads us to understand the unity of science along history:

> Wherein does the unity of history lie? In the continuous attempt to construct a realistic representation.[45]

MacIntyre illustrates the historical unity of science by using an image that implies a perspective very different from that of Laudan. Actually, just as Lau-

---

44. Ibid., p. 31.

45. Ibid., p. 33.

dan emphasizes the changing character of the ends of science, so MacIntyre stresses the continuity of the enterprise:

> the contemporary theory resembles not a twentieth-century building on the site of earlier buildings which it has replaced, so much as an originally eighteenth-century mansion, rebuilt in parts, with the foundation replaced, with many additions and much ornamentation, but still recognizably the same building for which, therefore, the original architects must be given credit even before those responsible for the most brilliant parts of the reconstruction.[46]

Along these lines, MacIntyre asserts that the historical unity of the scientific enterprise has a moral character, as the continuity of a communal project directed toward the search for truth:

> the continuities of history are moral continuities, continuities of tasks and projects which cannot be defined except with reference to the internal goods which specify the goals of such tasks and projects. Those tasks and projects are embodied in practices, and practices are in turn embodied in institutions and in communities. The scientific community is one among the moral communities of mankind and its unity is unintelligible apart from the commitment to realism. Thus the continuities in the history of that community are primarily continuities in its regulative ideals. . . . The building of a representation of nature is, in the modern world, a task analogous to the building of a cathedral in the medieval world or to the founding and construction of a city in the ancient world, tasks which might also turn out to be interminable.[47]

We can now understand why science is considered to be a moral activity; why objectivity is considered to be a moral concept insofar as it implies a commitment to the search of truth; and finally, why the historical perspective is so important:

> To be objective, then, is to understand oneself as part of a community and one's work as part of a project and part of a history. The authority of this history and this project derives from the goods internal to the practice. Objectivity is a moral concept before it is a methodological concept, and the activities of natural science turn out to be a species of moral activity. . . . Science is a morality . . . we can give good reasons for giving morality primacy over science. For science can only become intelligible to us through its history and the continuities of this history are moral continuities. Our knowledge of nature is immensely fallible; the best confirmed and most adequately justified theory in the whole history of science did, after all, turn out to be false. But our knowledge of our knowledge of nature, that is,

46. Ibid.
47. Ibid., pp. 36–37.

our knowledge of the history and philosophy of science, is far better founded. Yet its foundation depends in turn on our understanding of the history of human relationship to goods.[48]

MacIntyre accepts in some way the widespread fallibilist view of empirical science. I disagree with MacIntyre's implicit reference to Newton's mechanics as being false. Indeed, I do not think we have reasons to say that it is false; I could argue that even Popper, who was tremendously impressed by Einstein's theory superseding Newton's, was very cautious in this respect.

The main question, however, is a very different one: should we admit, with MacIntyre, that empirical science is a moral enterprise? The answer to this question heavily depends on our attitude to scientific realism. If we admit that the search for truth is a central aim of the scientific enterprise, then it is easy to agree that this enterprise possesses an ethical character and requires ethical involvement. In this case, empirical science can no longer be considered an activity moved only by particular interests. Searching for the truth implies disinterestedness and detachment from subjective perspectives; in addition, it corresponds with one of the most important aspirations of the human being. In this respect, I would have no hesitation to say that empirical science has an ethical character.

To end my commentary on MacIntyre's position, I think that something must be said about his apparent historicism. As already noted, history plays a central role in MacIntyre's position, and it may even seem that this position implies an overstrong kind of historicism. Indeed, Marjorie Grene speaks of MacIntyre as "a loyal Hegelian,"[49] and historicism appears in other places as closely related to his position.[50] Nevertheless, as far as my argument is concerned, I think he uses history wisely, as the context in which we can appreciate the real nature of human enterprise. His remarks fit quite well with my argument about the feedback of scientific progress on the presuppositions of science.

III. WHICH VALUES?

We speak of *values* when we refer to the goals of our actions or to the means used to achieve them. In consequence, as my argument centers around the general presuppositions of science, I am mainly interested in those values that are an essential part of the entire scientific enterprise, those related to the *gen-*

48. Ibid., pp. 37–39.

49. Marjorie Grene, "Response to Alasdair MacIntyre," in *Morals, Science and Sociality*, ed. H. Tristram Engelhardt, Jr. and Daniel Callahan (Hastings-on-Hudson, N.Y.: The Hastings Center, 1978), p. 41.

50. Giovanna Borradori, "Nietzsche or Aristotle? Alasdair MacIntyre," in *The American Philosopher. Conversations with Quine, Davidson, Putnam, Nozick, Danto, Rorty, Cavell, MacIntyre, and Kuhn* (Chicago and London: The University of Chicago Press, 1994), pp. 139, 147–148.

eral goals of science, on the one hand, and to the *institutionalized features* of science, on the other. These values are closely related, because science as an institution can be considered the social manifestation of the goal-directed scientific enterprise.

Values directly related to the general goals of science may be called *constitutive,* because they define the basic architecture of scientific work; those that correspond to the institutionalized social aspect of science may be called *institutional* (Figure 7.1).

1. CONSTITUTIVE VALUES

Constitutive values are those unchangeable values related to internal goals that characterize the scientific enterprise in itself, leaving aside particular purposes of individuals and communities, which are changeable. Actual motives of scientists may relate, for example, to success in their work, to recognition of their success, to the reward due their work; they will usually be present but do not influence the nature of scientific work in itself.

The enormous progress of science has important implications for technology, and technological progress, in its turn, becomes more and more inte-

CONSTITUTIVE VALUES
  EPISTEMIC VALUES
    Accuracy of explanations and predictions
    Internal coherence
    External consistency
    Scope or unifying power
    Fertility or fruitfulness
    Simplicity
  PRAGMATIC VALUES
    Effectiveness in problem solving
    The epistemic values listed above, considered
      in their practical aspect
INSTITUTIONAL VALUES
    Universalism, objectivity, intersubjectivity
    Cooperativeness
    Intellectual humility
    Disinterestedness
    Publicity
    Absence of fraud
    Open-mindedness

Fig. 7.1 Scientific values. Considered as a human enterprise, natural science carries within itself a double set of values: constitutive values, which refer to the general goals of natural science, namely, the search for truth (epistemic values) and for a controlled dominion over nature (pragmatic values) and institutional values, which refer to the social aspect of science. Some particular values of each kind are listed here.

grated in the practice of science, providing tools for research and even new goals. The intertwining of science and technology has provoked the development of the so-called "big science," a kind of research that requires resources that can only be provided by wealthy institutions, so that those institutions can easily intervene to set up the goals of scientific research. Even then, however, the constitutive values of science do not change. Establishing particular goals and providing resources and incentives are external to the essential nature of empirical science. Our interest in knowing the laws of nature cannot alter them. If we are interested in creating a certain kind of artifact, we need to use the laws of nature such as they are, independent of our will. As a search for the laws of nature, the scientific quest is always guided by the existence of an objective natural order. We can create new conditions but only if we use the natural laws in the appropriate way.

The twofold goal of empirical science indicates the most important values of the scientific enterprise: the *search for truth* and the *controlled domination over nature*. These values can be called *constitutive* because they are internal, characteristic, and necessary values of empirical science in all its modalities. They are presupposed by any other value, which will always be external and accidental in relation to them.

When we see empirical science under this perspective, its meaning in terms of values is twofold: it possesses a *cognitive* value that refers to the knowledge of the natural world and a *practical* one that refers to the controlled domination of nature. As I have already argued that in empirical science we reach what can be considered a true knowledge of nature, I say now that the cognitive value of science mainly consists in the *pursuit of truth*. On other grounds, we can argue that the practical value of science consists in its providing means for *service to mankind*. These are the central values that characterize empirical science in itself, regardless of the particular purposes that may be superimposed on them by individual scientists, extrascientific individuals, or societies.

1.1. EPISTEMIC VALUES

Considered as a unitary enterprise, the cognitive value of empirical science is the pursuit of truth. We approach this single large value, however, by successive steps that involve different kinds of evaluation. Thus, we can speak of *epistemic* values, in plural, as the characteristics scientific constructs should possess if they are to be effective in reaching the cognitive goal of science. Ernan McMullin calls this kind of value *epistemic* "because they are presumed to promote the truth-like character of science."[51] They can be considered values insofar as they refer to the properties we attribute to "good" constructs; properly speaking, however, they are only *instrumental* values, which serve to promote the search for truth.

We have already met such a value in Thomas Kuhn's discussion of scientific values, which include *accuracy, consistency, scope, simplicity,* and *fruitfulness.*

---

51. McMullin, "Values in Science," cit., p. 364.

McMullin comments on them, introducing some qualifications.[52] Now I will refer to some of these.

McMullin stresses, and I agree with him, that "*predictive accuracy* is the desideratum that scientists would usually list first"; he adds, as Lakatos and Feyerabend have emphasized, that "scientists must often tolerate a certain degree of inaccuracy, especially in the early stages of theory-development." However, "a high degree of predictive accuracy is in the long run something a theory *must* have if it is to be acceptable." I would add that accuracy is relative to the kind of problem we are facing. For example, the first observations of microwave background radiation were close enough to the theoretical predictions that they were considered as evidence in favor of the big bang theory, even though they were not completely accurate. Evidence is always circumstantial. McMullin insists on the all-pervasive character of value judgment at every step of scientific work.

Accuracy is a qualification of predictions and explanations. It is a link between theoretical explanations and predictions on one side, and their empirical control on the other. That is why it is a most relevant epistemic value. Greater accuracy means that our explanatory and predictive theories correspond increasingly well with the empirical data that support them. Searching for truth in empirical science can be translated as constructing theories that may be submitted to empirical control, and accuracy is a central value in this control.

McMullin also comments on *internal coherence, external consistency,* and *unifying power.* Then, he stresses the relevance of *fertility,* saying:

> This is rather a complex affair. The theory proves able to make novel predictions that were not part of the set of original explananda. More important, the theory proves to have the imaginative resources, functioning here rather as a metaphor might in literature, to enable anomalies to be overcome and new and powerful extensions to be made. Here is the *long-term* proven ability of the theory or research program to generate fruitful additions and modifications that has to be taken into account.[53]

Fertility is a crucial epistemic value. Scientists appreciate laws and theories that have a high heuristic power, even if they are so general that it is difficult to prove them. For instance, the principle of conservation of energy plays a most important role in the scientific study of nature, because it provides boundary conditions that must be satisfied in all natural processes and therefore can be used to limit the possible behavior of the systems we study. The potential range of its applications is so great that scientists are reluctant to abandon it; when faced with difficulties, they prefer to introduce new entities to save the principle, and this attitude has been extremely fruitful in some

52. Ibid., pp. 360–361.

53. Ibid., p. 361.

well-known cases (as in the "discovery" of neutrinos). In a similar vein, many features of theories about cosmological and biological evolution cannot be proved, but these theories still have a great explanatory and heuristic value, and this is why they are generally admitted despite the existence of many unexplained features in them.

The use of such epistemic values is necessary for the progress of empirical science. Both Kuhn and McMullin introduce them as a means to fill the gap between our constructs and the data that can serve to support them. This gap exists not only in some particular cases, but, as I have repeatedly underscored, in all cases: when we define concepts, when we formulate laws, when we build up theoretical systems, when we obtain empirical data.

Epistemic values do not provide infallible rules or algorithmic automatic procedures; they only indicate what kind of qualities we should appreciate if we are to pursue the cognitive goal of the scientific enterprise. There is always a risk when we decide to accept a particular experimental result or a basic statement that can be used to test a theory, when we decide to accept a theory that has successfully resisted our attempts to falsify it, or when we decide to accept a theory that at the moment cannot be supported by serious empirical evidence but possesses a great heuristic potential. Epistemic values are fallible means to achieve the general cognitive aim of science. As far as they represent ideal properties imposed on our constructs, they can evolve and may, at times, contradict other epistemic values. In this latter case, we must find a way to harmonize them, but there is no infallible algorithm that can take the place of our decision.

If we accept that the scientific enterprise has a realistic meaning, and even more if we accept that this realism is not limited to a regulative ideal but includes our attaining specific pieces of true knowledge, then the cognitive value of science in general and the particular epistemic values acquire meaning. This is the position I advocate. However, even those who admit weaker cognitive claims should admit that empirical science is meaningful insofar as it searches for models that must be empirically adequate; therefore, they admit that empirical science makes sense as a cognitive enterprise. In fact, empirical adequacy is a necessary requirement that scientific explanations must fulfill in any case, and so everyone should admit that empirical science has a cognitive value.

1.2. PRAGMATIC VALUES

The practical value of empirical science as a whole consists in the possibility of using its results to obtain a controlled dominion over nature.

From the historical point of view, the birth of empirical science in the seventeenth century was mostly motivated by the desire to achieve this practical goal. Ancient natural science was regarded as sterile, because it focused on theoretical speculations that could not be used to improve our dominion over nature. Francis Bacon was the prophet of the new science that, according to his account, would be a new and most powerful instrument to improve the conditions of human life. Bacon clearly foresaw what became the hallmark of the new science: its capacity to provide the basis for technological achievements that, in the long run, have dramatically changed the conditions of human life. If there is a point of general agreement, it is that practical achievements are due to the progress of empirical science.

Empirical science continues to be used to improve the conditions of human life, but we know that scientific advances can also be used for other purposes, and that some new technologies have a great destructive potential. Therefore, there is an asymmetry between the cognitive and the practical values of science. Cognitive advances always represent a positive value, whereas their practical applications can be positive or negative from an ethical point of view. The possibility of using science negatively clearly shows that science cannot be the ultimate reference in human life; we need to rely on ethical criteria that may help us use the achievements of science appropriately.

In the cognitive realm, I have distinguished the general cognitive value of science from the specific plural values that serve as instruments to decide the acceptability of particular theories. In a similar vein, we can distinguish now the general practical value of science from the particular specific values that are a part of it. This value can be identified with service to mankind, which is achieved through technology. Technology cannot be identified with science; although technology today is strongly science-dependent, it also possesses its own characteristics; scientific theories usually cannot be applied directly to solve technological problems. There is a distance between theoretical science and its practical usage, and this gap must be filled by specific technological rules. That is why, although technological progress is probably the main reason for the prestige of empirical science, it cannot be regarded as a simple and complete proof of the truth of scientific knowledge.

I will not analyze technological rules. They are enormously varied, as varied as the technologies they are applied to, and their analysis would have no relevance for my argument.

Leaving aside technological values, the practical value that is most relevant within science itself is the *problem-solving* potential of scientific theories. That the entire scientific enterprise can be considered a problem-solving activity was strongly underscored by Karl Popper and Larry Laudan. Popper often represents scientific research as a chain where we begin with a problem-situation, propose a tentative theory to explain it, submit that theory to empirical control and, if our test provides new elements, arrive at a new problem-situation that serves as a new starting point, so that this tetradic scheme is repeated in an unending quest. Following this line, Laudan articulated his theory of scientific rationality around the idea of problem solving and discussed the different kinds of problems, and therefore of problem solving, that we find in empirical science.

The application of scientific theories to specific scientific problems cannot be identified simply with technology. In most cases, technological problem solving requires specific rules that make it possible to apply the results of science to industry-like problems, a process that often requires simplifying scientific theories and introducing pragmatic methods. Many areas of scientific research today require using technological devices to perform empirical tests. The problems that originate scientific research are often provoked by the needs of technology. Moreover, the trial-and-error elimination method is used in both science and technology. Nevertheless, science and technology have quite different aims; for example, if we consider a particular chemical substance, in science we are interested in the investigation of its nature and properties, whereas technology is directed toward the production of that substance in a quantity that may serve for commercial uses.

Effectiveness in problem solving follows rules similar to those we have found when considering theory choice. Theories are constructed to solve scientific problems: therefore, theory choice and problem solving represent two perspectives of the same reality. The same kind of rules are applied to both; following Kuhn's perspective, they can be summarized as *accuracy, consistency, scope, simplicity,* and *fruitfulness,* or following McMullin as *predictive accuracy, internal coherence, external consistency, unifying power, fertility,* and *simplicity.* My favorite five criteria are *explanatory power, predictive power, accuracy of both explanations and predictions, variety of independent proofs,* and *mutual support regarding already accepted theories.*

These criteria represent instrumental values that are at the same time cognitive and practical, because the general goals of empirical science include both aspects in a single unitary aim; therefore, those values include both cognitive and other features related to empirical control. That is why the same instrumental values that are used to decide theory acceptance should also be used to decide problem-solving effectiveness. Theory acceptance and problem-solving effectiveness are two sides of the same coin.

2. Institutional Values

Institutional values refer to scientific work as it is institutionalized as a communal enterprise and implies an entire set of values that should be pursued by the members of the scientific community.

This kind of value has no source independent from that of the constitutive values, namely the general aims of science. All kinds of scientific values stem from the same source, because they are instrumental to achieving the general aims of science or, at least, are necessarily linked to them. However, institutional values also contain the requirements derived from the communal character of the scientific enterprise.

This can be easily perceived if we recall the institutional values enumerated by Robert Merton, which are *universalism, communism, disinterestedness,* and *organized skepticism.*

I would say that *universalism* is the principal institutional value. It is a central constitutive value as well, because it refers to the intersubjective character of scientific proofs and constructs, which is an essential feature of empirical science. Indeed, the requirement of empirical control implies that theories are formulated in an intersubjective form and that experiments can be repeated by anyone. The term "universalism" makes sense precisely when we consider the different individual members of the scientific community and make explicit the requirement that scientific procedures should be available to any of them if they desire to check the validity of a theory. *Objectivity*, or *intersubjectivity*, are values very close to universalism, but this term expresses better than the other two the communal character of the value.

Communism, a somewhat unfortunate term, expresses very clearly another aspect of universalism—public availability. In principle, scientific procedures and results could be intersubjective while remaining the private property of their discoverers or of some particular community. There is no guarantee that this cannot eventually happen. Considering communism as a value, however, indicates that the scientific community thinks that public availability should be pursued. Scientists rely on publication as a first step for any new finding that claims to be considered seriously within the scientific community.

Another feature that Merton included within his "communism" is *cooperation*, understood as readiness to collaborate with others. In their work, scientists usually need the cooperation of others and must behave in a cooperative way if they want to be admitted as members of the scientific community. Cooperativeness has always been important, but the importance of this value has increased as a result of the intense specialization provoked by the progress of science. The vast majority of scientific achievements result from the cooperative work of people associated in special teams. As a consequence, scientists tend to recognize the achievements of others.

Cooperation also includes awareness of one's dependence on the collaboration of others and, therefore, a kind of *intellectual humility*. This is not to say that scientists are free from vanity or pride. But work in empirical science, if it is to be effective, requires behavior that, as far as it involves cooperation, dependence on others, and recognition of other people's achievements, can be objectively labeled as intellectually humble.

Disinterestedness, in Merton's perspective, is linked to the fact that the activities of scientists are subject to rigorous control. He rightly states that this value is based on the public and testable character of science; even this institutional value is a consequence of the general aims of empirical science, which include empirical testability and, therefore, objectivity in the sense of intersubjectivity open to public control.

From the historical point of view, it is a fact that, when empirical science began to develop in a systematic way in the seventeenth century, scientific societies were immediately founded, as an expression of the communality of the new science. The requirement of *publicity* is essential to the scientific enterprise.

A natural consequence of this state of affairs is that *absence of fraud* should be the rule; this can be taken as a very important institutional value. Again, this has no direct bearing on the inner moral character of particular scientists; rather, it is a consequence of the institutionalization of science. Neither should we conclude that errors cannot be introduced within the scientific realm; we know that some errors have been admitted for centuries (Newton's absolute space and time are a clear example), yet the requirement of intersubjectivity and the simultaneous existence of a very large scientific community provide a guarantee of intersubjective, though not infallible, control.

Organized skepticism is closely related to the methodological attitude involved in the general aims of empirical science. We know that a method that includes empirical control as an essential ingredient is an effective means of reaching reliable knowledge about the natural world, but cannot lead us to complete certitude. Scientists must always remain open to new possibilities. *Open-mindedness* or readiness to incorporate new data or new ideas, and to change our minds when necessary, can be considered as an institutional value also. The methods of empirical science need to be applied rigorously; thus, *rigor* can be also considered an institutional value in this context.

This explains why empirical science is usually regarded as *public knowledge;* it includes the requirements of intersubjectivity and control. The existence of those institutional values in empirical science should be recognized as a fact, but we should remember that these values exist because we have deliberately chosen a method that by its very nature is limited to the study of those aspects of the natural world that are related to natural patterns and, therefore, may be submitted to empirical control.

Institutional values refer to the social dimension of science. I have repeatedly emphasized that these values are the social or communal consequences of the requirements inherent in the general aims of the scientific enterprise. Even in the hypothetical case of a scientist working in isolation, the methods used and the results obtained must be potentially intersubjective if they are to be admitted within the realm of empirical science; this implies the existence of the other institutional values. Institutional values are intrinsic to science and are derived from the constitutive values when the communal nature of the scientific enterprise is taken into account.

I have already noted that the institutional values of empirical science are not, properly speaking, ethical values, because scientists can pursue them for personal reasons independent from ethical motivations. Nevertheless, from an objective point of view, they possess an ethical character. This can be easily appreciated if we list them: seeking the truth, loyalty to the truth, telling the truth, honesty in reporting results, integrity, fairness in handling evidence running counter to one's views, openness, personal responsibility, intellectual humility, tolerance, freedom of thought and investigation, common loyalties. Such names possess an unmistakable ethical flavor.

The institutional values of science possess an ethical dimension because they derive from the general aims of science. These general goals have an ethical character that is transmitted to the institutional values derived from them. No scientist is obliged, by the fact of being a scientist, to admit ethical commitments as such; nevertheless, to work in empirical science implies striving to achieve those values and behaving in a way consistent with those values. In this sense, we can speak of an "institutionalized ethics of science." Institutionalized values are inherent to empirical science as a communal activity.

3. Values in the Four Types of Scientific Activity

We can speak of empirical science as a goal-oriented unitary activity. Nevertheless, this activity is complex, and we can distinguish within it several modalities. Our image of empirical science depends to a great extent on the kind of activity under consideration. Different epistemological perspectives usually emphasize one or several kinds of scientific activity.

I like to classify scientific activities into four types: *research,* which aims at obtaining new knowledge; *systematizing,* or synthesis of previously acquired knowledge; *transmission,* which refers to the ways of expressing the results obtained; and *application,* or use of scientific knowledge to solve scientific problems. These activities are interconnected but represent different contributions to the general goals of science.

3.1. RESEARCH

Research is related to *innovation* and *progress.* There are many kinds of innovation in empirical science. Very often, when we think about scientific progress, we have in mind big theoretical systems. Nevertheless, there are not many great theoretical systems in empirical science: there are a few of them in physics, such as classical mechanics, quantum mechanics, special and general relativity; but it is more difficult to formulate such general theories in other branches of science. However, there are many other innovations in empirical science: for example, building particular models (of, for example, the atom, the nucleus), formulating experimental laws, or proving the existence of entities, properties, or processes.

The Popperian account of empirical science is mainly centered around research and makes sense when applied to large innovations in the development of science. In some respects it could be labeled as a "heroic image" of science. This partly explains the confrontation between Popper's account and Kuhn's idea of science, which centers around "normal science" in which there is a generally accepted paradigm whose validity is not questioned in ordinary circumstances.

The main value associated with research is *progress.* Even though there is progress in systematizing, or in the application of knowledge to solve specific problems, these depend on the acquisition of new knowledge, and therefore on research. I would only add that progress represents in a single concept the basic goals of scientific research. This is a general value, rather than a specific one.

3.2. SYSTEMATIZING

Systematizing plays four important roles. First, it serves to *unify particular pieces of knowledge;* this is most important because research usually provides fragmentary pieces that must be united. It also plays a *heuristic role;* actually, a good systematization is likely to suggest ways to further our knowledge. Classic examples are the prediction of new elements that should fill the holes in the periodic table and some predictions of great theoretical systems, such as the discovery of Neptune on the basis of Newton's mechanics, or the production of electromagnetic waves as a consequence of Maxwell's electromagnetic theory. Systematizing also provides a greater *economy of thought,* enabling us to use our knowledge more easily, saving many intermediary steps already contained in the systems. Finally, systematizing plays a *critical* role, because it makes it easier to analyze and criticize scientific knowledge.

Systematizing is not an end but it is a very useful means to perform the functions just mentioned.

In the past philosophy of science was too often associated with systematizing, partly as a consequence of scientism. Neopositivists insisted on "rational reconstruction" of theories to allegedly show that only empirical science could be constructed rationally and, therefore, should be considered the paradigm of any valid knowledge claim.

The values associated with systematizing are related to its four functions: *order,* in relation to the unifying function; *progress,* as new discoveries are made possible by the heuristic role; *effectiveness,* as a consequence of economy of thought; and *openness,* as far as criticism helps to uncover errors that should be corrected.

3.3. TRANSMISSION

Transmission is a ubiquitous feature of science, for it is necessary in order to communicate with the rest of the scientific community and the public at large. It represents a specific type of scientific activity, because the same achievement can be formulated and explained in more than one way. For instance, great scientific systems can be formalized or axiomatized in different ways. In general, there is always some underdetermination of the upper levels by the inferior ones: a statement is never a mere addition of empirical data, empirical data are never a mere collection of observation reports, and so on. Therefore, there are different ways of formulating the same pieces of knowledge.

Transmission operates at three different levels. The first is the *specialized lev-*

el of research scientists, who use a specialized vocabulary and highly technical explanations understood only by them. The second is the *higher education*
level, where current knowledge is systematized and presented in an orderly
fashion, usually as a body of well-established knowledge accompanied by corresponding proofs. The third is the level of *popular science,* where scientific
knowledge is presented in terms understandable to ordinary people.

An image of science closely related to transmission, and especially to the
higher education level, is the accumulative image that represents empirical science as an ever-progressing activity with well-established contents. Taken to
extremes this image presents science as problem-free, as if there were no problems with already accepted theories. This simplified image has been used by
authors imbued by scientism and is still used in the same line today, mainly in
popular writings. It serves the illegitimate purpose of representing empirical
science as the model for any valid knowledge claim. The actual record of science shows, instead, that science is teeming with problems, and that every new
advance opens new problems. In addition, in science there is always room for
discussion, because theories are always underdetermined in relation to the evidence used to support them. Finally, even the best established knowledge is
contextual and partial, so that it can be superseded by better explanations.

Values associated with transmission are mainly *clarity* and *rigor.* We can also
mention here *universality* as a basic requirement implied by communication
in science, because the methods used in science and the knowledge obtained
by their application must be understandable and reproducible by everyone,
and everywhere, regardless of personal preferences.

3.4. APPLICATION

Application is used here as equivalent to problem solving in the scientific field.
Therefore, it does not mean applied science or technology, although problem
solving is a preliminary step that serves as the basis for technology.

Scientific activity in its entirety can be considered a problem-solving activity. However, an explicit consideration of this activity helps to remind us
that science is always in process. Very often we consider science as a body of
established knowledge. This view is incomplete, because the motive force of
empirical science is always provided by its unsolved problems. This was emphasized by Popper and, after him, by Laudan, who explicitly placed problem
solving at the center of a realistic picture of science.

This type of activity includes as many aspects as there are types of problems. It may refer to the existence of entities, properties, or processes; to the
validity of experimental laws, general principles, or theories; or to problems
that have a theoretical or practical character.

The corresponding image of science underscores the dynamic features of
scientific progress. At the same time, it includes static features, because problems are solved only by using good theories. The success of problem solving
is the best kind of corroboration a theory may receive.

The main value associated with application is *fitness*. If we were considering technology, the main value would be *usefulness*. Certainly, even within pure science we can speak of usefulness as a most relevant value; however, fitness is a more accurate expression, because here we are not dealing with usefulness in the pragmatic sense, but with explanations that aspire to be true.

IV. SCIENTIFIC VALUES AND SCIENTIFIC PROGRESS

That scientific progress exercises a feedback on the ethical presuppositions of empirical science seems quite obvious. Indeed, the more the sciences progress, the more we can say that their goals are achieved and that the values associated with them are divulged. In addition, scientific progress provides better means for the implementation of those goals and values, enriching and refining them.

1. Epistemic Implications

We could appreciate the cognitive relevance of empirical science even if we accepted some moderate form of conventionalism or instrumentalism. Nevertheless, if we recognize the realistic aim of science and the realistic character of its achievements, we will be able to fully appreciate the feedback of scientific progress on its presuppositions.

As previously noted, the historical unity of the scientific search for truth can be interpreted as a moral commitment that gives meaning to the entire scientific enterprise. I would add that to consider empirical science as meaningful, as a consequence of its commitment to the pursuit of truth, represents a very important claim in our scientific age. Indeed, it can help us to appreciate empirical science not only because it provides us with fascinating insights and with practical advantages, but, above all, because it represents a systematic effort in our search for truth, which is a central value in human life.

To consider truth as a central value in human life goes hand in hand with empirical science because of its realistic character. Realism is a key concept to fully appreciate empirical science. The ethical evaluation of science changes depending on whether we admit that science has a realistic meaning. Those who do not admit any kind of scientific realism must interpret empirical science in a merely instrumental or pragmatic way that does not do justice to the achievements of scientific progress.

I have already argued in favor of the possibility of reaching scientific truth. These further reflections on scientific realism aim to underline the role that commitment to truth plays as a central ethical dimension of science.

Nicholas Rescher, in a study of scientific realism, strongly criticizes instrumentalism and asserts that the aim of science is closely linked to realism. He lists several antirealist objections that propose to abandon the notion of truth in empirical science, and comments:

Why, then, not accept this verdict and follow the sceptical path in dropping all reference to "the pursuit of truth" as regards the aim of science? The answer is straightforward. It is manifestly the *intent* of science to declare the real capital-T Truth about things. Without this commitment to the truth we would lose our hold on the teleology of the aims that define the very nature of the enterprise of inquiry. The characterizing *telos* of science, after all, is the discovery of facts—the providing of presumptively true answers to our questions about what goes on in the world and why things go on as they do.[54]

I agree with this appreciation. Rescher is right in saying that commitment to the truth is essential to defining the aims and the very nature of the scientific enterprise. As mentioned before, I do not find Rescher's arguments in favor of realism completely convincing. This shows that scientific realism is not an easy matter.

Two passages previously quoted and a new one can be useful here. In the first, Ronald Giere says that some major sciences, or long periods in their life, fit the empiricist model, whereas many contemporary sciences seem decidedly realistic. Examples of the first case would be Greek astronomy, thermodynamics in the late nineteenth century, and quantum theory in the twentieth century; their realist counterparts would include chemistry, molecular biology, and geology.[55] In the second passage, Ernan McMullin tells us that in many parts of science, such as geology and cell biology, we have good reason to think that we obtain true knowledge; he adds that the opposite is true where theory is still extremely underdetermined (as in current elementary particle theory) or where the ontological implications of the theory are not clear (as in classical mechanics).[56] In the third passage, McMullin applies his realist views mainly to "such structural sciences as geology, astrophysics, and molecular biology."[57]

Both Giere and McMullin differentiate some cases in which we can reasonably provide a realistic interpretation of scientific knowledge from other cases in which, in spite of realistic commitments, it is more difficult to determine to what extent our results correspond with real structures of the natural world. If we combine the passages quoted, we obtain an interesting picture in which realistic results are attributed to chemistry, molecular biology, and geology (according to Giere) and to geology, astrophysics, molec-

54. Nicholas Rescher, *Scientific Realism: A Critical Reappraisal* (Dordrecht and Boston: Reidel, 1987), p. 42.

55. Ronald N. Giere, "Constructive Realism," in *Images of Science: Essays on Realism and Empiricism, with a Reply from Bas C. van Fraassen,* ed. Paul M. Churchland and Clifford A. Hooker (Chicago and London: The University of Chicago Press, 1985), pp. 96–97.

56. McMullin, "Values in Science," cit., pp. 367–368.

57. Ernan McMullin, "A Case for Scientific Realism," in *Scientific Realism,* ed. Jarrett Leplin (Berkeley: University of California Press, 1984), p. 30.

ular biology, and cell biology (according to McMullin); realism meets difficulties in thermodynamics in the late nineteenth century and in quantum theory in the twentieth century (according to Giere), and in current elementary particle theory and classical mechanics (according to McMullin). To sum up: geology and some parts of biology are considered the best candidates for realistic science, followed by chemistry and astrophysics. Nonrealistic examples refer in both cases to theories of mathematical physics, mainly to microphysics. Does this contain a meaningful message?

My answer is affirmative, and I think that the message is quite straightforward and most important: realism depends on the level of organization of the subject matter we study. Thus, as the subject matter of geology is a highly specific and organized system, our models to study it have to be realistic. It would be geological nonsense to propose abstract models that could not describe the real structure and processes of the earth. Something similar happens in the biological disciplines that study the highly organized features of the living world; we can also extend this consideration to a vast area of chemistry and to astrophysics. But when we study the most general properties of matter, as in the case of mechanics, or the smallest components of the physical world, as in quantum field theory, we must limit our study to quite abstract models. In such cases we also search for truth and eventually reach it, but we are not able to obtain realistic representations, so truth refers only to the correspondence between some abstract formulations and empirical data: it is the correspondence between theoretical mathematical relations and the measured values of the magnitudes involved.

Once we have obtained true knowledge in a field that is accessible to a realistic interpretation, it would be meaningless to try to falsify it. For example, we do not try to falsify basic truths about the structure of DNA and its role in genetics; instead we target the most cherished models in fields that can only be represented using abstract mathematical models.

It is interesting to note, however, that even when we study areas of the natural world outside our possibilities of direct or instrumental observation, realism provides the general framework of scientific research. Even when unable to attribute a precise realistic meaning to every component of our models, we are always trying to determine the properties of the real world as far as possible.

I shall refer, as an example in the field of the microphysical composition of matter, to the Standard Model, which admits six kinds of leptons and quarks and four interactions, as the basic components of the physical world. This model is regarded as a very well-tested one and, at the same time, is the subject of audacious research that tries to find a better model. This situation was described in 1997 by Gordon Fraser in the following terms:

> At a major international physics conference in Munich in 1988, review speaker Don Perkins spoke of a "festival of the Standard Model." For almost a decade now, major physics meetings have continued to be festivals of the conventional picture of six quarks and leptons

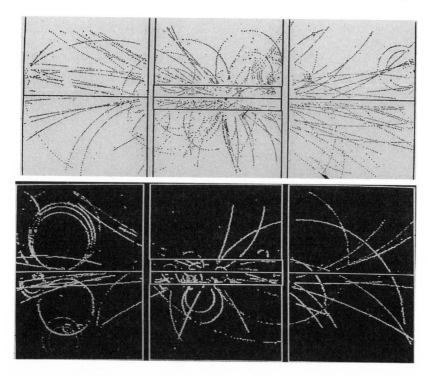

Fig. 7.2 Creativity and interpretation in empirical science. In empirical science we seek to know nonapparent features of nature. Therefore we must build up models and submit them to test. This requires a high dose of creativity and interpretation. These illustrations here are two characteristic computer pictures, the typical result of very sophisticated processes and calculations. They were obtained at the European Laboratory of Nuclear Physics (CERN: Geneva, Switzerland) by a team of more than 100 physicists who worked to detect the particles W and Z. Physicists are able to interpret this kind of picture as if they could see the traces of different kinds of subatomic particles, and they deduce the existence of invisible particles from the observable effects they produce. In this case the pictures show the decay products of the W and Z particles, whose existence was confirmed, using these and similar pictures, in 1983. Carlo Rubbia and Simon van der Meer received the 1984 Nobel Prize for physics for this discovery. (Photographs used by permission of CERN, Geneva.)

grouped pairwise into three families interacting via electroweak and interquark forces. All physicists agree that the Standard Model cannot be the full picture, with too many free parameters that can only be measured by experiment, and with the observed pattern of particle masses unexplained. But like a waterproof watch, the Standard Model had no visible crack to pry the case apart and get at the mechanism inside.[58]

58. Gordon Fraser, "Standard Model Hamburger," *Cern Courier,* 37 (1997), No. 7 (September 1977): 1.

Fraser reports the results collected in the Zeus and H1 experiments, at the Hera electron-proton collider at Desy (Hamburg), from 1994 to 1996, which seemed to suggest the existence of interactions with a new layer of matter deep inside the protons, deeper than the quarks themselves, at separations of 10^{-16} centimeters. The results were discussed in 1997 at an International Symposium held in Hamburg, and Fraser reports the following:

> Cautiously welcoming the result in his Standard Model summary talk at Hamburg, Guido Altarelli of CERN underlined the mismatch between the H1 and Zeus effects. While pointing to possible new physics implications, in his view a statistical fluctuation was the best "theoretical" explanation.[59]

Adding that anomalies persist in other sectors of physics, Fraser notes: "However the Standard Model still reigns supreme." This is not to say that he supports that model unconditionally; a month later in the same periodical, he asked, as if he were dealing with a future certain fact: "When will the Standard Model crack?" In his report on the Hamburg conference, Fraser tells us:

> It had long been a safe bet that major physics meetings would continue to revere the conventional picture of six quarks and leptons grouped pairwise into three families interacting via electroweak and interquark forces. From time to time unorthodox physics has been sighted, but nothing has stood the test of time.[60]

Referring to the new Hera results, Fraser adds:

> The Higgs particle, responsible for symmetry breaking in the electroweak sector, is the missing link in the Standard Model and remains the major objective. But even if the Higgs were to be found, the Standard Model would still be too empirical for comfort. A deeper understanding of the three quark/lepton generations and the widely disparate strengths of the different forces of nature is needed. Doubling the number of elementary particles and pairing each Standard Model lepton, photon or force carrier with a supersymmetric partner gives a beautifully balanced picture and has become the conventionally accepted dogma. "SUSY (Super-symmetry) has many virtues," declared Altarelli.[61]

These texts exemplify the attitude of scientists when studying features of the physical world that cannot be fully represented in a realistic way. Scientists do not give up realism; even though the task is very difficult, they engage in the search for true knowledge, using highly sophisticated conceptual resources and experiments. They know that their models have a provisory char-

59. Ibid.

60. Gordon Fraser, "Trying to Peer Behind the Standard Model," *Cern Courier*, 37 (1997), No. 8 (October 1997): 1.

61. Ibid.

acter and are ready to change them when necessary, but they make their decisions using serious reasoning and experimental evidence. In their evaluations they highly appreciate explanatory power; they feel uncomfortable with good results that are "too empirical" and with other unexplained results. I would say that, even in this extreme case—microphysical theories located on the frontiers of our conceptual and experimental possibilities—scientists maintain their realistic aim and behave in accordance with this aim.

Besides the difficulties involved in areas such as microphysics, other reasons explain the existence of nonrealistic tendencies in the philosophy of science. For a long time, epistemology has been centered around mathematical physics, the most advanced branch of empirical science, but also the most abstract, because it deals with the most general characteristics of all material beings and with the most basic components of the physical world. Many branches of physics are more abstract than other branches of empirical science. In the last decades of the twentieth century, however, progress in physics and chemistry has brought forth considerable progress in biology, which has become a new focus in both science and epistemology. Obviously, living beings occupy the center of the natural world in many respects, and biology should also occupy a central place among the sciences; however, modern biology has had to wait for physics and chemistry to provide the necessary base for its development as a rigorous branch of empirical science. A biologically centered epistemology would have more realistic tendency than an epistemology centered around mathematical physics, and so now it is easier to appreciate the realistic character of empirical science.

I would conclude that current progress in science and in epistemology supports, much more than in the past, a moderate kind of realism. In its turn, realism shows that the cognitive claim of empirical science has a firm foundation. Therefore, scientific progress retrojustifies the cognitive aims of science and enlarges their scope to include an ever-increasing number of natural phenomena. It also refines them, as it forces us to abandon a naive kind of realism and replace it with a more sophisticated version that takes into account the corresponding qualifications in particular cases.

2. Social Implications

Progress in the technological applications of science is so evident that it is probably the main reason for social support for the scientific enterprise. As Robert Merton puts it:

> Of course, the technological criterion of scientific achievement also has a social function for science. The increasing comforts and conveniences deriving from technology and ultimately from science invite the social support of scientific research. They also testify to the integrity of the scientist, since abstract and difficult theories which cannot be understood or evaluated by the laity are presum-

ably proved in a fashion which can be understood by all, that is, through their technological applications. Readiness to accept the authority of science rests, to a considerable extent, upon its daily demonstration of power. Were it not for such indirect demonstrations, the continued social support of that science which is intellectually incomprehensible to the public would hardly be nourished on faith alone.[62]

Even if we know that technology needs to supplement science with technological means that are not provided solely by science, current technology is doubtless based on science and would be completely impossible without a scientific foundation.

This means that scientific progress provides the practical advantages promised by the forerunners of empirical science. Francis Bacon was right when he emphasized the extraordinary social relevance of the new science, as Merton clearly expresses when he writes:

> It is probable that the reputability of science and its lofty ethical status in the estimate of the layman is in no small measure due to technological achievements. Every new technology bears witness to the integrity of the scientist. Science realizes its claims.[63]

It is also a well-known fact that, from the ethical point of view, technological progress is ambivalent. Even though the two general goals of empirical science are closely related and intertwined as two aspects of a unique goal, they possess a very different ethical status. Indeed, the theoretical goal, the search for truth, is always by itself a positive value; the only problem it may eventually provoke would be in relation to the means used in research. On the other hand, the application of scientific knowledge to controlled dominion over nature is essentially ambivalent. Science should be used in the service of mankind, but it can also be used for purposes that are ethically incorrect.

Therefore, there can be both an ethically positive and a negative feedback, from scientific progress on the pragmatic goal of empirical science. Scientific progress provides us with an increasing abundance of means that are extremely useful for many practical purposes. At the same time, it also poses new threats that must be faced with a creative responsibility, especially when they involve situations with a major impact on human life.

In a paper published in 1938, Merton reflected on the "Sources of Hostility toward Science." In the same paper he wrote:

> There is a tendency for scientists to assume that the social effects of science *must* be beneficial in the long run. This article of faith performs the function of providing a rationale for scientific research, but it is manifestly not a statement of fact.[64]

62. Merton, *The Sociology of Science,* cit., pp. 260–261.

63. Ibid., p. 277.

64. Ibid., p. 263.

He also referred very clearly on that occasion to hostility toward science, with allusion to:

an incipient revolt that is found in virtually every society where science has reached a high state of development. . . . Science is held largely responsible for endowing those engines of human destruction which, it is said, may plunge our civilization into everlasting night and confusion.[65]

Shortly afterward, August 6, 1945, marked the beginning of a new era. This date has often been regarded as the day that science lost its innocence. The nuclear era opened new dimensions in the history of mankind. But this was only the beginning; progress in biotechnology has provided unsuspected means that have opened ethically ambivalent roads. The power of human beings over the physical world, including their own physical dimensions, has increased in an unprecedented way.

Thus the practical feedback of scientific progress leads us to face new ethical responsibilities. We have already seen that the feedback of scientific progress on its ontological and epistemological presuppositions is completely consistent with the representation of the human being as part of nature but, at the same time, transcending nature as a responsible cooperator with God's plans. The feedback of scientific progress on its ethical presuppositions carries us a step further leading us to face ethical responsibilities that increase proportionally to the increased capabilities provided by the progress of science.

Apart from technological issues, scientific progress has other social consequences. Indeed, if we consider the institutional values of science, we can easily realize that scientific progress contributes to the divulgence of these values.

Although institutional values refer to rules that operate within the scientific community irrespective of ethical reasons, they are closely related to ethical values. They possess ethical dimensions and, therefore, when scientific progress makes them more widespread this has positive ethical implications in itself.

Pope John Paul II has described the spreading of scientific values as a positive feature of our epoch. Contrasting them with evils that exist in our world, he writes:

But at the same time we see in large sectors of the human community a growing critical openness towards people of different cultures and backgrounds, different competencies and viewpoints. More and more frequently, people are seeking intellectual coherence and collaboration, and are discovering values and experiences they have in common even within their diversities. This openness, this dynamic interchange, is a notable feature of the international scientific communities themselves, and is based on common interests, common goals and a common enterprise, along with a deep awareness that the

65. Ibid., pp. 261–262.

insights and attainments of one are often important for the progress of the other. In a similar but more subtle way this has occurred and is continuing to occur among more diverse groups.[66]

As a matter of fact, the number and prestige of scientific communities have grown dramatically in the contemporary world, resulting in the institutional values of empirical science being respected by an increasing number of influential people. Even though those values are sometimes respected for reasons that are not always properly ethical, the values possess an ethical value in themselves and, therefore, their spread implies the spread of ethical values. It seems possible to assert that ethical standards are becoming increasingly respected in many social realms as a consequence of scientific progress. One can object that this progress is often accompanied by ethically wrong conduct, but negative conduct is a manifestation of the ethical ambivalence of the technological consequences of scientific progress.

By its own nature, empirical science favors the growth of the values associated with it. Seeking the truth, telling the truth, honesty in reporting results, integrity, fairness in handling evidence, objectivity, rigor, cooperation, intellectual humility, and freedom of investigation are scientific institutional values that correspond to something we could call the "ethics of objectivity." Obviously, these values are not exclusive to empirical science; nevertheless, they form part of the institutional life of science, and scientific progress tends to spread them. Empirical science is a major source of means to improve the conditions of human life; but, as usually happens with human resources, the means provided by scientific progress can be used rightly or wrongly from the ethical point of view.

66. John Paul II, "Message to the Rev. George V. Coyne, June 1, 1988," in *Physics, Philosophy, and Theology: A Common Quest for Understanding,* ed. Robert J. Russell, William R. Stoeger, and George V. Coyne (Vatican City State: Vatican Observatory, 1988), p. M3.

8

The Meaning of
Scientific Progress

I shall focus now on the deepest meaning of scientific progress, including references to religious values. My analysis will cover only a small part of what can be said about religious values, because it centers around the feedback of scientific progress on the general presuppositions of empirical science. Nonetheless, this restricted perspective might illuminate some religious issues, precisely because I have deliberately limited my analysis so that it can provide a rigorous framework for the study of current problems and further research. I think that many attacks against religion in the name of science are the result of a misunderstanding of the real meaning of scientific progress, and I hope that my analysis will help to dissolve them.

I shall try to remain faithful to the commitments involved in my perspective. I think that the gap between science and religion is real, so I do not intend to obtain religious consequences directly from science. My argument is a philosophical analysis of the implications of scientific progress for the general presuppositions of empirical science. Therefore, the new perspectives I have explored and will develop in this chapter should be considered an attempt to establish links based on coherence rather than on demonstrative proof.

Nevertheless, in the second section of this chapter I shall examine the plausibility of my suggestions when confronted with naturalism, applying criteria similar to those we use to evaluate the acceptability of scientific theories. These criteria cannot be applied univocally in science and in philosophy, but they can be used in a broader sense to provide information about the comparative merits of the theistic and the naturalistic search for meaning. In the third section of this chapter, I shall provide some ideas for further research.

I. THE REENCHANTMENT OF THE WORLD

The systematic progress of modern empirical science since the seventeenth century has provided us with means to explain natural phenomena and to control them in an unprecedented way. Originally, the new science presented itself as a road that would lead us from nature to recognition of its Maker, promoting a new development of natural theology. However, from the mid-eighteenth century on, dissonant voices interpreted the new intellectual and practical powers provided by science as a road toward the independence of the human person from religious commitments. I will comment on this so-called "disenchantment" of the world and then explore some proposals to foster a new "reenchantment."

1. The Disenchantment of the World

Use of the term "disenchantment" of the world can be traced to the Romantic movement. Within the Romantic context, the "de-divinization" of the world was considered to be a consequence of the progress of empirical science that should be overcome either by supplementing the scientific image with a dose of spirituality taken from the arts, metaphysics, and religion, or by changing science itself. Hegel, for example, intended to change the basic concepts of physical science in his philosophy of nature but had very little success. Friedrich Schiller spoke about the "de-divinization" of the world, which was translated by Max Weber as the "disenchantment" of the world.

The de-divinization of the world has two different meanings. In a first sense, it means that the world is neither a part of God nor can be identified with God. Seeing the world as the handiwork of a personal transcendent God who governs it, emphasizing the rationality of the God-made and governed world, is a central tenet of Christianity and can be considered a positive factor that favored the birth of modern natural science. This kind of desacralization contrasts with ancient and modern pantheistic ideas, favors theism, and is completely consistent with the ontological presuppositions of empirical science.

In a second sense, de-divinization is sometimes interpreted as if there were not traces of God to be found in the world. This is the meaning of the word as used by Schiller and Weber.

In a lecture published in 1919, Weber included the disenchantment of the world as a major component of contemporary culture. I shall examine these views insofar as they are related to my argument.

The term "disenchantment" is a translation of the German *Entzauberung*, which Weber used several times in his essay. Related to "demystification," it expresses that, as the result of a process in which the progress of science plays a major role, the world and its scientific study are no longer considered to provide any means to see the hand of God acting in nature. As S. N. Eisenstadt puts it:

> *Entzauberung* refers mainly to the "contents" aspects of culture and describes the demystification of the conception of the world connected with growing secularism, with the rise of science, and with growing routinization of education and culture.[1]

According to Weber, the disenchantment of the world is closely related to a process of "rationalization," which replaces the ancient "magic" features of thinking with scientific naturalistic explanations. Empirical science plays a major role in that process and so, Weber concludes, the disenchantment of the world steadily grows as scientific thinking grows. Thus, speaking of the global process of increasing rationalization and intellectualization in the history of humankind, he says:

> it means that principally there are no mysterious incalculable forces that come into play, but rather that one can, in principle, master all things by calculation. This means that the world is disenchanted. One need no longer have recourse to magical means in order to master or implore the spirits, as did the savage, for whom such mysterious powers existed. Technical means and calculations perform the service. This above all is what intellectualization means.[2]

Weber compares concepts linked to intelligence, reason, progress, and control, to those linked to "magical means," "imploring the spirits," and "mysterious powers," such as they exist in the life of "the savage." In this line, he sees the disenchantment of the world as a very long process of rationalization that has existed in the Western world for millennia and that includes science as "a link and motive force." He presents the overall process as a conquest of the progressive rational mind, in which empirical science plays a central role.

I completely disagree with this evaluation, which resembles the three-stage law of Comte's positivism and is presented even today as if it were the result of an objective account of human history. I would say that fighting against religion in the name of science is as old as human history, adding that, in every epoch, naturalism presents itself as if it were the result of human progress. For example, in the first century before Christ, Titus Lucretius Carus wrote a long poem about nature arguing that the atomic theory, which had been proposed by Democritus and Leucippus in the fifth century before Christ and was restated by Epicurus one century later, provided the necessary basis for getting rid of religious superstition. Lucretius considered religion to be the cause of many evils in human affairs, because it would prevent human beings from

---

1. S. N. Eisenstadt, "Introduction," in Max Weber, *On Charisma and Institution Building* (Chicago and London: The University of Chicago Press, 1968), p. li.

2. Max Weber, "Science as a Vocation," in *On Charisma and Institution Building*, cit., p. 298.

searching for the true nature of the human condition: he thought that the real causes of everything are entirely material and could be reduced, in the last analysis, to atoms and their interactions. Physicists John Barrow and Frank Tipler, recognizing some scientific merit in Lucretius, write:

His great poem *De Rerum Natura* aimed to bury all superstitious speculation and philosophical dogma by outlining the vast scope of a purely materialistic doctrine.[3]

The argument for naturalism at that time was allegedly supported by a science that was hardly anything more than sheer speculation. Contemporary atomic theory has very little in common with its ancient predecessor, apart from the name. Whatever the merits of the ancients might be, it seems indisputable that the antireligious arguments presented by Lucretius are basically similar to those used now, insofar as materialism attempts to overcome metaphysics and religion in the name of modern science by reducing all explanations to those that address only two questions: what is this made of, and how does it work?

There is no doubt that contemporary naturalism presents its arguments in a much more sophisticated form than its ancient versions. Mario Bunge, in a book updating materialism, has written:

It must be owned that most materialists have not proposed satisfactory answers to the above crucial questions. Either they have not faced some of them or, when they have, their answers have tended to be simplistic . . . the interesting question is whether materialism is hopelessly dated and impotent, or can be revitalized and updated and, if so, how. This is the problem the present book addresses. This book can be regarded as an invitation to look at materialism as a field of research rather than a body of fixed beliefs.[4]

Bunge's sophisticated arguments include tools such as mathematical logic. I am mainly interested in the core of the argument, which is expressed by Bunge in this way:

it can be argued that materialism is not just one more ontology: that it is the ontology of science and technology. In particular, materialism is the ontological driving force behind certain scientific breakthroughs such as atomic and nuclear physics, evolutionary biology, the chemical theory of heredity, the scientific study of the origin of life, the physiology of ideation, and the most recent advances in paleoanthropology and historiography.[5]

I find this evaluation false and misleading, unless it is interpreted as meaning that empirical science studies the material world and, therefore, interest

3. John D. Barrow and Frank J. Tipler, *The Anthropic Cosmological Principle* (Oxford: Clarendon Press, 1986), pp. 41–42.

4. Mario Bunge, *Scientific Materialism* (Dordrecht: Reidel, 1981), p. xii.

5. Ibid., p. xiii.

in the material world favors its progress. But this is trivial, and if it is called materialism, all of us should be materialists. Nevertheless, this kind of materialism is useless and void of content.

If we take materialism in its nontrivial meaning, as the philosophical doctrine that denies the existence of nonmaterial realities, neither empirical science nor epistemology has anything to say about this. The reason is precisely because empirical science concentrates on the study of the material world and it makes no sense to derive from it assertions about spiritual realities. To interpret this as "the ontology of science" is also meaningless. Nevertheless, Bunge is not alone in supporting this view. In one way or another, supporters of the "disenchantment of the world" thesis argue in a similar vein, interpreting the methodological limitation of empirical science as the denial of the existence of anything that cannot be studied using the methods of empirical science.

Even if we admit as a sociological fact that modern times are witnessing an increasing process of secularization in Western societies, the causes and the meaning of this phenomenon are anything but simple and trivial. In any case, my point is that considering this phenomenon as a positive advance has nothing to do with scientific progress, which cannot be interpreted in favor of naturalism, materialism, or secularism.

If we return to Weber's argument, we see that he strongly emphasized that science is value-free. But he interprets this in terms of his disenchantment thesis; a value-free science would favor a value-free interpretation of the world, which would be incompatible with a religious interpretation. He then asks what disenchantment of the world means, and he says:

> To raise this question is to ask for the vocation of science within the total life of humanity. What is the value of science?[6]

Weber sees the process of intellectualization and rationalization as being as old as human history itself. He tells us that the Greeks of antiquity discovered the *concept,* one of the great tools of scientific knowledge, and were fully aware of the relevance of their discovery. The second great tool of scientific work—rational experiment as a means for controlling experience—was raised to a principle of research in the Renaissance. Weber adds that, during the period of the rise of the exact sciences, people no longer found the path to the hidden God among the philosophers, and they hoped to find in the new sciences traces of the divine plan. Then, Weber arrives at his first diagnosis of the contemporary world and writes:

> And today? Who—aside from certain big children who are indeed found in the natural sciences—still believes that the findings of astronomy, biology, physics, or chemistry could teach us anything about the *meaning* of the world? If there is any such "meaning," along what road could one come upon its tracks? If these natural

6. Max Weber, "Science as a Vocation," cit., pp. 298–299.

sciences lead to anything in this way, they are apt to make the belief that there is such a thing as the "meaning" of the universe die out at its very roots.[7]

On Weber's account, the sciences cannot provide a road to the divine. He refers to people who hold the opposite opinion as "big children" and manifests a certain skepticism regarding the very possibility of the existence of meaning in the world. He also says that the sciences are "irreligious" by their very nature, so that a religious life would require us to surpass the world of the sciences:

> And finally, science as a way "to God"? Science, this specifically irreligious power? That science today is irreligious no one will doubt in his innermost being, even if he will not admit it to himself. Redemption from the rationalism and intellectualism of science is the fundamental presupposition of living in union with the divine.[8]

Therefore, it seems we face a dilemma: either we accept the scientific outlook or we accept that our life has a divine meaning. Weber would regard this as a false dilemma, for he stresses that the scientific perspective does not include ultimate questions. His entire argument is based on recognizing the limits of science and, for this very reason, concludes in a form of skepticism.

In his subsequent analysis of the sciences, Weber stresses that they are value-free, but, if this is so, we might wonder how they could be irreligious, unless we interpret "irreligiosity" as mere methodological bracketing of religious issues. Weber insists that the sciences concern themselves only with means, regardless of the values of the ends they pursue. That their goals are valuable is something they must presuppose. Indeed, he says that "all scientific work presupposes that the rules of logic and method are valid," and then he goes on to say:

> Science further presupposes that what is yielded by scientific work is important in the sense that it is "worth being known." In this, obviously, are contained all our problems. For this presupposition cannot be proved by scientific means. It can only be *interpreted* with reference to its ultimate meaning, which we must reject or accept according to our ultimate position towards life.[9]

Weber speaks of what I have called the "ethical presuppositions of science," which refer to the general aims of science and the justification of these aims, and, therefore, to the meaning of science within the whole human life. He states that we cannot prove these presuppositions; but can only interpret them "according to our ultimate position towards life." Regarding the natural sci-

---

7. Ibid., pp. 301–302.

8. Ibid., p. 302.

9. Ibid., p. 303.

ences, which constitute the main focus of my argument, he strongly empha-sizes that they cannot prove anything about meaning:

> The natural sciences, for instance, physics, chemistry, and astronomy, presuppose as self-evident that it is worth while to know the ultimate laws of cosmic events as far as science can construe them. . . . Yet this presupposition can by no means be proved. And still less can it be proved that the existence of the world which these sciences describe is worth while, that it has any "meaning," or that it makes sense to live in such a world. Science does not ask for the answers to such questions. . . . Natural science gives us an answer to the question of what we must do if we wish to master life technically. It leaves quite aside, or assumes for its purposes, whether we should and do wish to master life technically and whether it ultimately makes sense to do so.[10]

Although, Weber is right when he says natural science by itself cannot prove anything about meaning, ethics, and religion, he seems to go further and accepts the "disenchantment" of the world as an irreversible, positive fact provoked to a great extent by scientific progress.

I do not want to overstate my point. Weber's position is a complex one and I do not intend to provide a full account of it. I use it only as a point of departure for my analysis of the disenchantment of the world, which is often presented as a consequence of scientific progress. In this case, a value-free sci-ence would possess a monopoly on objectivity. In the name of such a value-free science we are told either that there is no room for religious doctrines and values, or that ultimate questions constitute purely subjective matters.

Ultimate questions involve personal commitments. Nevertheless, this does not mean that they belong to a purely subjective ambit in which reasoning is no longer possible. I do not think that, objectively, scientific progress has es-sentially changed the nature of this problem, because ultimate questions have always required personal commitments. Therefore, it is unfair to present sci-entific progress as a major cause of the disenchantment of the world. Even an agnostic like Karl Popper, whose sympathies favor naturalism, clearly notes that "science does not make assertions about ultimate questions—about the riddles of existence, or about man's task in this world"; that "science has noth-ing to say about a personal Creator"; and, even more specifically, that "argu-ment from design may not be within the reach of science."[11]

I would conclude that scientific progress should not be considered a ma-jor cause of the disenchantment of the world. In addition, some contempo-rary reactions propose a reenchantment of the world.

---

10. Ibid., pp. 303–304.

11. Karl R. Popper, "Natural Selection and the Emergence of Mind," in *Evolutionary Episte-mology, Rationality, and the Sociology of Knowledge,* ed. Gerard Radnitzky and William W. Bartley (La Salle, Ill.: Open Court, 1987), pp. 141–142.

2. Reenchanting the World

I shall refer now to four different positions that coincide in their criticism of the disenchantment of the world, but advance different proposals to overcome it.

2.1. the reenchantment of science

The first position is represented by authors working in an area of thought mainly inspired by Alfred North Whitehead and Charles Hartshorne, but with a postmodern orientation. John B. Cobb, Jr., and David Ray Griffin are two preeminent representatives of this position, presented in a collective work, *The Reenchantment of Science,* an introduction to a series in constructive postmodern thought.[12]

This proposal aims to trigger a major change in science itself. Griffin writes:

> At the root of modernity and its discontents lies what Max Weber called "the disenchantment of the world." This disenchantment worldview has been both a result and a presupposition of modern science and has almost unanimously been assumed to be a result and a presupposition of science as such. What is distinctive about "modern" philosophy, theology, and art is that they revolve around numerous strategies for maintaining moral, religious, and aesthetic sensitivities while accepting the disenchanted worldview of modernity as adequate for science. These strategies have involved either rejecting modern science, ignoring it, supplementing it with talk of human values, or reducing its status to that of mere appearance. The postmodern approach to disenchantment involves a reenchantment of science itself.[13]

The two most widespread attitudes among philosophers and theologians who feel uncomfortable with modern science have been to ignore it or to reduce its status to a level that, in practice, could be ignored. Griffin's approach represents the opposite extreme, as he proposes to change science itself. It is important to note that change does not mean rejection, even though, insofar as something is to be changed, at least a part of it must be rejected.

This proposal involves a most difficult task. The immediate question that arises is: what would the reenchanted science be like? What is meant by a reenchanted physics, for example? This is the purpose of Griffin's work:

> The essays herein reflect some of the dimensions that would be involved in a reenchanted science. This introduction positions these essays by showing how they imply a reversal of the modern disenchantment of science and nature and how this reversal fits within the larger contemporary reassessment of natural science.[14]

12. David Ray Griffin, ed., *The Reenchantment of Science: Postmodern Proposals* (Albany: State University of New York Press, 1988).

13. David Ray Griffin, "Introduction: The Reenchantment of Science," in *The Reenchantment of Science,* cit., p. 1.

14. Ibid.

I must confess that I am very skeptical about this kind of proposal, which combines two different elements: on the one hand, science properly, and on the other, interpretations or worldviews associated with science that cannot be considered as science in a strict sense. Difficulties arise if we mix these two elements, presenting the interpretation or worldview as if it were science in a strict sense.

The difficulty with the distinction between science and worldview is, who decides what is science in a strict sense? Are not scientists always committed to interpretations that are the source of our difficulties? Griffin writes:

> Science as a cognitive system was thought to be essentially value-free, except for those values that are internal to science itself, i.e., its distinctive way of pursuing truth. But now it is widely held that this separation is not possible and that the social factors affect science essentially, not just superficially. Rather than standing as an impartial tribunal of truth, transcendent over the battle field of competing social forces, science is seen as one more interested participant, using its status to legitimate certain social, political, and economic forces and to delegitimate others. More than that, the scientific community's interest in its own social power relative to other professions and institutions is now seen to condition the picture of the world it sanctions as "scientific."[15]

I am ready to admit that something like this can eventually happen, especially in the social sciences. Nevertheless, saying that today it is "widely held" that "the social factors affect science essentially" is simply false, at least if we speak, as I do, of the natural sciences. The corresponding footnotes sends us to a list of writings, the first of which is *Against Method,* by Paul Feyerabend. We should remember that Feyerabend's motto was "anything goes"; therefore, Feyerabend's "epistemological anarchism" is not a reliable reference if we desire to respect the rigor of the natural sciences. Later, Griffin himself refers to Feyerabend's "anything goes," saying that such a viewpoint is surely too strong, but that it serves "to shake us free from parochial limitations on what counts as science."[16] We are faced with the same problem again: what should count as science, and what should be regarded as an interpretation of science?

Obviously, when we *interpret* empirical science, it is we who must decide which interpretation we accept. However, we should always distinguish what is being said by the scientists in their own field from what is said by them or by us as an interpretation. This distinction is not always a particularly sharp or easy one, but we should always try to respect it; otherwise, we will end up involved in meaningless talk.

Griffin is aware that many of his readers might think that to avoid mixing

15. Ibid., pp. 8–9.

16. Ibid., p. 26.

science with views at other levels it may be sufficient to point out the inherent limitations of science. To this objection he answers:

> The problem with this solution is that the ideal of an "inherently limited science" does not work in practice. Science is inherently not only realistic, trying to describe the way things really are, but also imperialistic, bent on providing the only genuine description. . . . The cultural effect of modern science has been to make scientists the only "acknowledged legislators" of humankind, because its worldview has ruled out the possibility that metaphysics, theology, or poetry would have anything to add. Unless science itself is seen as giving a different answer, the disenchantment of the world will continue.[17]

I do not agree that science is "inherently imperialistic." The natural sciences have the reputation of being extremely reliable and, in consequence, scientists may in some cases abuse their authority, but the remedy for this should not be the opposite abuse, to deny the reliability of empirical science. We can obtain in the natural sciences a kind of socially reliable knowledge that cannot be obtained in other fields, but the very spatiotemporal repeatable patterns that explain the reliability of the natural sciences also imply that they are incompetent to judge subjects that involve spiritual dimensions, freedom, and related matters.

It is well known that some scientists use their prestige to defend ideas that are not scientific and may possibly provoke confusion. Nevertheless, we should not conclude that science is "inherently imperialistic." It seems that scientists are today much more aware of the limits of their disciplines than they were previously, and most of them are ready to dialogue with philosophers and theologians. In any case, if we try to remedy an excess through the opposite excess, the result will not be clarification but increasing confusion.

The arguments presented in *The Reenchantment of Science* contain interesting criticisms and proposals. They rightly reject mechanism, determinism, reductionism, and materialism and show that recent developments in empirical science open interesting new perspectives and highlight the drawbacks of the classical mechanistic worldview. In some respects, their contributions can be combined with the worldview I am advocating here. Nevertheless, I think that their general approach may tend to confuse science with a philosophical and theological worldview that, even though presented as scientific, is neither scientific nor a necessary consequence of science.

Griffin proposes his own idea of empirical science,[18] one that is quite similar to the standard one but seems to leave room for a kind of natural philosophy within science itself. I think this is a serious problem that deserves care-

17. Ibid., p. 6.

18. Ibid., pp. 26–28.

ful study; indeed, empirical science may sometimes use implicit metaphysical assumptions that are incorrect. However, I think that the progress of an empirical science centered around repeatable natural patterns is one of the greatest advances in the history of mankind, and that this advance should be respected and protected, avoiding hybrid mixtures. Finally, I would add that respecting empirical science, which implies presenting philosophical and theological reflections on their own feet, is the only way to overcome the shortcomings of scientism. We should always distinguish science from scientism: the real source of confusions is scientism. And scientism is not science but a mistaken philosophy that presents itself as if it were science.

2.2 POSTMODERN SCIENCE

Other proposals have been advanced as contributions to the reenchantment of the world in the name of postmodern science. Generally they take advantage of new developments in science and present them as implying philosophical and even theological consequences that tend to bring the natural sciences and the search for meaning closer together.

Postmodern science plays an important role in Griffin's "postmodern organicism." Other interpretations of postmodern science are also available. For example, the emergence of fractal geometry and the revised understanding of dynamic systems are leading empirical science, according to D. L. Madsen and M. S. Madsen, toward a new view of nature that is essentially postmodern. The postmodern character of the new worldview would include the following facets:

> Predictability and certainty have been rendered problematic by chaos, and the concepts basic to conventional science have been undermined by a new emphasis upon the impossibility of objectivity and the unattainability of absolute knowledge . . . postmodern science must adopt a new approach which prioritises the provisional nature of our understanding of total structures, within the context provided by recent studies of the emergence of complex behaviour from simple subsystems.[19]

This view emphasizes the limits of scientific knowledge, which, it claims, are much more problematic, noncertain, and nonobjective than previously thought. Knowledge is presented as context dependent and hence relative. The authors who support this view clearly state their goal in these terms:

> We shall attempt to demonstrate that the purely postmodern aspects of science can be seen to provide an explicit deconstruction of the goals of modernist science. Understanding science as a postmodern *subculture,* or a loosely and contextually related set of subcultures, would release science from its empty and ultimately futile conflicts

19. Deborah L. Madsen and Mark S. Madsen, "Fractals, Chaos and Dynamics: The Emergence of Postmodern Science," in *Postmodern Surroundings,* ed. Steven Earnshaw (Amsterdam and Atlanta, Ga.: Rodopi, 1994), p. 119.

with literature, religion and politics; as well as from the vigorously
contested struggle for equality among the sciences. . . . Our intention
in this essay is to describe the construction of a genuinely postmodern science, based upon the structure of twentieth-century science as
it is presently understood and practised.[20]

The last words seem to imply that postmodern science is already in operation; the authors write:

How are we to construct a truly postmodern science? The answer lies
in the recognition that most of present day science already has the
structure of a postmodern discipline.[21]

The study of dynamic systems, chaos, and fractals is seen by the authors as
an example of postmodern science and the computer as a "quintessentially
postmodern tool of inquiry."

As we have seen, the argument centers around the dispensability of certainty or absolutism in favour of contextuality. The authors note that their
definition of postmodern science "does not lead to any conflict with experimental results" and requires no change in well-corroborated theories.
Changes occur in the relationship between different branches of science, as
scientific knowledge is conceived as representing relational, and hence provisional, models. Thus:

As a consequence of this relational modelling, different sciences are
equally important, since no branch of knowledge is more fundamental than any other. Indeed, it appears that by this criterion, social and
literary studies should be as important to human culture as scientific
disciplines.[22]

Thus, the authors of this proposal are not trying to change postmodern
science; they admit its existence and try to explain its characteristics and to
make its consequences explicit. There is a leveling of the different sciences;
natural science should cease to be a set of allegedly hard disciplines in which
a unique kind of objectivity and certainty exists, and would occupy a place
on the same level as other intellectual enterprises.

Although this perspective is very different from Griffin's postmodern organicism, there is a common interest in both cases, that of placing the author's
philosophical thought and empirical science on the same level. Griffin attempts to transform empirical science, so that his metaphysics may be introduced within science itself. The Madsens consider today's science to be
deprived of the absolutist claims of modern science, so that it should be considered as already belonging to the same level humanistic disciplines occupy.
In both cases the authors presuppose that metaphysics, or religion, or hu-

20. Ibid., pp. 120–121.

21. Ibid., p. 126.

22. Ibid., p. 130.

manistic perspectives, if they are to be regarded as respectable at all, must possess a rigor comparable to that of empirical science.

This presupposition is based on serious misunderstandings. My previous analysis of empirical science shows that it possesses a specific kind of reliability and that the very same reasons that explain the peculiar reliability of empirical science also explain its limits and its place within the larger context of human life. Building a distorted image of empirical science to accommodate it to one's ideas is not only unfair, but also untenable and unnecessary.

2.3 A HOLISTIC APPROACH

Another proposal for reenchanting the world has been articulated by Morris Berman.[23] I shall refer to some relevant features of his ideas to show that this subject can be approached from a wide variety of perspectives.

Berman's critique of modernity refers to the classical topics in this area, such as Cartesian dualism, materialistic science, and productivity and efficiency considered as central values. To those elements, however, Berman adds others that are not so common and that occupy a central place in his analysis. One of them is his insistence on the role played by occultism in the scientific revolution, another is the relevance he attributes to bodily factors, following Wilhelm Reich in his identification between the body and the unconscious. The main element of his critique closely follows ideas borrowed from Gregory Bateson, a complex personality and the author of *Mind and Nature: A Necessary Unity* and *Steps to an Ecology of Mind*.

Even as Berman refers to science and epistemology as central keys to the disenchantment of the world, his analysis includes many references to the esoteric tradition, including an entire chapter devoted to the recovery of eros, in which he tries to prove that the union between "eros" and "logos" is a scientific fact rooted in preconscious childhood and that, therefore, the holistic worldview has a physiologic base.

Berman's analysis contains some valid criticisms of modernity and valuable insights, such as his underscoring the relevance of a holistic view that may overcome the fragmentary modern perspective; however, I find his holism too comprehensive. We find there references to a future holistic society in which the repressed features of industrial society will occupy their proper place; these include the recovery of our bodies, our health, our sexuality, our natural environment, our archaic traditions, our unconscious mind, our earthly roots, our sense of being in touch with others.

I find this combination of science, epistemology, psychology, sociology, and politics not only too comprehensive, but also too pretentious to be taken as an objective account or a reliable guide. But it clearly shows that the disenchantment of the world represents a real sociologic problem that may waken the most varied feelings. I regret that the entire book is presented as a

---

23. Morris Berman, *The Reenchantment of the World* (Ithaca, N.Y.: Cornell University Press, 1981).

holistic attempt, because using the term "holism" so loosely tends to give a bad image to a concept that occupies an important place in the contemporary worldview.

2.4 SCIENCE AND MYTHICAL THINKING

Kurt Hübner's ideas are most relevant in the present context. Indeed, one of Hübner's main objectives is to overcome criticisms directed against religion in the name of science. I shall briefly refer to some ideas that he has articulated in much more detail.[24]

According to Hübner, both science and religion presuppose ontologies that ultimately can coexist. Naturalism is, he thinks, the ontology of science, whereas religion has a mythical structure. In this context, "mythical structure" does not imply the return to old mythical ideas but to the possibility of discovering divine dimensions in the world. Hübner concludes:

> it is impossible to scientifically attack the mythical structure of religion and consequently it is also impossible to criticize all the mentioned events in salvation as has been done again and again since the Age of Enlightenment.[25]

Hübner's use of the term "ontology" does not mean a generally valid set of concepts that represent the different dimensions of reality. Rather, it is related to a history-dependent set of categories. In his own words:

> Since ontologies neither rest on experience nor on pure reason but consist only of historical rules in the sense already mentioned, they are neither true nor false. They are only *instruments,* with the help of which we *organize* experience—mythically or scientifically.[26]

The "sense already mentioned" refers to Hübner's view that every historical situation determines what the facts and fundamental principles used in science will be.

Thus, Hübner tries to dissolve the alleged opposition between science and religion by arguing that both rest on special ontologies, although the content of these two ontologies is completely different. To express it in my own terms, I would say that an attack against religion in the name of science would be illegitimate because science rests on presuppositions that cannot be justified in an absolute sense; therefore, it cannot be used to attack a perspective based on a completely different kind of presupposition.

Hübner's argument may serve to show that the disenchantment of the world is not a consequence of scientific progress and that it would not be nec-

24. Hübner's ideas about the relationship between science and religion are mainly contained in Kurt Hübner, *Die Wahrheit des Mythos* (München: C. H. Beck, 1985).

25. Kurt Hübner, "Short Abstract of my Philosophical Conceptions and Ideas" (Personal communication with author, February 16, 1987), n. 11.

26. Ibid., n. 8.

essary to reenchant the world, because it has not really been disenchanted. The alleged disenchantment is the product of fallacious reasoning that opposes science to religion as if the progress of science meant the regress of religion. This kind of opposition is the effect of an illusion that does not withstand rigorous analysis.

Hübner's argument is more sophisticated; I have only considered what I think is his central claim. I agree with him that the so-called disenchantment of the world is not a neutral fact; rather, it is a sociological phenomenon whose meaning and causes involve a certain complexity. Nevertheless, I think that speaking of "ontologies" as he does may result in confusion, because it may be interpreted as an exaggerated historicism in which everything is dissolved into history.

Last but not least, I would say that naturalism is not the ontology of science. If we distinguish *science* from *scientism,* then naturalism can be considered a kind of scientism—an illegitimate extrapolation of the goals, methods, and results of empirical science as if they were the paradigm that should be followed for any legitimate cognitive claim. In empirical science we adopt a kind of *methodological* naturalistic perspective, but we know, or at least we should know, that this does not imply any kind of *ontological* naturalism.

3. UPDATING THE AGENDA

The preceding reflections show that analysis of the disenchantment of the world and the corresponding solutions are often posed in a somewhat misleading way. Weber's idea that scientific progress implies a de-divinization of the world is false. Proposals for reenchanting the world very often try to change science itself, which is a utopian claim, or assert that science has inherently changed its character, which is misleading.

The entire issue should be reformulated under a different perspective, by recognizing that empirical science on the one side, and metaphysics and theology on the other, are separated by a methodological gap that can only be bridged using philosophical reflection. We should renounce any kind of imperialism, be it scientific, philosophical, or theological. We should carefully respect each one of these approaches, requiring of them rigor and consistency, and realizing that they are not opposed but rather complementary. Joseph Zycinski expresses a similar view:

> Certain contemporary authors, indeed, dream about the possibility of deep transformations and revisions in the present scientific paradigm. The revisions are to introduce some existential problems into the domain of scientific investigations. Up till now, however, all attempts of *a priori* forcing upon science normative principles of its future evolution appeared failures. There are serious reasons to argue that the expectation of a future unity of the natural sciences and the humanities remains only a nice dream which has no chance of fulfillment. Instead of comforting oneself with the expectation of the internal evo-

lution of science, it seems to be better to develop philosophical reflection upon factors that divide the scientific thought from the religious one. Such factors are certainly mutual misjudgements and prejudices.[27]

Zycinski adds that one major factor of that kind results from a lack of proper understanding of the immanence of God in nature, a subject belonging to
natural theology, and he advances a proposal along those lines. I shall include
Zycinski's proposal among my final suggestions.

II. BUILDING NEW BRIDGES

To bridge the gap that exists between empirical science and metaphysics and
theology, I have proposed an approach that centers on the feedback of scientific progress on its general presuppositions. I will recapitulate my conclusions and evaluate them using criteria similar to those employed in the
sciences.

1. A RECAPITULATION OF MY ARGUMENT

General presuppositions of science are a part of science, being necessary conditions of the entire scientific enterprise; nevertheless, we do not find them
in scientific formulations. This is why my argument, based on the feedback
of scientific progress on those presuppositions, closely follows the path of science but does not interfere with any of its concrete results; it completely
avoids the danger involved in proposals that intend to find a meaning in empirical science by changing its methods or contents. Moreover, because the
argument is centered on scientific progress, it does not depend on particular
stages of the development of science; it will conserve its value at any future
time. Indeed, the more the sciences progress, the more we can apply this argument to new circumstances.

I have applied my argument to the concrete circumstances of science and
epistemology at the end of the twentieth century, circumstances that provide
an extremely interesting basis for the argument. On the ontological level we
have, for the first time in the history of humankind, a worldview that is, at
the same time, rigorous and complete, as it includes all natural levels. On the
epistemological level, it is possible to combine the logical, historical, and sociological aspects of science, avoiding the excesses characteristic of previous
epochs. On the anthropological level, we can now easily appreciate the benefits provided by scientific progress avoiding at the same time the dangers involved in scientistic ideologies.

---

27. Joseph M. Zycinski, *Three Cultures: Science, the Humanities and Religious Values* (Tucson, Ariz.:
Pachart Publishing House, 1990), pp. 59–60.

I shall now sketch the main lines of my argument, concentrating on the substantive developments that begin with Part II.

In Part II, I analyzed the feedback of scientific progress on the ontological presuppositions of empirical science, emphasizing the central role of self-organization in the current scientific worldview and adding that, in its turn, self-organization provides new evidence in favor of the existence of teleological dimensions in the natural world. I tried to show that the new scientific worldview is most coherent with the view that divine action on the world carefully respects the agency of created causes and uses them to achieve the plans of divine providence. I commented on Aquinas' remarkable definition of nature, when he wrote that "Nature is nothing but the plan of some art, namely a divine one, put into things themselves, by which those things move towards a concrete end." This definition aptly expresses the divine origin of nature, stressing at the same time God's immanence and transcendence; in addition, Aquinas accompanied his definition with an example that directly refers to self-organization. In a paradoxical but real sense, his explanation is more true today than it was when he proposed it.

In Part III, I analyzed the feedback of scientific progress on the epistemological presuppositions of empirical science and argued that the reliability of empirical science is a consequence of its concentration on the study of repeatable spatiotemporal patterns. I also stressed that this study requires a high dose of creativity and interpretation and that scientific creativity, which is necessary in every step of the construction of theories and of their empirical control, clearly shows the singularity of human beings, who belong to the natural world but, at the same time, transcend it. Thus, empirical science provides us with very effective means to participate in God's plans as created cocreators.

In Part IV, I first analyzed the feedback of scientific progress on the ethical presuppositions of empirical science, arguing that empirical science makes sense insofar as we accept that its twofold goal is meaningful. Searching for truth should be considered a value in itself, and service to mankind through practical applications is doubtless another central value of empirical science. Scientific progress has made it possible to attain both goals and thus has changed the conditions of human life dramatically. Possible abuses show that science should be complemented with the necessary dose of responsibility. Scientific progress has also contributed to spreading the institutional values that are required for empirical science to be considered as a collective enterprise.

Finally, I examined the alleged disenchantment of the world, which presents scientific progress as the cause of a de-divinization of the world and discussed proposals that attempt to supersede that situation. I found these proposals to be inadequate because, in some cases, they take for granted that science implies such de-divinization of the world and, in others, propose to change the very nature of empirical science, which seems unnecessary and utopian.

2. Applying Scientific Criteria to My Conclusions

I intend to evaluate my conclusions by applying criteria similar to those we use to evaluate scientific achievements. As my conclusions include philosophical and theological reflections, scientific criteria cannot be applied to them in the same way they are applied in empirical science, where we can always rely on empirical control. In a book on spirituality, Georges Chevrot aptly expressed this difficulty:

> The genius of man, with an admirable tenacity, discovers one after another the mysteries of nature and the secrets of the history of our planet. But however extended his field of knowledge may be, he is necessarily bound by the limits of the facts subject to his control. The realities which surpass these limits cannot be seized by the same means of investigation: there is then no other natural guide than reason, and the latter, which tries to explore the infinite, is incapable of penetrating and grasping it.[28]

Chevrot is right, because a necessary requirement for anything to be accepted in empirical science is that it can be submitted to empirical control. One can ask, then, how to use scientific criteria to judge philosophical and theological ideas.

Criteria similar to those used in science can be applied in our case. On the one hand, we can examine whether the analysis of the presuppositions of science and of the feedback of scientific progress on them corresponds to an objective picture of scientific activity. On the other hand, we can judge the philosophical and theological interpretation of the previous analysis according to scientific criteria, provided we adapt those criteria to the specific circumstances of the case. This accommodation is possible and may be illuminating.

Which criteria should we choose? Because I wish to be coherent and rigorous, I shall employ the five criteria that I feel offer the best yardstick for judging the acceptability of scientific theories: *explanatory power, predictive power, accuracy both of explanations and predictions, convergence of varied and independent proofs,* and *mutual support.*

Philosophers of science usually maintain that those criteria are used to decide between competing theories. I shall also consider the views opposed to my conclusions, analyzing them under the same five criteria.

2.1. EXPLANATORY POWER

Explanatory power is the basic requirement for any potential candidate in empirical science and other intellectual enterprises. In every particular case we must evaluate how this requirement is fulfilled in relation to the facts we try to explain. Nevertheless, explanation is not a univocal concept. In empirical

---

28. Georges Chevrot, *Simon Peter* (Dublin: Scepter, 1959), p. 111.

science, explanations are obtained by using laws or theories that include, as a particular case, that which we want to explain. But other kinds of explanation are possible: for example, the existence of a black hole or other kind of entity can be considered as an explanation of some particular effects. A feature common to all kinds of explanation is that there must be a *consistency* between the explanation and the phenomena being explained. Even in areas where scientists display great ingenuity, very often the most important results are presented by saying that experimental results are *consistent* with the particular hypothesis that should explain them.

In my argument, this criterion must be applied, first of all, to the *scientific worldview* formulated in Part II. I think it is clear that it corresponds to the present results and trends in empirical science. There is little room in it for personal interpretation, because on this point I have followed indications provided by the most conspicuous scientists and philosophers of science in our time. The central role played by self-organization in the present scientific worldview, and the corresponding emphasis on natural dynamism, patterning, and information, are commonplace in the contemporary literature on this subject. It can be safely said this there is no serious alternative to this worldview at the present moment.

Things are more complex, regarding my argument in favor of *scientific realism* in Part III. There is no generalized consensus on this topic among philosophers of science; however, my argument takes into account the present state of the art. Also, it adequately reflects the realistic aim of practicing scientists and the merits and limits of their achievements. I argue for a kind of moderate realism that basically coincides with the realism supported by well-known authors.

My version of scientific realism served two purposes. In Part III, I used it to argue in favor of *the singularity of human beings.* Nevertheless, I stressed there that, even if someone does not accept a realism like mine, human singularity would still be the conclusion of any objective analysis of the enormously sophisticated procedures used in empirical science. In Part IV, I used realism to characterize *the general aims of empirical science.* In this case, if we reject any kind of realism, we obtain a very impoverished image of science as an excellent tool for pragmatic uses but deprived of cognitive content. This picture of science would lead us to consider the realistic aim of scientists and the cognitive progress of science as illusory, and the success of science-based technology would appear a miracle; therefore, judged by the standards of explanatory power, that picture of science would not be correct.

Issues related to the scientific worldview and to scientific realism include philosophical evaluations, but remain quite close to the facts. Obviously, things are much more complex when we consider philosophical and theological views such as those I have included in my analysis. That is why, from the very beginning, I have remarked that I would propose interpretations based on *coherence* rather than on proof; I think I have remained faithful to this promise.

I would add, however, that my philosophical and theological *suggestions* are not the result of a purely personal speculation. I have tried to concentrate on interpretations that are accepted by well-known authors representing different philosophical and theological perspectives, and, whenever possible, I have included references that show this coincidence.

My conclusions in favour of theism and human spirituality possess a high explanatory power because they account for many phenomena that, when seen in the light of agnosticism or atheism, are left completely unexplained. Agnostics and atheists usually recognize this fact. Theism and spiritualist metaphysics have no problem in accepting all scientific explanations and, in addition, provide explanations about other problems that would otherwise remain veiled in mystery.

Doubtless, divine action is mysterious because it is different from any created activity, but we should not forget that science admits mysterious agencies when they are necessary to explain observed effects. Besides, divine action is not completely mysterious; we can reasonably conclude that it must exist, and its existence enables us to understand many facts that otherwise would remain unexplained. In this line, Gilbert K. Chesterton wrote:

> The one created thing which we cannot look at is the one thing in the light of which we look at everything. Like the sun at noonday, mysticism explains everything else by the blaze of its own victorious invisibility. Detached intellectualism is (in the exact sense of a popular phrase) all moonshine; for it is light without heat, and it is secondary light, reflected from a dead world.[29]

This holds also in the case of teleology, which is closely linked to the existence of a divine plan. Teleology does not contradict the agency of efficient causes; on the contrary, it presupposes the existence of that agency, since it expresses the directionality inherent to natural processes, but adds directionality and meaning. We know of the existence of teleology because we observe directionality in the world, but also because the world we observe, if it were the mere product of natural forces alone, would be, in the last analysis, completely unreasonable. The present worldview provides a great amount of highly sophisticated evidence in favor of a teleological interpretation of the world.

2.2. PREDICTIVE POWER

Philosophical and theological ideas cannot be used to obtain predictions related to the control of empirical facts. Nevertheless, we can speak of their predictive power, because we can explore the consequences of using such views to evaluate natural facts and human conduct.

---

29. Gilbert K. Chesterton, *Orthodoxy*, in *The Collected Works of G. K. Chesterton*, vol. I, ed. David Dooley (San Francisco: Ignatius Press, 1986), p. 231.

In this sense, we can attribute very good predictive power to the theistic view because it provides a rational basis for responsible and creative human activity, whereas atheists, if they are coherent with their position, have no basis at all for moral behavior. Although they can sometimes be more honest than believers, they will be honest in spite of the fact that they are atheists or agnostics; when believers are dishonest, they are so in spite of the fact that they are believers.

We can also underscore that atheism and materialism usually have a promissory character that does not fit well with the rigor characteristic of empirical science and could eventually provoke the collapse of scientific progress. Indeed, when ideological factors are introduced in science, some provisional results might be considered as definitive and bring research to a halt. Let us consider, for example, the explanations for evolutionary theory. Some supporters of neo-Darwinism strongly maintain that natural selection provides a complete explanation of evolution; since the necessary evidence is lacking, they are probably motivated by the desire to show that evolution is already basically explained. Their attitude unconsciously prevents investigation in promising fields such as self-organization, which can elucidate the constructive results of evolution. A materialistic or atheistic position can easily provoke this kind of difficulty for the progress of science. Insofar as materialists search for evidence to support their position in the results and promises of science, they tend to attribute to scientific discoveries more importance than they really have.

A different kind of prediction is related to the existence of teleology and a divine plan. Many difficulties that arise in this area stem from the assumption that a divine plan should manifest itself in the form of regularities. More specifically, the contingency of the evolutionary process that leads to the human being is sometimes considered a counterexample that is inconsistent with the existence of a divine plan. Apparently, we cannot say that human beings occupy a special place in God's plan if the origin of man is marked by accident and chance. Nevertheless, the contingency involved in evolution should not be used as evidence contrary to the existence of a divine plan. Ernan McMullin has posed the problem this way:

> Does the contingency of the evolutionary account of origins, particularly of human origins, make it more difficult to see the universe as the work of a Creator? Does it, effectively, rule out purpose at the cosmic level and leave us in a world from which religious meaning has departed?[30]

McMullin notes that we tend to think about teleology, plan, and purpose by using notions related to temporality. But he argues that:

> if one maintains the age-old doctrine of God's eternality, the contingency of the evolutionary process leading to the appearance of *Homo*

---

30. Ernan McMullin, "Evolutionary Contingency and Cosmic Purpose," in *Finding God in All Things,* ed. Michael J. Himes and Stephen J. Pope (New York: Herder, 1996), p. 140.

sapiens makes no difference to the Christian belief in a special destiny for humankind.[31]

McMullin rightly remarks that the existence of a divine plan does not imply that natural events should develop in a perfectly linear and regular way:

A Creator who brings everything to be in a single action from which the entirety of temporal process issues, does not rely on the regularity of process to know the future condition of the creature or to attain ends. God's knowledge of how a situation will develop at a later time is not discursive; God does not infer from a prior knowledge of how situations of the sort ordinarily develop. It makes no difference, therefore, whether the appearance of *Homo sapiens* is the inevitable result of a steady process of complexification stretching over billions of years, or whether on the contrary it comes about through a series of coincidences that would have made it entirely unpredictable from the (causal) human standpoint.[32]

In fact, the existence of emerging levels of organization that are unpredictable from a human point of view appears to be the consequence of highly sophisticated processes that lead to the most sophisticated of all organizations, the human being. The overall process, including the contingent factors involved in it, can be interpreted as the deployment of a divine plan; otherwise, the result of the entire process, the existence of natural beings who at the same time transcend the natural level because they are rational, would be a complete enigma.

The existence of disorder and evil is the most serious objection against the theistic view. Indeed, it seems that the existence of an omnipotent God who governs the world should entail a perfection in his works that should not leave room for natural disorder. Thus, a central prediction of theism would be false. The classical answer to this well-known objection lies in remembering that disorder and evil can be included within God's plan if preventing their existence would entail greater evils or prevent the existence of higher goods. The present scientific worldview adds an important argument. Indeed, if the natural world is the result of evolution, then the existence of disorder and physical evil in nature seems unavoidable except by a continuous miracle. In addition, evolution seems reasonable if God wants to produce the world by using and respecting natural causes.

2.3 ACCURACY

In empirical science, accuracy is a qualification of explanations and predictions. Here we can interpret it as the faithfulness with which our interpretations represent the real facts.

Regarding the scientific worldview, I have already argued that my proposal corresponds quite well to the accepted facts. Further tests of its accuracy

---

31. Ibid., p. 157.

32. Ibid., pp. 156–157.

can be obtained by examining the different features of this worldview. A similar argument holds for scientific realism. I have also examined the facts that constitute new scientific evidence in favor of teleology.

If we consider the theistic perspective, I would say that it respects the real complexity of the world and does not interfere with natural explanations but provides them with their adequate radical foundation. On the other hand, as already noted, naturalism basically leaves everything unexplained and tends to overvalue those scientific explanations that appear to provide fuel for its arguments. I would recall in this context Karl Popper's remark that "positivists, in their anxiety to annihilate metaphysics, annihilate natural science along with it"; indeed, naturalism and materialism, to present themselves as a consequence of scientific progress, as usually happens, must rely on a distorted image of empirical science.

Sometimes pantheism is presented as the position most coherent with scientific progress. Indeed, it can be argued that the only serious alternative to theism is pantheism, because atheism and naturalism imply, in some degree, a renunciation of the exercise of reason, which is contrary to the scientific spirit. Nevertheless, pantheist views, even if endowed with religious and moral appeal, are incoherent and contradictory, because they identify the universe or its parts with divine features.

Faithfulness in building the scientific worldview, and in interpreting the aims and value of empirical science, should lead to mutual respect and help between the scientific outlook and philosophical and theological perspectives. Pope John Paul II described the fruits of a dialogue between science and theology, in his 1988 message to the Rev. George V. Coyne:

> Can science also benefit this interchange? It would seem that it should. For science develops best when its concepts and conclusions are integrated into the broader human culture and its concerns for ultimate meaning and value. Scientists cannot, therefore, hold themselves entirely aloof from the sorts of issues dealt with by philosophers and theologians. By devoting to these issues something of the energy and care they give to their research in science, they can help others realize more fully the human potentialities of their discoveries. They can also come to appreciate for themselves that these discoveries cannot be a genuine substitute for knowledge of the truly ultimate. Science can purify religion from error and superstition; religion can purify science from idolatry and false absolutes. Each can draw the other into a wider world, a world in which both can flourish. . . . Only a dynamic relationship between theology and science can reveal those limits which support the integrity of either discipline, so that theology does not profess a pseudo-science and science does not become an unconscious theology.[33]

33. John Paul II, "Message to the Rev. George V. Coyne, June 1, 1988," in *Physics, Philosophy, and Theology: A Common Quest for Understanding,* ed. Robert J. Russell, William R. Stoeger, and George V. Coyne (Vatican City State: Vatican Observatory, 1988), pp. M 13, M 14.

Accuracy in representing the world and the scientific knowledge of it should lead us to recognize that, when we pose questions that refer to meaning, empirical science alone cannot provide a reliable guide; it needs a metaphysical complement, which, to be really complete, should include the religious dimension. In a speech addressed to Nobel Prize winners, John Paul II expressed this as follows:

> Science alone is incapable of giving a complete answer to the issue of the basic significance of human life and activity. Their significance is revealed when reason, going beyond the physical datum, uses metaphysical methods to attain to the contemplation of the "final causes" and there discovers the supreme explanations that can throw light on human events and give them meaning. . . . The search for final significance is complex by nature and exposed to the danger of error, and man would often remain groping in the dark if he were not aided by the light of faith. The Christian revelation has made an inestimable contribution to the awareness that modern man has been able to attain of his own dignity and his own rights.[34]

2.4. VARIETY OF INDEPENDENT PROOFS

One of the most remarkable features of the current scientific worldview is that is integrates in a unitary representation a multiplicity of phenomena belonging to different natural levels. The classical worldview was mainly based on the success of classical Newtonian physics. The processual worldview centered around evolution. The present worldview includes the valid features of the preceding ones and adds further elements that connect the microphysical, macrophysical, and living components of nature. In consequence, philosophical and theological reflections based on this worldview refer to a great variety of independent scientific achievements that have at last been combined in a unitary picture.

More specifically, the existence of teleology is supported by a great variety of phenomena that belong to quite different fields. I argue that the world is full of teleological dimensions, not only in the case of the living beings, but also on the physicochemical level. The mechanistic worldview seemed to exclude teleology from the physical world, and the evolutionary worldview seemed to exclude it also from the biological level. The present worldview clearly shows directionality on all levels, so that teleological concepts, sometimes under the name of teleonomy, have become respectable again.

The singularity of the human being, a natural being who transcends the natural level, is coherent with a great variety of data provided by analysis of the scientific enterprise. Epistemology centered itself around the logic of science in the first half of the twentieth century; then, historical and sociological perspectives became predominant. Data emerging from these three per-

---

34. John Paul II, Speech to a Group of Twelve Nobel Prize Winners, December 22, 1980 (Vatican), *Insegnamenti di Giovanni Paolo II*, III, 2 (1980), pp. 1782–1783.

spectives coincide now in highlighting the role that creativity and interpretation play in the development of science.

Finally, the theological interpretations of divine action that have been suggested are coherent with scientific data stemming from a variety of sources, such as deterministic chaos, evolutionary theory, and natural dynamism. Actually, because my argument refers to the general presuppositions of science and to the feedback of scientific progress on them, it covers the entire spectrum of the scientific enterprise, and that is why I have developed it considering a great diversity of scientific data.

2.5. MUTUAL SUPPORT

My philosophical and theological suggestions can be integrated in a chain of mutual support with other generally accepted views: mainly with those of science, because they have been developed in a way consistent not only with the present scientific worldview, but also with the central core of most religious views and with basic human aspirations. Here we could find a common ground acceptable to most religious people and that could foster religious views.

In empirical science, mutual support is an intrascientific criterion; when we judge the acceptability of a physical theory, we examine its coherence with other physical theories and, eventually, with theories belonging to other related disciplines. In my case, mutual support refers to a wider coherence among different perspectives. We are dealing here with an interdisciplinary approach, and we should require that the different components be coherent and complementary.

The components of this interdisciplinary approach are empirical science, epistemology, metaphysics, ethics, and theology. Science prevails in the case of the worldview, epistemology in the case of scientific realism, metaphysics in the case of human singularity, ethics in the case of scientific values, and theology in the case of divine action. Nevertheless, science is present in all cases, because the entire argument is built on science. Epistemology is always present, because in every step an evaluation of the methods and results of science must be used. A certain dose of metaphysics is necessary to build the worldview and to argue about divine action. Therefore, the five approaches are closely related. I think it useful to comment on some particular aspects of those relations.

One of them refers to the origin of modern empirical science. If we admit the historical influence of Christianity, we can easily understand the existence of the necessary ontological, epistemological, and ethical presuppositions that provided the soil in which the new science developed. Otherwise, we would be facing a real mystery, because we would have to admit the existence of an abrupt origin to this extremely difficult enterprise. The positivist cliché that presents empirical science developing in opposition to metaphysics and religion should be replaced by a more realistic picture in which science, metaphysics, ethics, and religion have mutually interacted over a long period of time, until the excesses of positivism and idealism in the nineteenth century provoked their complete separation.

The general presuppositions of the scientific enterprise can be considered as a multiple hinge linking the different perspectives. In fact, my entire argument has been developed considering the feedback of scientific progress on these presuppositions. If we forget or deny the existence of these presuppositions, we may come to consider empirical science in a purely pragmatic way, merely as a tool useful to provide the basis for technology.

The "mutual support view" supposes the existence of perspectives that are different but complementary. It stresses cooperativity. Other views tend to artificially turn differences into opposition and conflict.

III. FURTHER PERSPECTIVES

In this last section I shall examine some issues that are closely related to my argument and could serve as subjects for further research. In some way they are the conclusions of my argument that deserve a more detailed study.

1. GOD'S INVOLVEMENT WITH CREATION

The current worldview is highly consistent with the emphasis on God's respect toward creation. Divine action should not be conceived as opposed to natural agency; rather, it makes possible the very existence of created causes and fosters their own agency. Thus, we are led to underscore God's involvement with creation.

As already noted, Joseph Zycinski strongly stresses divine immanence in creation. He realizes that asserting God's immanence in nature is anything but new, but, at the same time, he writes:

> The gap between scientific and religious vision of the world is to a great extent the result of the fact that in classically understood natural theology the thesis of God's immanence in nature did not obtain sufficient attention.[35]

It is not necessary to analyze in detail the historical issue.[36] I shall concentrate on some of Zycinski's suggestions about God's involvement in nature as contained in a 1996 lecture.[37] Zycinski presents them as purely philo-

---

35. Zycinski, *Three Cultures: Science, the Humanities and Religious Values,* cit., p. 60.

36. Zycinski provides some hints on the historical reasons for neglecting in practice the doctrine of divine immanence that obviously was always accepted at the doctrinal level. See Ibid., p. 82.

37. Joseph M. Zycinski, "The Laws of Nature and the Immanence of God in the Evolving Universe," Templeton closing lecture of the 6th ESSSAT Congress, Cracow, 26-30 March, 1996, in *The Interplay Between Scientific and Theological Worldviews,* ed. Niels H. Gregersen, Ulf Görman, and Christoph Wassermann, part I (Geneva: Labor et Fides, 1999), pp. 3–19.

sophical suggestions that do not intend to cover supernatural mysteries of faith, and he explains his goals as follows:

> In this paper, after assessing critically certain new models of God's interaction with nature on microcosmic level, I will try to defend the thesis that God's immanence in nature is expressed by cosmic order and evolutionary novelty. Among many physical forms of manifestations of the divine immanence we have to notice in particular: 1. the very existence of the laws of nature in a world which would exist as a lawless disorder; 2. the emergence of new attributes that constituted the domain of pure possibilites in the earlier stages of the cosmic evolution.[38]

Zycinski tells us that, among other attributes, God is "the ground of cosmic order." He refers to two interpretations of the laws of nature: the "regularity theory" defended by the empiricist tradition, which sees in the laws of nature nothing but observed regularities, and the "necessitarian theory" defended by some neo-Platonists, who argue that the laws of nature presuppose the existence of hidden necessary links or purely possible regularities that constitute the order of nature, even if in a specific situation no empirical procedures reveal physical instantiations of these links. He adds that many scientists today pose metascientific questions such as the following: Why are there laws of physics at all? Why is this particular set of physical laws instantiated in nature?

Among the scientists who pose such questions, even some agnostics refer to "the neo-Platonic cosmic Logos," conceived as a principle of cosmic order immanent in the laws of nature. Zycinski refers to Newton who, on the basis of his mathematical account, called into question the adequacy of empirical data provided by John Flamsteed. This procedure, Zycinski tells us,

> merely expressed the basic conviction that scientific research aims not at a simple description of the observed facts but at the discovery of hidden stable relations that are instantiated in physical processes.[39]

Zycinski suggests a new emphasis on looking for God's immanence, on the one hand, in the constant regularities submitted to the universal laws of nature, and on the other hand, in those natural laws that were uninstantiated in earlier cosmic epochs:

> The uninstantiated laws of nature revealed their actual existence in the process of cosmic evolution when more complex structures emerged. . . . The immanence of God in (uninstantiated) natural laws constitutes the ultimate ground for cosmic rationality because these laws determine the realms of the possible cosmic evolution. Heinz Pagels' analogy with the genetic code seems appropriate here to ex-

38. Ibid., p. 5.
39. Ibid., p. 12.

plain the role of God who influences the process of cosmic evolution.[40]

The modal actualism developed by Alvin Plantinga and Robert Stalnaker, which is close to the position developed in the fifteenth century by Nicholas of Cusa, are presented by Zycinski as especially adequate explanations of the results of contemporary science. God is the immanent as well as the transcendent Creator in whom are unfolded all possibilities before their instantiation in the actual visible world, so that:

> the process of cosmic changes discloses the presence of immanent God who unfolds the possible in making them the actual. God, understood by Cusanus as *posse ipsum*, constitutes the ultimate rationality of the cosmic evolution and makes the cosmic order rational not only on the level of observed regularities but also on the level of unactualized possibilities of the physical growth. God's role cannot be reduced to the role of an additional factor filling up the newly discovered gaps in our knowledge because he himself overcomes the basic distinctions between the possible and the actual. On the one hand, by determining the domain of the possible he constitutes the final ground of cosmic rationality and defines its laws of physico-biological evolution. This form of immanence in nature can be described in universal categories. On the other hand, his creative presence can be discovered in particular processes, in which there are actualized events that originally belonged to the domain of pure possibilities. These two forms of God's immanence in cosmic order, the order understood statically as well as dynamically, represent two basic forms of God's interaction with nature. Laws of nature and evolutionary novelties can be regarded as their counterparts described in modern science.[41]

The divine grounding of nature is most coherent with the present worldview, centered around the deployment of natural dynamism, which produces new kinds of dynamism and patterns that arrive at the level of organization that makes possible the appearance of rational human beings. Patterning is a central feature of our world. If we admit that properly speaking, no pure passive matter exists and that the organization of our world is the result of a huge process of self-organization, we should conclude that from the very beginning there have existed the potentialities whose actualization would produce successive levels of complex organization that lead up to the human being. John M. Templeton and Robert L. Herrmann underscore that, following this road, we are led beyond the realm of science:

> What is the meaning of a universe in which the primeval assembly of fundamental particles eventually manifests the potential for organiza-

40. Ibid., p. 14.
41. Ibid., p. 15.

tion into complex forms that are conscious and self-conscious, and that thereby transcend that matter from which they were derived? Science thus paradoxically seems to lead us, in our search for intelligibility and meaning, beyond the realm of science.[42]

This suggests that we should think of a God who is not a mere architect working to order a preexisting material from outside. Divine action is conceived as the cause of the very nature of the material components of our world, including their interaction, patterning, and successive steps of self-organization. We are encouraged to think of a God who is not only, as Templeton and Herrmann put it, a machine-tender or caretaker, but:

> an immanent Creator, whose involvement with his vast creation every moment ensures its very existence as well as its order. The extent of the Creator's power and the sense of his presence at every level of the created order is awesome. And by this order he brings coherence and rationality to make intelligible what would otherwise be baffling. It is as though the scientific history of our world was like a great musical masterpiece composed for our ears. Indeed, Arthur R. Peacocke makes just such an analogy.[43]

This insight leads us to the idea of purpose, which plays a central role as a bridge that joins science to metaphysics and religion.

2. God's Purposeful Action

The very same reflection on the current scientific worldview that suggests we should admit God as the creator who is always acting from within in his creatures, providing them with their being, potentialities, and effectiveness, clearly suggests that the created world corresponds to God's purposive action. Acceptance of divine purpose makes it possible to understand how necessity, chance, and purpose can be combined to bring about our world. Indeed, if naturalist explanations were to be considered ultimate, we would be forced to attribute to blind natural forces a subtlety and foresight they cannot possess. Along these lines, Zycinski notes:

> The acceptance of a rational principle of the dynamism of nature makes possible the evasion of many former controversies connected with the dilemma "either necessity or purpose," and enables rational explanations of the ultimate causes of biological evolution.[44]

The current worldview strongly underscores the interconnectedness of the different parts of the world, not only in the form of extrinsic cooperation,

---

42. John M. Templeton and Robert L. Herrmann, *The God Who Would be Known: Revelations of the Divine in Contemporary Science* (San Francisco: Harper & Row, 1989), p. 38.

43. Ibid., p. 126.

44. Zycinski, *Three Cultures: Science, the Humanities and Religious Values,* cit., p. 44.

but also in the much more subtle form of intrinsic relations necessary to produce the results we know. Templeton and Herrmann put it this way:

> Science has gradually made it more clear that all entities are continuously and intrinsically interconnected, so that we can now see the world as a mighty organic whole in which every single thing is related to everything else. The world in which we live presents itself to us not as a machine, artificially contrived, but as an organism building itself up from within; an organism in which all entities have appeared through a stage-by-stage process of growth.[45]

According to the theological counterpart of this cosmological view, divine plan does not exclude created agency but rather includes it as a necessary ingredient: God's commitment to his creation implies that, even though God's power is not limited by the natural behavior of created causes, God himself provides the created causes with their specific potentialities and makes possible their actualization, so that it is God who freely has chosen to follow, as the general rule, the order that He himself has created. This theological view is most coherent with the existence of natural tendencies and cooperativeness in the world as it is represented in the present worldview. In this line, Templeton and Herrmann refer to the work of Manfred Eigen and coworkers on the problem of the origin of living systems:

> The key to the success of the process is in the balance of deterministic and random events, the former ensuring that useful macromolecular species will survive, the latter providing the capacity for creative experimentation within existing structures. Here again the random component appears to be anything but blind. Instead it appears peculiarly well situated to achieve a very purposeful end.[46]

Indeed, the combination of lawfulness and chance seems most fitting for the development of a historical course that follows the laws of nature and is also directed by God's design.

One of the most relevant innovations in the current scientific worldview is that nature is seen as the source and result of a huge process of self-organization with a historical character. I have already referred to natural dynamism as requiring a divine foundation that accounts both for the existence of that dynamism and for its directionality. John Haught suggests that the picture of the cosmos as an unfolding story can be assimilated to a narrative pattern, which can be meaningfully contextualized by the religious historical tradition:

> Science up until recently has been very abstract and law-oriented. It has not taken into account the *story* underlying the laws. And as long as the universe was seen as essentially storyless—as unoriginated,

---

45. Templeton and Herrmann, *The God Who Would be Known*, cit., p. 55.

46. Ibid., p. 60.

eternal, and necessary—it was difficult for science to think of it as having any possible point to it. Today, however, the universe has taken on a discernibly narrative mien. The laws of nature are themselves not the offspring of an underlying eternal necessity but the contingent outcome of a definite story with a definite past . . . science has recently brought to our attention some surprising ways in which the cosmic story corresponds with the basic religious sense of reality as rooted in a promise that invites from us the response of hope. It is now possible to connect this hope to the cosmic story.[47]

Haught carefully notes that this proposal should be interpreted neither as a new conflation of cosmology and religion, or as a desire to force the data of science into a preexisting theological scheme. Empirical science is no longer limited to timeless explanations whose temporal direction would be completely indifferent. On the contrary, contemporary developments focus on the role time plays in science, including the irreversible character of natural processes. The entire process of cosmological and biological evolution appears to be ruled by laws while at the same time, including many accidental coincidences. This combination of lawfulness and chance can be interpreted as the divine way to carry out the divine plan respecting the course of nature. Paradoxically, what we attribute to chance may be a way God chooses to act. As Templeton puts it, after reflecting on the numerous coincidences necessary for the evolutive origin of the physical conditions that make our existence possible:

> One can call such a coincidence only happenstance, but it would seem to be repeated throughout the evolutionary process, and to suggest that something much deeper and more profound is going on. Someone has said that coincidence is God's way of remaining anonymous![48]

3. GOD'S TRANSCENDENCE

To say that God is transcendent has two related but different meanings. On the one hand, it means that God is different from the created world. On the other, it means that we cannot completely conceptualize God.

The first meaning underscores the difference between God the creator and created beings. I have suggested that a theological interpretation of the present scientific worldview should stress God's immanence in the created world, but this view has to be completed by considering God's transcendence. Indeed, the Creator cannot be identified with His creatures, so that, when we assert that God is present in the creatures in a most intimate way, we presuppose the distinction between them. Otherwise, it would be meaningless to

---

47. John F. Haught, *Science & Religion: From Conflict to Conversation* (New York and Mahwah, N.J.: Paulist Press, 1995), pp. 175–176.

48. John M. Templeton, "Introduction," in *Evidence of Purpose: Scientists Discover the Creator,* ed. John Marks Templeton (New York: Continuum, 1994), p. 16.

stress God's presence. This presence should be interpreted as the presence of the radical cause of all being and becoming. As the source from which all being springs, God is more intimate to the creatures than they are to themselves. But the creatures cannot be a part of God. The creatures can be seen as a manifestation of God, who is their First Cause in every moment, not because they are in any way a part of God, but because they manifest in the most varied ways the power, wisdom, and goodness of God.

The second meaning underscores the infinite perfection of God. A consequence of God's transcendence is that, even though we can know the existence and the attributes of God, and the place we occupy in his plans, this knowledge is always limited. We cannot exhaust God's perfection. God transcends any model or representation. Our world does not exhaust God's creativity and perfection. As in philosophy of science we speak of the empirical underdetermination of our theories, so here we face God's transcendence as indicating that God is above any particular data or representation. Any representation of God will always be partial and imperfect.

Scientific progress shows the immensity of the universe and discloses an enormous variety of subtle mechanisms underlying the working of nature. We can discover God's power and wisdom behind the increasingly marvelous discoveries of science. This points toward a God who completely transcends our capacity of imagination. Actually, as the source of all being, God's being must be completely self-sufficient and not dependent on any particular circumstance. This is why it is nonsense to ask: who created God?

God can be discovered through the works of nature, but we should not represent God as one more cause in the line of natural causes, even if this cause was the first and the strongest. When theologians speak of God as the First Cause, this should not be interpreted in this way. God's causality is unique and completely different from the causality of created causes.

I have quoted Templeton and Herrmann reminding us that "coincidence is God's way of remaining anonymous." This is coherent with God's respect for our freedom. If our entire life is dependent on God, there is only one thing God can expect from us: our gratitude, our love, our joyful cooperation in the divine plan. If our freedom is God's idea, God desires that beings capable of love exist and will always help us while respecting our freedom; otherwise, our loving correspondence to God's love would be impossible. In this line, John Haught underscores God's respect toward the entire creation with these words:

> Remarkable as it may seem, if God is to create a world truly distinct
> from the divine Self, such a world would have to have an *internal*
> "self-coherence" or autonomy. Simply in order to be the "world" and
> not God, the creation has to be different from its Creator. This implies, then, that divine creativity allows the world to be itself.[49]

---

49. Haught, *Science & Religion: From Conflict to Conversation*, cit. p. 160.

In practice, this means that an important part of the role we play in God's plan is to become personally involved in it using our personal responsibility. As intelligent and responsible creatures, we should employ our capacities to figure out what we should do. It is left to our free responsibility to recognize our role in God's plan and to venture toward its implementation with a sense of ethical responsibility. Nobody can replace us. There is an essential openness in nature, in human affairs, and in the construction of our future.

Obviously, we should always be ready to realize that God's plans perhaps do not coincide with our standards. Nevertheless, we should also expect that, if we really desire to collaborate with God's plans, God will let us know them. Even though our knowledge of God and of God's plans is incomplete, it can provide the necessary basis for our responsible decisions in such a way that we may discover the meaning of our lives and may understand in every particular case what should we do.

4. The Divine Pathways on Earth

Haught suggests that progress in the sciences of chaos and complexity can be considered theologically significant:

> the sciences of chaos and complexity are theologically (and we might add, ecologically) significant because of their emphasis on "sensitivity to initial conditions." This fact brings out the significance or value of everything in the world, no matter how incidental it may seem to be. . . . This fact should have implications for interpreting the unique and special character of every existing thing, including ourselves and our lives and actions. It is not just abstract universal laws that possess significance, for every concrete thing and every person makes a difference in shaping the whole character of the universe. Ours would not be the same world if even the tiniest part of it did not exist.[50]

This consideration is reinforced and acquires a much deeper meaning when we take into account God's immanence in nature and the existence of a divine purpose in which human beings occupy a special place. In this framework, human life acquires a new religious meaning. A religious attitude basically implies openness toward God and a new outlook that stems from the contemplation of the divine dimension of the world and every one of its parts, especially other human beings. Insofar as scientific progress favors this outlook, it can be considered a source of religious inspiration.

In the light of scientific progress, nature can be seen as a multiform manifestation of the power and wisdom of God. All human beings, also considered in their natural dimensions, represent a most sophisticated kind of natural organization that can easily become a pointer toward the divine. Any kind of event can be considered an opportunity to find a divine meaning in

---

50. Ibid., p. 156.

our lives; we should not identify the divine with extraordinary circumstances. God's involvement with creation is so deep that He can be found in the most ordinary circumstances of any human life.

This perspective, which can be reached on grounds common to different religions, acquires a special relevance in Christianity. Since its very beginnings, Christianity strongly emphasized this perspective, and it became the usual pattern of Christian life during the first centuries. In the contemporary scene, Vatican Council II has solemnly proclaimed the sanctifying value of ordinary life, a message that has reached a multitude of persons from 1928 onward through the life and preaching of Blessed Josemaría Escrivá, founder of Opus Dei. In an interview with Tad Szulc for *The New York Times*, on October 7, 1966, he said:

> The spirit of Opus Dei reflects the marvelous reality (forgotten for centuries by many Christians) that any honest and worthwhile work can be converted into a divine occupation. In God's service there are no second-class jobs; all of them are important. To love and to serve God, there is no need to do anything strange or extraordinary. Christ bids all men without exception to be perfect as his heavenly Father is perfect. Sanctity, for the vast majority of men, implies sanctifying their work, sanctifying themselves in it, and sanctifying others through it. Thus they can encounter God in the course of their daily lives.[51]

He used to say, speaking of Opus Dei as a way of sanctification in daily life and in the fulfillment of ordinary duties, that "the divine paths of the world have been opened up."[52] On October 8, 1967, he addressed the following words to some 20,000 people:

> God is calling you to serve him *in and from* the ordinary, material and secular activities of human life. He waits for us everyday, in the laboratory, in the operating theatre, in the army barracks, in the university chair, in the factory, in the workshop, in the fields, in the home and in all the immense panorama of work. Understand this well: there is something holy, something divine hidden in the most ordinary situations, and it is up to each of you to discover it. . . . We discover the invisible God in the most visible and material things . . . the christian vocation consists in making heroic verse out of the prose of each day. Heaven and earth seem to merge, my sons, on the horizon. But where they really meet is in your hearts, when you sanctify your everyday lives.[53]

I dare say that the current scientific worldview strongly underscores the relevance of ordinary, small, usual things. Roughly speaking, our world is ba-

---

51. Josemaría Escrivá de Balaguer, *Conversations with Monsignor Escrivá de Balaguer* (Shannon: Ecclesia Press, 1972), p. 65 (n. 55).

52. Josemaría Escrivá de Balaguer, *Christ is Passing By* (New York: Scepter, 1985), p. 40 (n. 21).

53. Josemaría Escrivá de Balaguer, *Conversations with Monsignor Escrivá de Balaguer*, cit. pp. 137–139 (nn. 114, 116).

sically composed of three subatomic particles (protons, neutrons, and electrons) that form 92 types of atoms. Combinations of this small list of components produce an extraordinary variety of beings and processes that constitute a permanent source of awe.

In ordinary life, nature exhibits power, beauty, simplicity, and efficiency. Scientific progress enlarges our knowledge of nature in such a way that these characteristics do not vanish; rather, we can illustrate their existence in much more detail. Therefore, science can be considered as transcending itself. Indeed, even though it does not explicitly include metaphysical or religious components, it provides us with a deeper knowledge that can foster metaphysical thinking and religious experience.

Nature can be seen as containing messages that can be deciphered only by using the appropriate code. As Wolfgang Smith has put it,

> We should remember that the Book of Nature can be read in various ways and on different levels, and that no one knows it all.[54]

Scientific progress is possible because we have created codes that can be used to obtain scientific knowledge about spatiotemporal patterns. The more the sciences progress, the more we know how the cosmic codes work, and the more we can become impressed by the dazzling, striking, and majestic features of the natural world. In this way, contemplation of the natural world through the results of scientific progress can provide a pointer to the deepest meaning of nature, leading us to recognize nature as the handiwork of a transcendent God who, as the cause of all being, is also immanent to his creatures and is the source of meaning in human life.

John Puddefoot has stressed that, to recognize the hand of God in nature, we need to be in tune with God's way of manifesting himself through his work:

> The plasticity of creation ensures that no scientist, however well-placed, would be able unequivocally to detect the agency of God . . . *no system of observations is ever sufficient to determine its own interpretation.* This is another aspect of the fact that we cannot state in language how language relates to reality.[55]

Puddefoot represents our deciphering the messages encoded in nature as a *recreation* of the patterns originated by God's *creation,* so that our recreation is possible if we are tuned at the right frequency to the Creator. He stresses that we are free and can fail:

> Seen from outside brains follow biological laws; seen from inside minds are free. And we do exercise that freedom by refusing daily to

---

54. Wolfgang Smith, *Cosmos and Transcendence* (Peru, Ill.: Sherwood Sugden, 1990), pp. 140–141.

55. John C. Puddefoot, "Information and Creation," in *The Science and Theology of Information,* ed. Christoph Wassermann, Richard Kirby, and Bernard Rordorf (Geneva: Labor et Fides, 1992), p. 16.

participate in the only living harmony, the only living interpretative and recreative framework that can make sense of the universe and our places in it.[56]

5. HUMAN INSIGNIFICANCE AND GRANDEUR

When seen in the light of scientific progress, human beings appear as a most fragile kind of natural being who, at the same time, represent the highest peak of a marvelous process of self-organization. There is much that could be said about this from the biological point of view, which provides the basis for the specifically human dimensions that make possible the very existence of empirical science. Also, from the ethical point of view, the scientific enterprise plays a most important role in human life.

When considered as a search for truth, empirical science acquires a deep ethical meaning and can be considered in itself, independent of the usefulness of its results, as one of the most admirable achievements of humankind. This ethical meaning of science can be easily connected with religion. Zycinski expresses the Christian perspective on science thus:

> The Christian attitude towards human intellectual efforts necessarily implies recognition of the objective value of the natural sciences. Regardless of its possible practical functions, the so-called scientific truth possesses an objective value because of the very nature of truth. . . .
> In the Christian hierarchy of values, any efforts to discover objective truth appear as being related to Christ, Who named himself the Way, the Truth, and the Life. Scientific research, based on objective principles of scholarly investigations, is therefore objectively related to the truth which, according to Christ himself, is to liberate mankind (John 8:32). . . . Both the spiritual heritage of contemplative tradition and the scientific reflection aimed at the truth represent objective values that are essential for richness of human culture.[57]

The rigor characteristic of the scientific approach favors an interdisciplinary cooperation that recognizes the value of the different scientific disciplines and of the philosophical and theological perspectives as well. Addressing a group of Nobel Prize winners, Pope John Paul II underscored this point and added that a complete perspective on the human being should contemplate humans as deserving unconditional respect. Thus, the theoretical and the pragmatical dimensions of empirical science are united in promoting the service of mankind:

> The efforts you will devote to this inter-disciplinary exchange, together with the corresponding efforts of the experts in 'the science of God,' will encourage significant progress in the comprehension of

56. Ibid., p. 21.

57. Zycinski, *Three Cultures: Science, the Humanities and Religious Values*, cit., pp. 80–81.

truth, which is a complex unity that can be grasped only if viewed from many sides, only if it is the meeting point of different forms of openended and complementary knowledge. In particular, it will encourage more complete knowledge of man, of the components of his being, and of the historical and yet transcendental dimensions of his existence. Man will then be seen ever more clearly for what he is: an end, never a means; a subject, never an object; a goal, never merely a stage on the way to a goal. In a word, man will be seen as a person, the only legitimate attitude to whom is that of unconditional respect. Respect for man will therefore become the supreme test for judging every employment of science.[58]

The coexistence of insignificance and grandeur in the human being was forcefully underscored by the Pope in a speech to a Symposium on the Frontiers of Cosmology, in which he described the role of scientific progress in helping us to know our limits and our unique place in a world that in so many ways cooperates with our existence and with the development of our potentialities:

Through the natural sciences, and cosmology in particular, we have become much more aware of *our true physical position within the universe,* within physical reality—in space and in time. We are struck very forcibly by our smallness and apparent insignificance, and even more by our vulnerability in such a vast and seemingly hostile environment. Yet this universe of ours, this galaxy in which our sun is situated and this planet on which we live, is our home. And all of it in some way or other serves to support us, nourish us, fascinate us, inspire us, taking us out of ourselves and forcing us to look far beyond the limits of our unaided vision. What we discover through our study of nature and of the universe in all its immensity and rich variety serves on the one hand to emphasize our fragile condition and our littleness, and on the other hand to manifest clearly our greatness and superiority in the midst of all creation—the profoundly exalted position we enjoy in being able to search, to imagine and to discover so much.[59]

Finally, addressing a meeting organized by the International Center for Relativistic Astrophysics, John Paul II referred to the relationship that connects the search for truth, appreciation for the Creator's wisdom, and respect for the dignity of every person. He referred to the benefits derived from the collaboration between science and religion, expressing:

the Church's deep conviction that *scientific research,* undertaken in a spirit of humility and reverence for the truth, *leads to a deeper apprecia-*

58. John Paul II, Speech to a Group of Twelve Nobel Prize Winners, December 22, 1980, cit., pp. 1784–1785.

59. John Paul II, Speech to the Participants in a Symposium on the Frontiers of Cosmology, July 6, 1985 (Vatican), *Insegnamenti di Giovanni Paolo II,* VIII, 2 (1985), p. 90.

tion of the Creator's wisdom and, consequently, to a greater respect for the inalienable dignity and freedom of every person. Religion and science ought to collaborate closely in promoting the fundamental human values of peace, mutual understanding and effective solidarity among all peoples.[60]

6. Integral Naturalism

Naturalism usually argues that we should limit our explanations to what can be examined using the rigorous methods of the natural sciences. Nowadays, supporters of naturalism try to avoid a reductionist language, because the prestige of reductionism has been undermined by its repeated failures. However, they continue to claim that only naturalistic explanations are valid; they claim that there exists *nothing but* what can be studied by means of empirical science or can be related to physical or material dimensions.

Aquinas used the very same expression *nothing but* to express a completely different view of nature in which metaphysical and theological dimensions played a central role. Aquinas stated that "nature is *nothing but* the plan of some art, namely a divine one, put into things themselves, by which those things move towards a concrete end." Aquinas does not deny natural beings their own consistency and dynamism; rather, he speaks of nature as developing following a process of self-organization and stresses that the radical foundation of nature is to be found in the divine.

I would add that the naturalist *nothing but* is closed, excluding all dimensions except the material. In contrast, the metaphysical *nothing but* is open; it is intended to underscore that nature, in the last analysis, must rely on a transcendent basis. The metaphysical and theological perspectives respect the natural level and integrate it within a larger framework. The naturalist framework is closed, self-contained, and univocal, whereas the metaphysical framework is open, integrative, and analogical.

In empirical science we use a kind of methodological agnosticism that brackets those dimensions that cannot be studied through the scientific method. If we desire to represent nature in a complete way, we should include three dimensions: the *physical, ontological,* and *metaphysical*.

I call *physical* dimensions those directly related to spatiotemporal structures, which are the subject of the natural sciences. Spatiotemporal structures, however, do not exist by themselves; they are properties of systems or processes. Thus, if we desire to obtain a more complete picture of the natural world, we must include systems and processes with their properties and tendencies; therefore, we are led to admit ontological dimensions. Concepts such as system, process, property, and tendency refer to *ontological* dimensions; they have

---

60. John Paul II, Speech to the Participants in a Meeting Organized by the International Center for Relativistic Astrophysics, September 14, 1990 (Vatican), *Insegnamenti*, XIII, 2 (1990), p. 613.

a philosophical meaning, because they refer to the modalities of being that exist beyond their particular manifestations.

To exemplify the existence of ontological dimensions in nature, a case in point is that of *tendencies*. If something like natural tendencies exists, it will have observable consequences, although tendencies in themselves are not observable. We must assume their existence on the basis of some observable effects: this is why there is no agreement about this issue. For example, Quentin Gibson has analyzed the explanatory role of statements about tendencies and concludes that they cannot be tested and therefore are useless. He also warns us against the use of such statements, because they could favor metaphysical abuses and anthropomorphic reasoning. Gibson's favorite example is that of states of affairs in which the absence of observable effects is attributed by supporters of the existence of tendencies to the equilibrium between them.[61] Gibson follows the path of Richard Bevan Braithwaite and others who are suspicious of introducing entities and properties that cannot be tested. In contrast, I would say that tendencies are real, as real as the directionality of natural processes, though sometimes it is difficult to build up concepts representing tendencies that can be useful in science.

Supporters of the existence of tendencies argue that natural beings possess properties corresponding to their specific nature and that, therefore, they possess tendencies. They add that difficulties involved in their detection result from tendencies acting in combination; to detect them, we must isolate them in experimental conditions. Authors who assume this usually favour realistic interpretations of science. For example, Rom Harré, arguing for the existence of tendencies, defines them as a kind of power:

> A tendency is a power in abeyance, a power in the course of coming to be exercised, a power about to be exercised or manifested.[62]

Harré has analyzed the concept of power, trying to show that it is not only legitimate, but necessary if science is to make sense at all:

> I propose to show that the concept of "power" can play a central role in a metaphysical theory appropriate to a realist philosophy of science. . . . I shall show in this paper that not only are powers indispensable in the epistemology of science, but are the very heart and key to the best metaphysics for science. In so doing, I shall show that the concept of power is neither magical nor occult but is as empirical a concept as we could well ask for, yet richer in capacity than those concepts it succeeds . . . we must have the concept of power for making sense of science.[63]

---

61. Quentin Gibson, "Tendencies," *Philosophy of Science,* 50 (1983): 296–308.

62. Rom Harré, *The Principles of Scientific Thought* (London: Macmillan, 1970), p. 278.

63. Rom Harré, "Powers," *The British Journal for the Philosophy of Science,* 21 (1970): 81, 83, 85.

Roy Bhaskar has also argued along these lines, presenting his realism as an ontology that is needed to explain the very existence of empirical science:

> every account of science presupposes an ontology . . . it presupposes a schematic answer to the question of what the world must be like for science to be possible.[64]

One may or may not agree with the analysis of these authors. However, I find their argument in favor of a philosophy of nature underlying empirical science, which should be admitted if science is to make any sense, to be very sound. Concepts belonging to philosophy of nature would be typical examples of the *ontological* dimensions of nature.

Philosophy of nature describes and interprets the modalities of being that exist in the natural world and it is, therefore, a kind of ontology. But ontology is not enough. If we pose the problem of being itself, namely the problem of the radical foundation of nature, we are led to the realm of properly *metaphysical* dimensions. Insofar as the natural world is not self-contained, it requires a metaphysical foundation. Moreover, if we admit God's immanence in nature, we should admit that natural entities, properties, and processes include a kind of "metaphysical coefficient" that corresponds to the founding divine action. This opens new vistas for an interpretation that would include the physical, ontological, and metaphysical dimensions of nature in a unitary account, and should be considered as a full or integral kind of naturalism.

A fully developed naturalism should include all the dimensions of the natural world; therefore, it would include the ontological dimensions that reflect the modalities of being and the metaphysical dimensions that refer to the founding divine action, whose causality is different from natural causation but has concrete natural effects. This perspective could be used to illuminate the spiritual character of the human being, another kind of metaphysical dimension. Actually, human spirituality can be regarded as the effect of a specific divine action that produces a unique participation in God's nature. Then, we could combine God's universal action on all created beings with the unique effect God's action produces in the case of the human being.

In accord with his view of science as a value-free enterprise, Max Weber pointed out that scientific views should not become contaminated with subjective judgments:

> whenever the man of science introduces his personal value judgment, a full understanding of the facts *ceases.*[65]

This view is widely accepted today. Personal value judgments are taken to include all subjects that cannot be studied by the methods of empirical science, among them religious views, and what I have called ontological and meta-

---

64. Roy Bhaskar, *A Realist Theory of Science* (Leeds: Leeds Books, 1975), pp. 28–29.

65. Max Weber, "Science as a Vocation," cit., p. 306.

physical dimensions. But for my part, I think it necessary to introduce a qualification, lest we become prisoners of a methodological error. We must distinguish two cases that are quite different.

First, when we work in empirical science, we should avoid arguments that cannot be formulated using the intersubjective approach characteristic of empirical science. However, we should remember that we need to reach a consensus on many kinds of stipulation, must rely on our personal capacities of knowledge, and must decide many issues that cannot be settled by logic and experience alone. If we evaluate Weber's ban on personal value judgments by the contemporary standards of philosophy of science, we should introduce important qualifications to it.

I underscore here qualifications of a different kind, those which we must introduce in fields other than empirical science. In such cases we use approaches that eventually may provide access to dimensions other than the purely physical. Of course, we will not reach the kind of reliability found in the empirical sciences, but this does not mean that our knowledge will not be true, or that we cannot reach "a full understanding of the facts." Such full understanding is impossible unless we complement the scientific perspective with philosophical and religious views. We cannot understand science itself unless we adopt a philosophical perspective to evaluate the scientific enterprise, its presuppositions, its methods, and its results.

Weber, and many others after him, seem to think that if you seriously accept the scientific perspective you will find difficulties in combining it with metaphysical and theological views. Some even think that such combination is impossible. But if science is to have any meaning at all, the combination is not only possible, but also necessary. If we take into consideration the present scientific worldview, one may wonder how someone aware of the results of scientific progress can be an atheist or a materialist today.

Because we are natural beings who, at the same time, transcend nature, we need a spiritual reference; otherwise, our life becomes pointless. My proposal intends to bridge the gap between science and spirituality, respecting the specificity of both. Therefore, it is most germane with these highlights of John Templeton's thought:

> True happiness comes from bringing a wonderfully creative idea from the world of spirit into the world of matter or form. The flow between the spiritual and material world needs to be honored if we are to live fully and with purpose."[66]

The flow between the spiritual and material world really exists. When we contemplate the natural world from the point of view of its creation, it appears to be the deployment of a divine plan in which matter is endowed with a natural dynamism whose successive deployments and integrations produce

---

66. John M. Templeton, *Worldwide Laws of Life* (Philadelphia and London: Templeton Foundation Press, 1997), p. 324.

an immense variety of systems and processes that make possible the appearance of the human being. In virtue of our rationality and freedom, we possess a personal character that implies a special participation in the nature of God. We are God's collaborators. God has created a world in becoming, destined to reach more and more evolved goals, and has created human beings as created cocreators who are able to know God's plans and to collaborate with God in a spirit of love and responsibility.

7. Creativity: Natural, Human, and Divine

The new scientific worldview presents a creative universe that has made possible the appearance of creative intelligent beings who are, at the same time, bearers of insignificance and of grandeur. John Paul II writes:

> The scientific disciplines too, as is obvious, are endowing us with an understanding and appreciation of our universe as a whole and of the incredibly rich variety of intricately related processes and structures which constitute its animate and inanimate components. This knowledge has given us a more thorough understanding of ourselves and of our humble yet unique role within creation. Through technology it also has given us the capacity to travel, to communicate, to build, to cure, and to probe in ways which would have been almost unimaginable to our ancestors. Such knowledge and power, as we have discovered, can be used greatly to enhance and improve our lives or they can be exploited to diminish and destroy human life and the environment even on a global scale.[67]

The progress of science and of science-based technology solves problems, but it also creates new ones of a humanistic character. Therefore, this progress is a source of new challenges that must be faced with a sense of ethical responsibility. All this reinforces the idea that man cooperates with God and has an ethical responsibility toward himself and other people.

Only a personal, creator God can provide the radical foundation of being, creativity, and values. Neither nature nor human beings possess the capacity of creating in an absolute sense; nevertheless, they can considered creative in an analogous sense. Indeed, in both cases effects can be produced that are truly new.

On the natural level, natural creativity plays a central role in the current worldview. Self-organization implies creativity. New creative processes may occur through the integration of different kinds of information; technological advances lead to the production of new kinds of beings that previously did not exist, some of which are completely artificial, whereas others possess a modality of being similar in unity and consistency to that of natural beings.

---

67. John Paul II, Message to the Rev. George V. Coyne, cit., p. M 5.

On the human level, creativity plays a central role in the progress of science. Contemporary epistemology points out that creativity is an essential ingredient of the scientific enterprise: we need it every time we formulate a new hypothesis, propose a new experiment, perform an experiment and interpret it, or establish new stipulations. Scientific creativity has to be adapted to the constraints imposed by coherence and experience, but it is indubitably a central feature of science.

Scientific creativity is one of our most astonishing capacities. Empirical science steadily progresses in spite of the fact that, on purely logical grounds, we can never be sure of having obtained true knowledge. We are able to build on foundations that, even though not completely firm, are good enough to hold up impressive skyscrapers. Commenting on Popper's simile that represents empirical science as a building erected on piles driven from above into a swamp, Henry Margenau points out:

> There is one aspect, however, which this account (and Popper's) ignores, an aspect of growing importance in contemporary physics. It is this. We sometimes sink a floating submarine platform down to a certain depth and build up from there. Some of the most spectacular modern theories arise from postulates deep below the surface. The structures built upon them (by rules of logic and mathematics) finally reach the surface at points dotted with known or previously unrecognized objects or peculiarities, hence "explaining" them. To name but one, the mathematical principle of invariance (of nature's laws) is such a submarine platform of extreme, almost miraculous efficacy.[68]

Creativity is a central feature in nature and in human life. It does not always lead to success; novelties in nature, as well as in human life, may fail. Karl Popper represented all living beings as searching for a better world, and used to comment that one of the greatest differences between other living beings and humans is that they die if their innovations fail, whereas humans have learned to build up theories that can be submitted to empirical testing and that eventually can die in our place. Although creativity may lead to blind alleys, it is a most powerful force that plays a central role in human life.

Recognizing the role of creativity may prevent us from becoming prisoners of our own creations. Scientism is self-defeating because it makes us prisoners of one of our most impressive achievements: empirical science. If we always remember that it is *we* who create science, interpret its results, and use them, it will be much easier to behave in a truly human way, according to the ethical principles that should guide our entire creativity. Indeed, ethical behavior is the highest level at which creativity can be displayed in the form of personal responsibility, in the fulfillment of our tasks, and in the service of mankind.

---

68. Henry Margenau, "On Popper's Philosophy of Science," in *The Philosophy of Karl Popper,* ed. Paul A. Schilpp (La Salle, Ill.: Open Court, 1974), p. 756.

Natural and human creativity are rooted, in the final analysis, in the radical foundation provided by God. We can represent our world as an unfinished symphony where we have a role to play. We can even understand that God permits the existence of evil so that we may really play our role with freedom, responsibility, and merit. If we live a divine life, we will live with God forever. But this is another story.

Bibliography

Agazzi, Evandro. "L'objectivité scientifique." In *L'objectivité dans les différentes sciences,* edited by Evandro Agazzi, pp. 13–25. Fribourg: Éditions Universitaires, Fribourg 1988.

———. "Eine Deutung der wissenschaftlichen Objectivität." *Allgemeine Zeitschrift für Philosophie* 3 (1978): 20–47.

———. *Philosophie. Science. Métaphysique.* Fribourg: Éditions Universitaires, 1987.

———. *Temi e problemi di filosofia della fisica.* 2d ed. Roma: Abete, 1974.

Albert, Hans. "Science and the Search for Truth." In *Rationality: The Critical View,* edited by Joseph Agassi and Ian C. Jarvie, pp. 69–82. Dordrecht: Nijhoff, 1987.

Andersson, Gunnar. "Presuppositions, Problems, Progress." In *The Structure and Development of Science,* edited by Gerard Radnitzky and Gunnar Andersson, pp. 3–15. Dordrecht, Boston, and London: Reidel, 1979.

Aquinas, Thomas. *In duodecim libros Metaphysicorum Aristotelis Expositio.* Torino-Roma: Marietti, 1964.

———. *In octo libros Physicorum Aristotelis Expositio.* Torino-Roma: Marietti, 1965.

———. *Summa Theologiae.* Torino-Roma: Marietti, 1952.

Aris, Rutherford; Davis, H. Ted; and Stuewer, Roger H., eds. *Springs of Scientific Creativity: Essays on Founders of Modern Science.* Minneapolis: University of Minnesota Press, 1983.

Artigas, Mariano. "Three Levels of Interaction between Science and Philosophy." In *Intelligibility in Science,* edited by Craig Dilworth, pp. 123–144. Amsterdam and Atlanta, Ga.: Rodopi, 1992.

———. *Filosofía de la ciencia experimental. La objetividad y la verdad en las ciencias.* 2d ed. Pamplona: Eunsa, 1992.

Ayala, Francisco J. "Teleological Explanations in Evolutionary Biology." *Philosophy of Science* 37 (1970): 1–15.

Barbour, Ian G. "Experiencing and Interpreting Nature in Science and Religion." *Zygon* 29 (1994): 457–487.

———. "Ways of Relating Science and Theology." In *Physics, Philosophy, and Theology: A Common Quest for Understanding*, edited by Robert J. Russell, William R. Stoeger, and George V. Coyne, pp. 21–48. Vatican City State: Vatican Observatory, 1988.

———. *Ethics in an Age of Technology*. San Francisco: Harper, 1993.

———. *Religion in an Age of Science*. San Francisco: Harper, 1990.

Barrow, John D., and Tipler, Frank J. *The Anthropic Cosmological Principle*. Oxford: Clarendon Press, 1986.

Bartley, III, William W. *The Retreat to Commitment*. 2d. ed. La Salle, Ill., and London: Open Court, 1984.

Bedau, Mark. "Naturalism and Teleology." In *Naturalism: A Critical Approach*, edited by Steven J. Wagner and Richard Warner, pp. 23–51. Notre Dame, Ind.: University of Notre Dame, 1993.

Berman, Morris. *The Reenchantment of the World*. Ithaca, N.Y.: Cornell University Press, 1981.

Bertolet, Rod. "Presupposition." In *The Cambridge Dictionary of Philosophy*, edited by Robert Audi, general editor, pp. 641–642. Cambridge: Cambridge University Press, 1995.

Bhaskar, Roy. *A Realist Theory of Science*. Leeds: Leeds Books, 1975.

Blackburn, Simon. "Presupposition." In *The Oxford Dictionary of Philosophy*, pp. 300–310. Oxford and New York: Oxford University Press, 1994.

Blanpied, William A., and Weisman-Derner, Wendy. "Value Images of Science and the Values of Science." *Proceedings of the AAAS Interdisciplinary Workshop on the Interrelationships between Science and Technology, and Ethics and Values*, Reston, Virginia, 10–12 April 1975. Washington, D.C.: American Association for the Advancement of Science, 1975.

Borradori, Giovanna. "Nietzche or Aristotle? Alasdair MacIntyre." In *The American Philosopher. Conversations with Quine, Davidson, Putnam, Nozick, Danto, Rorty, Cavall, MacIntyre, and Kuhn*, pp. 137–152. Chicago and London: The University of Chicago Press, 1994.

Boyd, Richard; Gasper, Philip; and Trout, J. D., eds. *The Philosophy of Science*. Cambridge, Mass.: The MIT Press, 1991.

Bresch, Carsten. "What Is Evolution?" In *Evolution and Creation*, edited by Svend Andersen and Arthur Peacocke, pp. 36–57. Aarhus: Aarhus University Press, 1987.

Brooke, John H. "Science and the Fortunes of Natural Theology: Some Historical Perspectives." *Zygon* 24 (1989): 3–22.

———. *Science and Religion: Some Historical Perspectives*. Cambridge: Cambridge University Press, 1993.

Brown, Harold I. "Response to Siegel." *Synthese* 56 (1983): 91–105.

————. *Perception, Theory and Commitment: The New Philosophy of Science.* Chicago: Precendent Publishing, 1977.

Bunge, Mario. *Scientific Research. The Search for Systems.* Vol. I. New York, Heidelberg, and Berlin: Springer, 1967.

————. *Scientific Materialism.* Dordrecht: Reidel, 1981.

Campbell, Donald T. "Evolutionary Epistemology." In *The Philosophy of Karl Popper,* edited by Paul A. Schilpp, pp. 413–463. La Salle, Ill.: Open Court, 1974.

Carnap, Rudolf. "The Old and the New Logic." In *Logical Positivism,* edited by Alfred J. Ayer, pp. 133–146. Glencoe, Ill.: The Free Press, 1960.

————. *The Logical Structure of the World and Pseudoproblems in Philosophy.* London: Routledge, 1967.

Carnap, Rudolf; Hahn, Hans; and Neurath, Otto. *The Scientific Conception of the World: The Vienna Circle.* Reproduced in Otto Neurath, *Empiricism and Sociology,* edited by Marie Neurath and Robert Sonné Cohen, pp. 298–318. Dordrecht: Reidel, 1973.

Carroll, William E. "Big Bang Cosmology, Quantum Tunneling from Nothing, and Creation." *Laval Théologique et Philosophique* 44 (1948): 59–75.

————. "Reductionism and the Conflict between Science and Religion." *The Allen Review* (Oxford), 15, Trinity 1996: 19–22.

Chesterton, Gilbert K. *Orthodoxy. The Collected Works of G. K. Chesterton,* Vol. 1. Edited by David Dooley. San Francisco: Ignatius Press, 1986.

Chevrot, Georges. *Simon Peter.* Dublin: Scepter, 1959.

Churchland, Patricia S. "Do We Propose to Eliminate Consciousness?" In *The Churchlands and Their Critics,* edited by Robert N. McCauley, pp. 297–300. Oxford: Blackwell, 1996.

————. *Neurophilosophy: Toward a Unified Science of the Mind / Brain.* Cambridge, Mass.: The MIT Press, 1993.

Churchland, Paul M. *A Neurocomputational Perspective: The Nature of Mind and the Structure of Science.* Cambridge, Mass.: The MIT Press, 1992.

Churchland, Paul M., and Churchland, Patricia S. "Intertheoretic Reduction: a Neuroscientist's Field Guide." In *The Mind-Body Problem. A Guide to the Current Debate,* edited by Richard Warner and Tadeusz Saubka, pp. 41–54. Oxford: Blackwell, 1994.

Clarke, W. Norris. "Is a Natural Theology Still Possible Today?" In *Physics, Philosophy, and Theology: A Common Quest for Understanding,* edited by Robert J. Russell, William R. Stoeger, and George V. Coyne, pp. 103–123. Vatican City State: Vatican Observatory, 1988.

Cline, David B.; Mann, Alfred K.; and Rubbia, Carlo. "The Search for New Families of Elementary Particles." *Scientific American* 234, 1 (January 1976): 44–54.

Collingwood, Robin George. *The Idea of Nature.* Oxford: Clarendon Press, 1945.

Cournand, André, and Meyer, Michael. "The Scientist's Code." *Minerva* 14 (1976): 79–96.

Craig, William Lane. "Finitude of the Past and God's Existence." In *Theism, Atheism, and Big Bang Cosmology,* edited by William Lane Craig and Quentin Smith, pp. 3–76. Oxford: Clarendon Press, 1993.

Crick, Francis. *The Astonishing Hypothesis: The Scientific Search for the Soul.* New York: Charles Scribner's Sons, 1994.

Darden, Lindley, and Maull, Nancy. "Interfield Theories." *Philosophy of Science* 44 (1977): 43–64.

Davies, Paul. "Is the Universe a Machine?" In *The New Scientist Guide to Chaos,* edited by Nina Hall, pp. 213–221. London: Penguin, 1992.

———. "The New Physics: A Synthesis." In *The New Physics,* edited by Paul Davies, pp. 1–6. Cambridge-New York: Cambridge University Press, 1989.

———. "The Unreasonable Effectiveness of Science." In *Evidence of Purpose: Scientists Discover the Creator,* edited by John Marks Templeton, pp. 44–56. New York: Continuum, 1994.

———. *The Mind of God: The Scientific Basis for a Rational World.* New York and London: Simon & Schuster, 1993.

———. *The Cosmic Blueprint: Order and Complexity at the Edge of Chaos.* London: Penguin Books, 1989.

Davies, Paul, and Gribbin, John. *The Matter Myth.* London: Penguin Books, 1992.

Dawkins, Richard. *The Blind Watchmaker: Why the Evidence of Evolution Reveals a Universe without Design.* New York and London: Norton, 1987.

Denifle, Henricus. *Chartularium Universitatis Parisiensis,* Paris, 1891. Bruxelles: Culture et Civilisation, 1964.

Duhem, Pierre. *The Aim and Structure of Physical Theory.* Princeton, N. J.: Princeton University Press, 1951.

Duve, Christian de. *A Guided Tour of the Living Cell.* New York: Scientific American Books–The Rockefeller University Press, 1984.

Eccles, John C. *Evolution of the Brain: Creation of the Self.* London and New York: Routledge, 1991.

Eisenstadt, S. N. "Introduction." In Max Weber, *On Charisma and Institution Building,* pp. i–lvi. Chicago and London: The University of Chicago Press, 1968.

Emerton, Norma. *The Scientific Reinterpretation of Form.* Ithaca, N.Y., and London: Cornell University Press, 1984.

Escrivá de Balaguer, Josemaría. *Christ is Passing By.* New York: Scepter, 1985.

———. *Conversations with Monsignor Escrivá de Balaguer.* Shannon: Ecclesia Press, 1972.

Feigl, Herbert. "The Scientific Outlook: Naturalism and Humanism." In *Readings in the Philosophy of Science,* edited by Herbert Feigl and May Brodbeck, pp. 8–18. New York: Appleton-Century-Crofts, 1953.

Ferguson, Kitty. *The Fire in the Equations: Science, Religion & the Search for God.* Grand Rapids, Mich.: Eerdmans, 1995.

Feyerabend, Paul K. "More Clothes for the Emperor's Bargain Basement. A

Review of Laudan's *Progress and Its Problems.*" Reprinted in Paul K. Feyerabend, *Problems of Empiricism,* Philosophical Papers, Vol. 2, pp. 231–246. Cambridge: Cambridge University Press, 1981.

————. "On the Critique of Scientific Reason." In *Method and Appraisal in the Physical Sciences,* edited by Colin Howson, pp. 309–339. Cambridge: Cambridge University Press, 1976.

Fraassen, Bas C. van. *The Scientific Image.* Oxford: Oxford University Press, 1980.

Fraser, Gordon. "Standard Model Hamburger." *Cern Courier* 37 (7) (September 1977): 1.

————. "Trying to Peer Behind the Standard Model." *Cern Courier* 37 (8) (October 1977): 1–8.

Friedman, Kenneth. "Is Intertheoretic Reduction Feasible?" *The British Journal for the Philosophy of Science* 33 (1982): 17–40.

Galileo Galilei. *Opere,* reimpression of the national edition, edited by A. Favaro. Firenze: Barbèra, 1968.

Gibson, Quentin. "Tendencies" *Philosophy of Science* 50 (1983): 296–308.

Giere, Ronald N. "Constructive Realism." In *Images of Science. Essays on Realism and Empiricism, with a Reply from Bas C. van Fraasen,* edited by Paul M. Churchland and Clifford A. Hooker, pp. 74–98. Chicago and London: The University of Chicago Press, 1985.

————. "Introduction: Cognitive Models of Science." In *Cognitive Models of Science,* edited by Ronald N. Giere, pp. xv–xxviii. Minneapolis, Minn.: University of Minnesota Press, 1992.

————. "Philosophy of Science Naturalized." *Philosophy of Science* 52 (1985): 331–356.

————. "What the Cognitive Study of Science Is Not." In *Cognitive Models of Science,* edited by Ronald N. Giere, pp. 481–484. Minneapolis, Minn.: University of Minnesota Press, 1992.

————. *Explaining Science: A Cognitive Approach.* Chicago: The University of Chicago Press, 1988.

————. *Understanding Scientific Reasoning.* New York: Holt, Rinehart and Winston, 1984.

Gilkey, Langdon. "Nature as the Image of God: Reflections on the Signs of the Sacred." *Zygon* 29 (1994): 489–505.

————. *Nature, Reality, and the Sacred: The Nexus of Science and Religion.* Minneapolis, Minn.: Fortress Press, 1993.

Gleick, James. *Chaos. Making a New Science.* New York: Viking, 1987.

Gould, Stephen Jay. "The Evolution of Life on the Earth." *Scientific American* 271 (4) (October 1994): 63–69.

Graham, Loren R. "Commentary. The Multiple Connections between Science and Ethics: Response to Stephen Toulmin." In *The Roots of Ethics: Science, Religion, and Values,* edited by Daniel Callahan and H. Tristram Engelhardt, Jr., pp. 424–438. New York and London: Plenum Press, 1981.

————. *Between Science and Values.* New York: Columbia University Press, 1981.

Granada, Luis de. *Introducción del Símbolo de la fe,* edited by José M. Balcells. Madrid: Cátedra, 1989.

Grant, Edward, ed. *A Source Book in Medieval Science.* Cambridge, Mass.: Harvard University Press, 1974.

————. *Physical Science in the Middle Ages.* Cambridge: Cambridge University Press, 1977.

Grene, Marjorie. "Response to Alasdair MacIntyre." In *Morals, Science and Sociality,* edited by H. Tristram Engelhardt, Jr., and Daniel Callahan, pp. 40–47. Hastings-on-Hudson, N.Y.: The Hastings Center, 1978.

Griffin, David Ray. "Introduction: The Reenchantment of Science." In *The Reenchantment of Science. Postmodern Porposals,* edited by David Ray Griffin, pp. 1–46. Albany: State University of New York Press, 1988.

Habermas, Jürgen. *Knowledge and Human Interests.* London: Heinemann, 1972.

Haken, Hermann, "Pattern Formation and Pattern Recognition: An Attempt at a Synthesis." In *Pattern Formation by Dynamic Systems and Pattern Recognition,* edited by Hermann Haken, pp. 2–12. Berlin-Heidelberg-New York: Springer, 1979.

————. *Synergetics. An Introduction.* Berlin-Heidelberg-New York: Springer, 1977.

Harré, Rom. "Powers." *The British Journal for the Philosophy of Science* 21 (1970): 81–101.

————. *Great Scientific Experiments: Twenty Experiments that Changed our View of the World.* Oxford-New York: Oxford University Press, 1984.

————. *The Principles of Scientific Thought.* London: Macmillan, 1970.

Hartmann, Nicolai. *Philosophie der Natur. Abriss der speziellen Kategorienlehre.* Berlin: Walter de Gruyter, 1980.

————. *Teleologisches Denken.* Berlin: Walter de Gruyter, 1951.

Haught, John F. *Science & Religion: From Conflict to Conversation.* New York and Mahwah, N. J.: Paulist Press, 1995.

Hawking, Stephen. *A Brief History of Time.* New York: Bantam, 1988.

Hefner, Philip. "The Evolution of the Created Co-Creator." In *Cosmos as Creation: Theology and Science in Consonance,* edited by Ted Peters, pp. 211–233. Nashville, Tenn.: Abingdon Press, 1989.

————. *The Human Factor: Evolution, Culture, and Religion.* Minneapolis, Minn.: Fortress Press, 1993.

Hegel, Georg Willhelm Friedrich. *Enzyklopädie der philosophischen Wissenshaften im Grundrisse.* In *Gesammelte Werke,* herausgegeben von der Rheinisch-Westfälischen Akademie der Wissenschaften, Band 20. Hamburg: Felix Meiner Verlag, 1992.

Hempel, Carl G. "The Empiricist Criterion of Meaning." In *Logical Positivism,* edited by Alfred J. Ayer, pp. 108–129. Glencoe, Ill.: The Free Press, 1960.

Hodgson, Peter. "Presuppositions and Limits of science." In *The Structure and*

Development of Science, edited by Gerard Radnitzky and Gunnar Andersson, pp. 133–147. Dordrecht, Boston, and London: Reidel, 1979.

Holton, Gerald. "The End of Science is Nowhere in Sight." *Scientific American* 273 (4) (October 1995): 191.

Hooft, Gerard't. "Gauge Theories of the Forces Between Elementary Particles." *Scientific American* 242 (6) (June 1980): 104–138.

Howard, John N. "Principal Scientific Contributions of John William Strutt, Third Baron Rayleigh." In *Springs of Scientific Creaetivity: Essays on Founders of Modern Science,* edited by Rutherford Aris, H. Ted Davis, and Roger H. Stuewer, pp. 163–187. Minneapolis: University of Minnesota Press, 1983.

Howson, Colin, ed. *Method and Appraisal in the Physical Sciences. The Critical Background to Modern Science, 1800-1905.* Cambridge: Cambridge University Press, 1976.

Hoyningen-Huene, Paul. *Reconstructing Scientific Revolutions: Thomas S. Kuhn's Philosophy of Science.* Chicago: The University of Chicago Press, 1993.

Hübner, Kurt. "La naissance de l'age scientifique, resultat des lois ou du hasard? *Epistemologia 10* (1987): 27–38.

———. "The Problem of Metaphysical Presuppositions in and of Science." In *The Nature of Metaphysical Knowledge,* edited by George F. McLean and Hugo Meynell, pp. 129–134. Washington, D.C.: University Press of America, 1988.

———. *Critique of Scientific Reason.* Chicago and London: The University of Chicago Press, 1983.

———. *Die Wahrheit des Mythos.* München: C. H. Beck, 1985.

———. "Short Abstract of my Philosophical Conceptions and Ideas" Personal communication with author. February 16, 1987.

Isak, Rainer. *Evolution ohne Ziel? Ein interdisziplinären Forschungsbeitrag.* Freiburg: Herder, 1992.

Jaki, Stanley L. "From Scientific Cosmology to a Created Universe." *The Irish Astronomical Journal* 15 (1982): 253–262.

———. "The Role of Faith in Physics.: In *Chance or Reality and Other Essays,* pp. 144–160. Lanham, Mass.: University Press of America, 1986.

———. "Theological Aspects of Creative Science." In *Chance or Reality and other Essays,* pp. 161–181. Lanham, Mass.: University Press of America, 1986.

———. *Angels, Apes, and Men.* La Salle, Ill.: Sherwood Sugden, 1983.

———. *Science and Creation: From Eternal Cycles to an Oscillating Universe.* 2d ed. Edinburgh: Scottish Academic Press, 1986.

———. *The Relevance of Physics.* Chicago and London: The University of Chicago Press, 1966.

———. *The Road of Science and the Ways to God.* Chicago: The University of Chicago Press; Edinburgh: Scottish Academic Press, 1978.

John Paul II, "Message to the Rev. George V. Coyne, June 1, 1988." In *Physics, Philosophy, and Theology: A Common Quest for Understanding,* edited by

Robert J. Russell, William R. Stoegen, and George V. Coyne, pp. M1– M14. Vatican City State: Vatican Observatory, 1988.

———. "Speech to a Group of Twelve Nobel Prize Winners, December 22, 1980 (Vatican)." *Insegnamenti di Giovanni Paolo II* III, 2 (1980): 1780– 1785

———. "Speech to the Participants in a Meeting Organized by the International Center for Relativistic Astrophysics, Vatican, September 14, 1990." *Insegnamenti di Giovanni Paolo II* XIII, 2 (1990): 612–614.

———. "Speech to the Participants in a Symposium on the Frontiers of Cosmology, July 6, 1985 (Vatican)." *Insegnamenti di Giovanni Paolo II* VIII, 2 (1985): 89–92.

———. "Message to the Pontifical Academy of the Sciences, October 22, 1996." *L'Osservatore Romano,* October 24, 1966, 6–7.

Karakash, Clairette, and Schäffer-Guignier, Otto. "Typologie des articulations entre science et foi religieuse." In Pierre Bühler, Pierre-Luigi Dubied, Clairette Karakash, Otto Schäffer-Guignier, and Gerd Theissen, *Science et foi font système. Une approche herméneutique,* pp. 45–72. Genève: Labor et Fides, 1992.

Kauffman, Stuart. *At Home in the Universe: The Search for Laws of Self-Organisation and Complexity.* London: Viking, 1995.

———. *The Origins of Order: Self-Organisation and Selection in Evolution.* New York-Oxford: Oxford University Press, 1993.

Kiesewetter, Hubert. "Ethical Foundations of Popper's Philosophy." In *Karl Popper: Philosophy and Problems,* edited by Anthony O'Hear, pp. 275– 288. Cambridge: Cambridge University Press, 1995.

Krohn, Wolfgang; Küppers, Günther; and Nowotny, Helga. "Introduction" In *Selforganisation: Portrait of a Scientific Revolution,* edited by Wolfgang Krohn, Günther Küppers, and Helga Nowotny, pp. 1–10. Dordrecht-Boston-London: Kluwer, 1990.

Kuhn, Thomas S. "Objectivity, Value Judgment, and Theory Choice." In *The Essential Tension,* pp. 320–339. Chicago and London: The University of Chicago Press, 1977.

———. "Second Thoughts on Paradigms." Reprinted in Thomas S. Kuhn, *The Essential Tension,* pp. 293–319. Chicago and London: The University of Chicago Press, 1977.

———. "The Road Since Structure." In *Science and the Quest for Reality,* edited by Alfred I. Tauber, pp. 231–245. Washington Square, N.Y.: New York University Press, 1997.

———. *The Structure of Scientific Revolution.* 2d enlarged ed. Chicago: The University of Chicago Press, 1970.

———. *The Copernican Revolutions: Planetary Astronomy in the Development of Western Thought.* Cambridge, Mass.: Harvard University Press, 1957.

Kuntz, Paul G. "Introduction." In *The Concept of Order,* edited by Paul G. Kuntz, pp. ix–xxxix. Seattle and London: The University of Washington Press, 1968.

Lakatos, Imre. "The Social Responsibility of Science." In *Mathematics, Science and Epistemology*. Philosophical Papers, Vol. 2. Edited by John Worrall and Gregory Currie, pp. 256–258. Cambridge: Cambridge University Press, 1978.

———. *The Methodology of Scientific Research Programmes*. Philosophical Papers, Vol. 1. Edited by John Worrall and Gregory Currie. Cambridge: Cambridge University Press, 1984.

Laudan, Larry. "A Confutation of Convergent Realism." *Philosophy of Science* 48 (1981): 19–49.

———. *Beyond Positivism and Relativism: Theory, Method, and Evidence*. Boulder, Colo.: Westview Press, 1996.

———. *Progress and Its Problems: Towards a Theory of Scientific Growth*. Berkeley: University of California Press, 1977.

———. *Science and Values: The Aims of Science and their Role in Scientific Debate*. Berkeley: University of California Press, 1984.

Lederman, Leon M. "The Upsilon Particle." *Scientific American* 239 (4) (October 1978): 60–68.

Leibniz, Gottfried Wilhelm. "De primae philosophiae Emendatione, et de Notione Substantiae." In *Die philosophische Schriften von Gottfried Wilhelm Leibniz*, edited by C. J. Gerhardt. Hildesheim: Georg Olms, 1965.

Leplin, Jarrett. "Methodological Realism and Scientific Rationality." *Philosophy of Science* 53 (1986): 31–51.

Linder, Maurine E., and Gilman, Alfred G. "G Proteins." *Scientific American* 267 (1) (July 1992): 36–43.

MacIntyre, Alasdair. "Objectivity in Morality and Objectivity in Science." In *Morals, Science and Sociality*, edited by H. Tristram Engelhardt, Jr. and Daniel Callahan, pp. 21–39. Hastings-on-Hudson, N.Y.: The Hastings Center, 1978.

Mackie, John L. *The Miracle of Theism: Arguments For and Against the Existence of God*. Oxford: Clarendon Press, 1982.

Madsen, Deborah L., and Madsen, Mark S. "Fractals, Chaos and Dynamics: The Emergence of Postmodern Science." In *Postmodern Surroundings*, edited by Steven Earnshaw, pp. 119–132. Amsterdam and Atlanta, Ga.: Rodopi, 1994.

Marcuse, Herbert. *One-Dimensional Man*. London: Routledge, 1964.

Margenau, Henry. "On Popper's Philosophy of Science." In *The Philosophy of Karl Popper*, edited by Paul A. Schilpp, pp. 750–759. La Salle, Ill.: Open Court, 1974.

Masterman, Margaret. "The Nature of a Paradigm." In *Criticism and the Growth of Knowledge*, edited by Imre Lakatos and Alan Musgrave, pp. 59–89. Cambridge: Cambridge University Press, 1990.

Mayr, Ernst. *Towards A New Philosophy of Biology*. Cambridge, Mass.: Harvard University Press, 1988.

McMullin, Ernan. "A Case for Scientific Realism." In *Scientific Realism*, edited by Jarrett Leplin, pp. 8–40. Berkeley: University of California Press, 1984.

———. "Evolutionary Contingency and Cosmic Purpose." In *Finding God in All Things,* edited by Michael J. Himes and Stephen J. Pope, pp. 140–161. New York: Herder, 1996.

———. "How Should Cosmology Relate to Theology?" In *The Sciences and Theology in the Twentieth Century,* edited by Arthur Peacocke, pp. 17–57. Notre Dame, Ind.: University of Notre Dame Press, 1981.

———. "Natural Science and Belief in a Creator: Historical Notes." In *Physics, Philosophy, and Theology: A Common Quest for Understanding,* edited by Robert J. Russell, William R. Stoeger, and George V. Coyne, pp. 49–79. Vatican City State: Vatican Observatory, 1988.

———. "The Goals of Natural Science." In *Scientific Knowledge Socialized,* edited by Imre Hronszky, Márta Fehér, and Balázs Dajka, pp. 27–58. Dordrecht: Kluwer, 1988.

———. "Values in Science." In *Introductory Readings in the Philosophy of Science,* edited by E. D. Klemke, Robert Hollinger, and A. David Kline, pp. 349–373. Buffalo, N.Y.: Prometheus Books, 1988.

Merton, Robert K. *The Sociology of Science: Theoretical and Empirical Investigations.* Chicago and London: The University of Chicago Press, 1973.

Miller, David. *Critical Rationalism: A Restatement and Defence.* Chicago and La Salle, Ill.: Open Court, 1994.

Monod, Jacques. "On Chance and Necessity." In *Studies in the Philosophy of Biology: Reduction and Related Problems,* edited by Francisco J. Ayala and Theodosius Dobzhansky, pp. 357–365. Berkeley and Los Angeles: University of California Press, 1974.

———. *Chance and Necessity: An Essay on the Natural Philosophy of Modern Biology.* New York: Alfred A. Knopf, 1971.

———. *Chance and Necessity.* New York: Vintage Books, 1972.

Murphy, Nancey. *Theology in the Age of Scientific Reasoning.* Ithaca, N. Y., and London: Cornell University Press, 1990.

Nagel, Ernest. *The Structure of Science.* London: Routledge, 1961.

Nambu, Yoichiro. "The Confinement of Quarks." *Scientific American* 235 (5) (November 1976): 48–60.

Neurath, Otto. "Sociology and Physicalism." In *Logical Positivism,* edited by Alfred J. Ayer, pp. 282–317. Glencoe, Ill.: The Free Press, 1960.

Newell, Alan C.; Passot, Thierry; and Lega, Joceline. "Order Parameter Equations for Patterns." *Annual Review of Fluid Mechanics* 25 (1993): 399–453.

Oresme, Nicole. *Nicole Oresme and the Medieval Geometry of Qualities and Motions: A Treatise on the Uniformity and Difformity of Intensities Known as "Tractatus de configurationibus qualitatum et motuum."* Edited by Marshall Clagett. Madison, Wis.: University of Wisconsin Press, 1968.

Pannenberg, Wolfhart. *Towards a Theology of Nature: Essays on Science and Faith.* Louisville, Ky.: Westminster–John Knox Press, 1993.

Pap, Arthur. "Does Science Have Metaphysical Presuppositions?" In *Readings in the Philosophy of Science,* edited by Herbert Feigl and May Brodbeck, pp. 21–33. New York: Appleton-Century-Crofts, 1953. A briefer version is contained in Philip P. Wiener, *Readings in Philosophy of Science,* pp.480–484. New York: Charles Scribner's Sons, 1953.

————. *Analytische Erkenntnistheorie.* Wien: Springer, 1955.

Peters, Ted. "Editor's Introduction: Pannenberg on Theology and Natural Science." In Wolfgang Pannenberg, *Towards a Theology of Nature: Essays on Science and Faith,* edited by Ted Peters, pp. 1–28. Louisville, Ky.: Westminster-John Knox Press, 1993.

Plantinga, Alvin. *God and Other Minds: A Study of the Rational Justification of Belief in God.* Ithaca, N.Y. and London: Cornell University Press, 1967.

Polkinghorne, John C. "A Revived Natural Theology." In *Science and Religion. One World: Changing Perspectives on Reality,* edited by Jan Fennema and Ian Paul, pp. 87–97. Dordrecht-Boston-London: Kluwer, 1990.

————. *One World.* London: SPCK; Princeton: Princeton University Press, 1987.

————. "Chaos Theory and Divine Action." In *Religion and Science: History, Method, Dialogue,* edited by W. Mark Richardson and Wesley J. Wildman, pp. 243–252. New York and London: Routledge, 1996.

Popper, Karl R. "Campbell on the Evolutionary Theory of Knowledge." In *The Philosophy of Karl Popper,* edited by Paul A. Schilpp, pp. 1059–1065. La Salle, Ill.: Open Court, 1974.

————. "Natural Selection and the Emergence of Mind." In *Evolutionary Epistemology, Rationality, and the Sociology of Knowledge,* edited by Gerard Radnitzky and William W. Bartley, III, pp. 139–155. La Salle, Ill.: Open Court, 1987.

————. "Replies to My Critics: Introduction." In *The Philosophy of Karl Popper,* edited by Paul A. Shilpp, pp. 961–976. La Salle, Ill.: Open Court, 1974.

————. *A World of Propensities.* Bristol: Thoemmes Antiquarian Books, 1990.

————. *In Search of a Better World: Lectures and Essays from Thirty Years.* London and New York: Routledge, 1992.

————. *Objective Knowledge: An Evolutionary Approach.* Oxford: Clarendon Press, 1989.

————. *The Open Society and Its Enemies.* London: Routledge, 1977.

————. *The Open Universe: An Argument for Indeterminism.* London: Hutchinson, 1982.

————. *The Logic of Scientific Discovery.* London and Cambridge, Mass.: Unwin Hyman, 1990.

Popper, Karl R., and Eccles, John C. *The Self and Its Brain.* New York-London-Heidelberg-Berlin: Springer, 1977.

Preus, Anthony. *Science and Philosophy in Aristotle's Biological Works.* Hildesheim and New York: Georg Olms Verlag, 1975.

Prigogine, Ilya. *From Being to Becoming.* San Francisco: Freeman, 1979.

Puddefoot, John C. "Information and Creation." In *The Science and Theology of Information,* edited by Christoph Wassermann, Richard Kirby, and Bernard Rordorf, pp. 7–25. Geneva: Labor et Fides, 1992.

Putnam, Hilary. *Representation and Reality.* Cambridge, Mass.: The MIT Press, 1988.

Radnitzky, Gerard, ed. *Centripetal Forces in the Sciences,* Vol. 2. New York: Paragon House, 1988.

Rebbi, Claudio. "The Lattice Theory of Quark Confinement." *Scientific American* 248 (2) (February 1983): 36–47.

Rescher, Nicholas. *Scientific Realism: A Critical Reappraisal.* Dordrecht and Boston: Reidel, 1987.

Richardson, W. Mark. "The Theology of Human Agency and the Neurobiology of Learning." In *Religion and Science. History, Method, Dialogue,* edited by W. Mark Richardson and Wesley J. Wildman, pp. 351–371. New York and London: Routledge, 1996.

Rohrlich, Fritz. "Pluralistic Ontology and Theory Reduction in the Physical Sciences." *The British Journal for the Philosophy of Science* 39 (1988): 295–312.

Schlick, Moritz. "The Turning Point in Philosophy." In *Logical Positivism,* edited by Alfred J. Ayer, pp. 53–59. Glencoe, Ill.: The Free Press, 1960.

———. "Positivism and Realism." In *Logical Positivism,* edited by Alfred J. Ayer, pp. 82–107. Glencoe, Ill.: The Free Press, 1960.

Seneca, Lucius Annaeus. *Quaestiones naturales.* Paris: Les Belles Lettres, 1961.

Shapere, Dudley. "Meaning and Scientific Change." In *Scientific Revolutions,* edited by Ian Hacking, pp. 28–59. Oxford: Oxford University Press, 1981.

Sharon, Nathan, and Lis, Halina. "Carbohydrates in Cell Recognition." *Scientific American* 268 (1) (January 1993): 82–89.

Siegel, Harvey. "Brown on Epistemology and the New Philosophy of Science." *Synthese* 56 (1983): 61–89.

———. *Relativism Refuted: A Critique of Contemporary Epistemological Relativism.* Dordrecht: Reidel, 1987.

Sinclair, John, *Collins Cobuild English Language Dictionary.* London and Glasgow: Collins, 1987.

Sklar, Lawrence. "Types of Inter-Theoretic Reduction." *The British Journal for the Philosophy of Science* 18 (1967): 109–124.

Smith, Quentin. "The Uncaused Beginning of the Universe." In *Theism, Atheism, and Big Bang Cosmology,* edited by William Lane Craig and Quentin Smith, pp. 108–140. Oxford: Clarendon Press, 1993.

———. "The Uncaused Beginning of the Universe." *Philosophy of Science* 55 (1988): 39–57.

Smith, Wolfgang. *Cosmos and Transcendence.* Peru, Ill.: Sherwood Sugden, 1990.

Sosa, Ernest. "Condition." In *The Cambridge Dictionary of Philosophy,* edited by Robert Audi, general editor, p. 149. Cambridge: Cambridge University Press, 1995.

Spradlin, Wilford W., and Porterfield, Patricia. *The Search for Certainty.* New York-Berlin-Heidelberg-Tokyo: Springer, 1984.

Stanesby, Derek. *Science, Reason and Religion.* London: Routledge 1988.

Stöckler, Manfred. "A Short History of Emergence and Reductionism." In *The Problem of Reductionism in Science,* edited by Evandro Agazzi, pp. 71–90. Dordrecht: Kluwer, 1991.

―――. "Reductionism and the New Theories of Self-Organisation." In *Advances in Scientific Philosophy,* edited by Gerhard Schurz and Georg J. W. Dorn, pp. 233–254. Amsterdam and Atlanta, Ga.: Rodopi, 1991.

Storer, Norman W. "Prefatory Note." In Robert K. Merton, *The Sociology of Science. Theoretical and Empirical Investigations,* pp. 223–227. Chicago and London: The University of Chicago Press, 1973.

Stroll, Avrum. "Presupposing." In *The Encyclopedia of Philosophy,* edited by Paul Edwards, editor in chief, Vol. 6, pp. 446–449. New York: Macmillan & The Free Press, 1967.

Swinburne, Richard. *The Existence of God.* Oxford: Clarendon Press, 1989.

Templeton, John M. "Introduction." In *Evidence of Purpose: Scientists Discover the Creator,* edited by John Marks Templeton, pp. 7–20. New York: Continuum, 1994.

―――. *Worldwide Laws of Life.* Philadelphia and London: Templeton Foundation Press, 1997.

Templeton, John M., and Herrmann, Robert L. *The God Who Would be Known: Revelations of the Divine in Contemporary Science.* San Francisco: Harper & Row, 1989.

Torrance, Thomas F. *Divine and Contingent Order.* Oxford: Oxford University Press, 1981.

Toulmin, Stephen. "How Can We Reconnect the Sciences with the Foundations of Ethics?" In *The Roots of Ethics: Science, Religion and Values,* edited by Daniel Callahan and H. Tristram Engelhardt, Jr., pp. 403–423. New York and London: Plenum Press, 1981.

Trigg, Roger. *Rationality and Science: Can Science Explain Everything?* Oxford: Blackwell, 1993.

Vollmer, Gerhard. "On Supposed Circularities in an Empirically Oriented Epistemology." In *Evolutionary Epistemology, Rationality, and the Sociology of Knowledge,* edited by Gerard Radnitzky and William W. Bartley, III, pp. 163–200. La Salle, Ill.: Open Court, 1987.

Weber, Max. "Science as a Vocation." In *On Charisma and Institution Building,* pp. 294–309. Chicago and London: The University of Chicago Press, 1968. Excerpt from H. H. Gerth and C. Wright Mills, eds. *Max Weber: Essays in Sociology.* Oxford: Oxford University Press, 1946.

Weinberg, Steven. *Dreams of Final Theory.* New York: Pantheon Books, 1992.

Whitehead, Alfred North. *Science and the Modern World.* New York: Macmillan, 1967.

Whitrow, Gerald J. "The Role of Time in Cosmology." In *Cosmology, History, and Theology,* edited by Wolfgang Yourgrau and Allen D. Breck, pp. 159–177. New York and London: Plenum Press, 1977.

Williams, L. Pearce. "Preface." In Norma Emerton, *The Scientific Reinterpretation of Form,* pp. 7–8. Ithaca and London: Cornell University Press, 1984.

Worrall, John. "Why both Popper and Watkins Fail to Solve the Problem of Induction." In *Freedom and Rationality,* edited by Fred d'Agostino and Ian C. Jarvie, pp. 257–296. Dordrecht: Kluwer, 1989.

Zamulinski, Brian. "Review of: M. A. Corey, 'God and the New Cosmology: The Anthropic Design Argument,'" *Australasian Journal of Philosophy* 72 (1994): 405.

Zeldovich, Yacov B. "Spontaneous Birth of the Closed Universe and the Anthropic Principle." In *Astrophysical Cosmology,* edited by H. A. Brück, G. V. Coyne, and M. S. Longair, pp. 575–579. Vatican City: Pontificia Academia Scientiarum, 1982.

Ziman, John. *Reliable Knowledge. An Exploration of the Grounds for Belief in Science.* Cambridge: Cambridge University Press, 1991.

———. *Public Knowledge: The Social Dimension of Science.* Cambridge: Cambridge University Press, 1967.

Zycinski, Joseph M. "The Anthropic Principle and Teleological Interpretations of Nature." *The Review of Metaphysics* 41 (1987): 317–333.

———. "The Laws of Nature and the Immanence of God in the Evolving Universe." Templeton closing lecture of the 6th ESSSAT Congress, Cracow, 26–30 March, 1996. In *The Interplay Between Scientific and Theological Worldviews,* ed. Niels H. Gregersen, Ulf Görman, and Christoph Wassermann, part I, pp. 3–19. Geneva: Labor et Fides, 1999.

———. *Three Cultures: Science, the Humanities and Religious Values.* Tucson, Ariz.: Pachart Publishing House, 1990.

Index